Foreword:

Thank you, reader, for looking at our book. We wanted to explain the thinking behind it: Death is a very difficult concept for adults, never mind, for children to grasp. We wanted to normalise the feelings experienced and to use straight forward language rather than words such as lost or passed away which tend to cause misunderstandings for children. If the person is merely lost maybe he/she can be found.

We haven't explored what happens when people die as we don't know, but we do know that children who have been bereaved struggle with their feelings and can quickly become overwhelmed and frightened by them.

When children have someone significant die their remaining caregivers are often overwhelmed by their own grief and may be unavailable for a time, meaning that the children have to cope alone with their maelstrom of feelings.

We have worked with troubled children for many years, all of whom have struggled with loss and bereavement. We have built up our own libraries of resources and have our favourites but wanted to create this book as a way of helping children who have been bereaved feel less isolated. The book is divided into three parts: The first part is a handbook of the many feelings felt by children who are grieving. These are explained and normalised. Our idea is that this part is read with the children by an adult and discussed with them.

The second part is the story of Frankie. Frankie is trying to cope with her mother's death and does not want to do anything she used to do. Nothing brings her joy anymore.

The third part is Albie's story. Albie is very angry following his father's death and keeps getting into trouble at school. He does not understand what is happening to him.

Each of the children is helped by a kind, caring adult who notices and accepts what is going on for them and helps them to express what they are thinking and feeling inside so that they can begin to make sense of it and to heal.

We hope you find it useful.

When someone you love dies it is very hard.

It can cause lots of tricky feelings:

Numb

You might not feel anything at all because you are in shock and are feeling numb or blanking out, not wanting to feel anything.

This usually happens just after the person you love has died and can last a long time.

This is your brain's way of protecting you from the hurt of what has happened.

Confused

You might feel confused because you don't understand what has happened or weren't expecting it because it was so sudden.

It might be because you are trying to work out what's going on and how you feel about it.

This can make it hard to sleep or concentrate and listen at school.

Sometimes it might feel as if you are in a fog or walking through mud.

You might feel as if you're living in a bubble, constantly thinking about the person who has died.

You might want to keep busy so that you don't have time to think or feel anything at all.

Angry

You might feel angry for lots of different reasons; because when someone you love dies it can feel very unfair and frightening and just... all wrong.

Sometimes you might feel cross with the person who has died because they have left you and you feel very alone.

4

You might not want to feel angry but you do. A lot!

And at people you like and love, and who might be trying to help you.

This can make you feel bad about yourself and even angrier.

Sad

You might feel sad because you didn't want the person you love to die and you miss them all the time.

You might not be able to stop crying.

You might not be able to feel happy or might feel that nothing is good anymore.

You might not want to feel happy because you feel guilty if you are happy that the person you love isn't there to enjoy things with you anymore.

Worried

You might feel worried because you don't feel well with headaches or tummy aches. You might be worried about other people being ill and someone else you love dying.

You might be worried that something you did or said or didn't do or didn't say caused the person to die.

You might feel worried that the last thing you remember saying to them wasn't very nice.

Embarrassed

You might feel embarrassed because sometimes other people don't know what to do or say when someone has died. Sometimes they make a fuss or get things wrong. Sometimes they might avoid you. Sometimes they act as if nothing has happened.

You might feel different from everyone else around you because you feel that no-one else has had someone they love die and even if they have they won't understand how you feel.

Tired

You might feel really tired because someone dying and having all these thoughts and feelings can be very tiring.

It's a lot for your brain and your body to cope with. You might not be able to sleep, or want to sleep a lot because then you don't have to think or feel anything. You might not want to do anything at all.

You might feel little again

You might feel as if you are very little again and need lots of cuddles and to be close to those you love.

You might not be able to talk about the person who has died.

Or you might want to talk about them all the time.

Questions

You might have a lot of questions that you want answers to.

It's important that you can ask all of your questions and talk about your thoughts and feelings and worries with someone you trust whenever you're ready.

It's very important that you have someone to help you.

This is far too big to cope with all by yourself.

Can you think of someone you trust who you can talk to?

Here are some people you might be able to talk to:

· A grown up in your family

· A grown up at school

· A family friend

· A grown up you know at a club or activity you do

If you don't feel that you can talk to someone yet can you draw or write down your thoughts and feelings and share them with someone on the list above?

FRANKIE'S STORY

Once there was a little girl called Frankie. She was a happy, little girl who lived with her Mum, her Grandma and her dog, Jason.

Jason was a lovely dog with long, golden fur, a waggy tail, floppy ears, three good legs and one that wasn't as good as the other three and sometimes stuck out to the side when he was running.

Jason loved to bark especially in the mornings when he first went outside. Frankie was sure that Jason was saying 'Good morning' to the animals in the other gardens and to the birds in the sky.

Frankie loved her Mum but often her Mum was poorly and had to go to the hospital.

"Will the doctors make her better?" Frankie asked her Grandma.
"I hope so, Frankie", said her Grandma, "but I don't know; sometimes doctors can't make people better."

One day Frankie's Mum didn't come home from the hospital, and her Grandma told Frankie that her Mum had died.
"What does that mean?" Frankie wondered.

Grandma told her that when somebody dies they never come back. Frankie was very upset and wanted to know where her Mum had gone.

"I don't know Frankie," said Grandma, "but I do know that's it's very sad for you and for me that your Mum's body didn't work anymore. I'm going to look after you now," Grandma told Frankie as she put her arm around her to give her a cuddle.

Frankie was very sad. Lots of people came to the house; they talked quietly to Grandma. Some cried. Some brought dinners. Some smiled at Frankie and others looked away.

Frankie didn't understand. People asked her if she was okay but she didn't know what to say. Sometimes she felt empty inside, sometimes she felt really cross and sometimes she felt sad. And sometimes she didn't know what she was feeling. It was all really confusing.

Grandma suggested that she play with her friend, Sam, next door. Frankie didn't want to do that. She didn't feel like it.

Frankie wasn't a happy girl anymore.

But Frankie loved Jason. When Frankie watched TV, Jason sat next to her and licked her hand; when Frankie didn't want to talk Jason put his head on Frankie's lap.

Sometimes Jason wobbled his head, which made Frankie smile. Jason slept on the floor next to Frankie's bed. Frankie felt a bit better knowing that he was there.

Frankie didn't like playing with her friend or talking to grown-ups, but she did like being outside in the garden with Jason.

"Don't get muddy", said Grandma.

But Frankie liked to dig in the mud and sometimes she made castles; sometimes she had big battles with different armies.

Frankie loved to play in the rain and feel the drops on her face and hands and sometimes she felt it running down inside her wellies; Jason shook the rain off his coat like a giant rain making machine which made Frankie laugh.

Frankie carried on digging and sometimes found interesting looking stones of different sizes and colours.

Once she found a beautiful pebble, which she popped into her pocket to look at later.

Frankie also found some green shoots in the garden which grew into white flowers and others that turned into lovely, yellow flowers.

Frankie noticed that the weather was getting a bit warmer and that her fingers and toes were not quite as cold, and her nose felt a bit warmer to touch.

Jason's nose still felt very cold. Grandma said that was a good thing as it meant Jason was healthy just like Frankie.

"I want my Mum", Frankie told Grandma.

"I know you do", Grandma said. "I'm so sorry that I can't make her come back.

Your Mum really loved you and was very proud of you.

She was very happy that you were her girl.

Your Mum made you, and she's in you; in your heart and your eyes and your smile."

One day Frankie said to Grandma, "Jason wants to go to the park today and play with some other dogs and children."

"I'm very pleased to hear that", said Grandma.

Frankie turned round and at that very moment saw a beautiful rainbow that covered the whole sky in the most amazing colours.

Frankie smiled and felt warm all over as she put her wellies on and got Jason's lead and together, she and Jason (and Grandma of course!) went to the park to play.

ALBIE'S STORY

Albie was a boy who sometimes liked school and sometimes didn't.

Sometimes he liked to play with his friends.

And sometimes he didn't....

Some days Albie felt like his body wasn't his own; some days it felt strange. When he felt like this sometimes Albie pushed the other children, and one time even hurt someone . . .

"You're such an angry boy", said Mrs King, a teacher.

Albie didn't know that he was angry. But he did know that sometimes his tummy felt strange and his head felt so muddled, it was like his body was being taken over by something very big and scary.

Often he would dream of his Dad.

In his dreams sometimes his Dad was really big and he would, "Tell that teacher off."

Sometimes his Dad was a superstar footballer.

Sometimes his Dad would bring him lots of presents.

Or take him to the park. They always had such good times together in his dreams.

One day Albie was sitting outside his classroom as he didn't want to go inside, and he knew the funny feeling was happening again.

A kind teacher came and sat beside him and said, "Hello Albie, I've been watching you for a while now and I wonder if sometimes you feel very cross, sometimes you feel very sad, sometimes very happy when you're playing with your friends and sometimes just so mixed up?"

"I wonder if sometimes you might also feel angry with your Dad for leaving you. I think you miss your Dad very much and sometimes it's so hard to understand why he isn't with you anymore and he can't come back."

Albie looked up at the teacher and he nodded, just a little bit.

The kind teacher then said; "I think it's really hard for children when people they love die, and especially hard for you when your Dad died.

Sometimes our feelings are so confused that we don't know what to feel.

Sometimes we don't feel anything at all. But it's okay to feel all of these things. It's really hard for grown-ups as well." She led him by the hand and took him to a quiet part of the classroom.

She reached for a tin and opened it.

She then sprinkled a circle of gold dust around them both. "This is our magic, safe place where we can talk, without the other children."

The kind teacher told Albie that it is good to talk to grown-ups about feelings.

She then asked Albie to tell her three people who he could talk to when things get hard and he has lots of tricky feelings.

Albie thought for a while and suggested his Mum, his Aunty and the nice man, Mr Todd, who helped in his classroom. The kind teacher was so pleased that Albie had told her who he could talk to.

She then gave Albie a card; an ordinary, orange card.

She told him that "When you are feeling that school is getting too much, or too hard, you can show this to the teacher and then she will know that you want to talk, or even just have some quiet time away from the other children."

The teacher explained that sometimes it's easier to show the card rather than have to say lots of words.

During the next few weeks Albie practised talking about his worries more and more.

He sometimes showed the teacher the orange card, which worked well and he gradually started to tell people how he was feeling.

He also practised drawing the circle around himself when he needed a little bit of extra time on his own.

Slowly he learned that it's okay to talk about feelings and worries, and he didn't have to try to keep them inside and deal with them all by himself anymore.

Gradually the weeks turned into months and Winter turned to Spring, and Summer into Autumn and then it was Christmas.

Still Albie didn't always like school.

Still he didn't always like playing with his friends.

But he liked it so much more and the teacher never again said to him, "What an angry boy you are". Most of the time Albie was happier and he had fun; he still felt sad about missing his Dad, but he knew now that was okay too.

About the Authors

The authors have worked with children in a professional capacity for many years.

 **Wendy Picken** is a social worker who is employed by Daisy's Dream, a children's bereavement charity based in Berkshire as well as working in private practice. Prior to working with bereaved children Wendy worked for children's social care as a social worker and manager and has specialist knowledge of working in the field of fostering and adoption, and therefore, has an understanding of the impact of loss and separation.

 **Jane Foulkes** trained as a social worker and has worked as an independent psychotherapist since 1996. In total she has over thirty years' experience of working with children and their families, the majority of whom have been traumatised by loss.

 **Jenny Picken** is now retired. Her career in NHS paediatric services enabled her to work in supporting families and their children with special needs. She has recently developed an interest in art and, in particular, in painting.

ResultsPlusRevision

Edexcel GCSE

Statistics

Gill Dyer

With diagnostic tests on CD-ROM

ALWAYS LEARNING

PEARSON

How to use the book and CD-ROM

Welcome to the ResultsPlus Revision guide for Edexcel's GCSE Statistics.

This book will help you prepare for your exams with more confidence. It contains the key information you need to know, along with plenty of practice questions and tips.

But before you start revising, why not take a diagnostic test? This will help you to identify what you already know and where you need to improve.

Insert the CD-ROM and follow the easy installation instructions. Then choose a test from the Tests menu. You can take each diagnostic test as many times as you want! Your latest results will be saved on your computer.

After taking a test, click on the Results tab. The Analysis screen shows your scores, question-by-question. Test review lets you look back at your answers and compare them with the correct answers. And your personalised skills map shows you how you performed in each area of your course. By copying across the red, amber and green symbols to the revision tracker at the front of your book, you can see where to spend more time revising.

Which tier are you taking?

Higher – you need to cover all the material in this book.

Foundation – you can leave out the sections marked with the 'Higher tier' tabs.

The book is divided into the 8 topics from your specification.

At the start of each section you'll find a list of skills. A complete list of the skills is given in your revision tracker at the start of the book.

Each section explains what you need to know about that topic. We've also included some helpful ResultsPlus features.

CD tests

There are 6 tests on the CD-ROM. Tests 1-3 cover the Foundation tier. Tests 1-6 all need to be taken to cover the Higher tier.

Need more help? details of where to look in the main student book for more information. (978-1-846904-54-7)

Collecting data

1.3: Non-random sampling

- ✓ Understand and use systematic, quota and cluster sampling
- ✓ Have a basic idea of the concept of bias, how it might occur in a sampling procedure and how it might be minimised
- ✓ Collect or obtain data by convenience sampling
- ✓ Understand the strengths and weaknesses of various sampling methods, including bias, influences and convenience

Cluster sampling

This is a non-random sampling method that is used when the population splits naturally into groups, or clusters. A sample of the groups is selected randomly and observations are taken from each member of these groups.

For example, a county might contain a number of hospitals, and to question the whole population of nurses would take a long time and be expensive. Instead, a number of hospitals could be selected and every nurse in these hospitals could be questioned. Each hospital would be a cluster.

Quota sampling

A researcher is told to interview a number (quota) of people who have a certain combination of characteristics, e.g. 20 men over 20 years old, 20 women over 20 years old, 20 teenage boys and 20 teenage girls.

People may be classified in terms of age, sex, social class, etc.

Systematic sampling

A systematic sample takes every n^{th} person on a list. If there are N in the population and you want to take a sample of size n, then you would take every $\frac{N}{n}$ th on the sampling frame. A random number $\leq n$ is used in order to decide where on the list to start. A systematic sample is very convenient when the population is large.

To take a sample of 30 from a population of size 600, start at a random number between 0 and 29 and take every $\frac{600}{30} = 20$ th person or unit on the sampling frame.

Convenience sampling

Sometimes it is only possible to take a sample in one particular way, or time may be too short to use most sampling methods. When this happens any convenient sample may be used.

Need more help? For more on this topic, see pages 11–12 of the main Edexcel textbook (ISBN 978-1-84690-454-7).

Higher tier

edexcel key terms

cluster sampling A sample of the groups is selected randomly and observations are taken from each member of these groups.
quota sampling Pre-specified numbers of the population are taken with certain combinations of characteristics such as sex, age, etc.
systematic sampling Every n^{th} person or unit on an unordered list is selected, beginning at a random point.

ResultsPlus Exam tip

Remember, when taking a systematic sample you must choose a starting point randomly. Many students forget to do this when answering questions.

Higher tier indicates material which only Higher tier students need to revise. Higher tier skills and questions are indicated by blue tick-circles and question numbers.

Edexcel key terms words and phrases that you need to recall and use in your exams.

Watch out! common mistakes that students make in the exams. Make sure that you don't fall into the same traps!

Build Better Answers commentary on exam-style questions.

Exam tip advice and guidance to help improve your results.

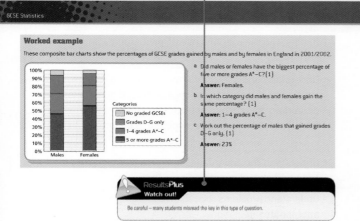

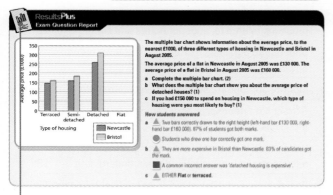

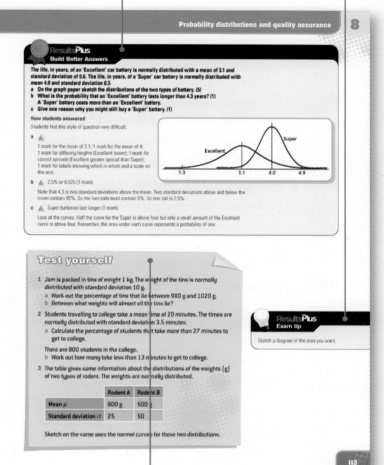

Exam Question Reports past exam questions with real data on how well students answered them.
- Red shows the proportion of students who scored low marks (under 35%)
- Orange shows the number of students who did okay
- Green shows the proportion of students who did well (70% of marks or higher)
They explain how students achieved top marks.

Test yourself practice questions on the topic you have just revised.

1.1 The collection of data

1.1.2 Types of data

- [X] [?] [✓] Understand that data can be obtained from primary or secondary sources   15
- [X] [?] [✓] Recognise the difference between quantitative and qualitative variables   8
- [X] [?] [✓] Recognise the difference between discrete and continuous data   8
- [X] [?] [✓] Recognise, understand and use scales of measurement   8
- [X] [?] [✓] Categorise data through the use of well defined, precise definitions, intervals or class boundaries   8
- [X] [?] [✓] Appreciate the implications of grouping for loss of accuracy in both calculations and presentations (higher)   36
- [X] [?] [✓] Understand the meaning of bivariate data which may be discrete, continuous, grouped or ungrouped   8
- [X] [?] [✓] Understand, use and define situations for grouped and ungrouped data   36

1.1.3 Population and sampling

- [X] [?] [✓] Understand the meaning of the term population   10
- [X] [?] [✓] Understand the word census   10
- [X] [?] [✓] Understand the reasons for sampling and that sample data is used to estimate values in the population   10
- [X] [?] [✓] Understand the terms random, randomness and random sample   10
- [X] [?] [✓] Generate, use **and understand the use of** random numbers   10
- [X] [?] [✓] Understand, design and use a sampling frame   10
- [X] [?] [✓] Be able to select a simple random sample or a stratified sample by **more than** one category as a method of investigating a population   10
- [X] [?] [✓] Understand and use systematic, quota and cluster sampling (higher)   13
- [X] [?] [✓] Have a basic idea of the concept of bias, how it might occur in a sampling procedure and how it might be minimised   13
- [X] [?] [✓] Understand the strengths and weaknesses of various sampling methods, including bias, influences and convenience (higher)   13

1.1.4 Collecting data

- [X] [?] [✓] Collect or obtain data by observation, surveys, experiments, counting, data logging, **convenience sampling**, questionnaires and measurement   13, 15
- [X] [?] [✓] Obtain primary data by questionnaires, experiment **or simulations**   18, 99
- [X] [?] [✓] Understand the effects of accuracy on measurements   8
- [X] [?] [✓] Understand the advantages and disadvantages of using interviews versus questionnaires   15, 18
- [X] [?] [✓] Design and use efficient and effective data capture sheets and methods of recording data   15
- [X] [?] [✓] Understand the role, and use of, pilot studies and pre-testing   15
- [X] [?] [✓] Understand and account for the problems of design, ambiguity of wording, leading and biased questions, definitions and obtaining truthful responses **with simplest form of random response in sensitive cases**   15, 18
- [X] [?] [✓] Understand the advantages and disadvantages of open and closed questions   15
- [X] [?] [✓] Understand problems related to identifying the appropriate population   15
- [X] [?] [✓] Understand the distribution and collection of, and problems related to, questionnaires and surveys   15
- [X] [?] [✓] Understand problems related to errors in recorded answers, non-responses and missing data
- [X] [?] [✓] Identify appropriate sources of secondary data   15
- [X] [?] [✓] Extract data from secondary sources, including those based on ICT
- [X] [?] [✓] Understand the aspects of accuracy, reliability, relevance and bias as related to secondary data   18
- [X] [?] [✓] Design simple statistical experiments to obtain data   18
- [X] [?] [✓] Understand the meaning of explanatory and response variables

Skills in blue are higher tier skills; skills in grey or light blue are linked to controlled assessment or have otherwise been omitted from this book. They are included here for completeness.

1.2 Processing, representing and analysing data

1.2.1 Tabulation

Construct frequency tables by tallying raw data — 21

Tabulate using class intervals as appropriate **including open ended classes and classes of varying width** — 21, 36

Tabulate using various forms of grouping the data — 36

Combine categories to simplify tables with an understanding of the problems of over simplification, the effects on readability, the identification or masking of trends and the loss of detail — 36

Read and interpret data presented in tabular or graphical form — 21

Design suitable tables, including summary tables; design and use appropriate two-way tables — 21

Design, construct and present summary tables

Convert raw data to summary statistics, design, construct and present summary tables (higher) — 21

1.2.2 Diagrams and representations

Label all forms of diagrams with correct and precise labelling — 25

Construct, use and understand pictograms for qualitative, quantitative and discrete data — 25

Construct, use and understand stick graphs for discrete data and bar charts for qualitative, quantitative and discrete data — 25

Construct, use and understand multiple bar charts or composite bar charts for qualitative, quantitative and discrete data — 31

Construct, use and understand pie charts for qualitative, quantitative, discrete and continuous data — 28

Construct, use and understand pie charts and comparative pie charts with area proportional to frequency (higher) — 34

Construct, use and understand histograms with equal class intervals, **histograms with unequal class intervals and the concept of frequency density**, for continuous data — 40, 42

Construct, use and understand cumulative frequency step polygons (higher) — 30

Construct, use and understand frequency diagrams and cumulative frequency diagrams for continuous data — 38

Construct, use and understand stem and leaf diagrams for discrete and continuous data — 28

Construct, use and understand population pyramids for continuous data — 44

Construct, use and understand line graphs and time series — 84

Construct, use and understand choropleth maps (shading) — 44

Understand the distinction between well presented and poorly presented data — 46

Construct, use and understand scatter diagrams for bivariate data (higher) — 70

Understand the shape and simple properties of frequency distributions — 40

Understand symmetrical, positive and negative skew — 40, 57

Understand the potential for visual misuse, by omission or misrepresentation — 46

Understand the transformation from one presentation to another

Understand how to **look for and** discover errors in data and recognise data that do not fit a general trend or pattern **including outliers** — 57

Know that many populations can be modelled by the normal distribution (higher) — 111

1.2.3 Measures of central tendency

Work out and use the mean, mode and median of raw data presented as a list — 48

Work out the mean, mode and median for discrete data presented as a frequency distribution — 48

Identify the modal class interval for grouped frequency distributions for discrete or continuous data — 50

Work out and use estimates for the mean and median of grouped frequency distributions for discrete or continuous data — 50

Understand the effects of transformations of the data on the mean, mode and median (higher) — 52

Understand the effect on the mean, mode and median of changes in the data including the addition or withdrawal of a population or sample member (higher) — 52

Understand the appropriateness, advantages and disadvantages of each of the three measures of central tendency — 52

Be able to make a reasoned choice of a measure of central tendency appropriate to a particular line of enquiry, **nature of the data and purpose of the analysis** — 52

Calculate and use a weighted mean (higher) — 52

1.2.4 Measures of dispersion

Work out and use the range for data presented in a list or frequency distribution — 54

Work out the quartiles, percentiles, **deciles** and interquartile range for discrete and continuous data presented as a list, a frequency table, a grouped frequency table, **frequency distribution or grouped frequency distribution** — 54

Work out interpercentile ranges for discrete and continuous data presented as a list, frequency distribution or grouped frequency distribution (higher)

Construct, interpret and use box plots — 57

Calculate and use variance and standard deviation (higher) — 60

Understand the advantages and disadvantages of each of the measures of dispersion range, quartiles, interquartile range, percentiles, **deciles, interpercentile range, variance and standard deviation** — 60

Use an appropriate measure of central tendency together with range, quartiles, interquartile range, and percentiles, **deciles, interpercentile range, variance and standard deviation** to compare distributions of data — 63

Calculate, interpret and use standardised scores to compare values from different frequency distributions (higher) — 63

1.2.5 Further summary statistics

Understand simple index numbers — 66

Use and understand chain base index numbers (higher) — 66

Use weighted index numbers (higher) — 66

Understand the retail price index (RPI) (higher) — 66

1.2.6 Scatter diagrams and correlation

Plot data as points on a scatter diagram — 70

Recognise positive, negative and zero linear **and non-linear** correlation by inspection — 70, 79

Understand the distinction between correlation, causality and a non-linear relationship — 70

Draw a line of best fit passing through the mean of the points on a scatter diagram — 70

Find the equation of a line of best fit in the form $y = ax + b$ and a practical interpretation of a and b in context (higher) — 76

Fit non-linear models (higher) — 79

Use interpolation and extrapolation and understand the pitfalls — 73

Interpret data presented in the form of a scatter diagram — 73

Calculate and use Spearman's rank correlation coefficient as a measure of agreement or for comparisons of the degree of correlation (higher) — 81

1.2.7 Time series

Plot points as a time series — 84

Draw a trend line by eye and use it to make a prediction — 86

Calculate and use appropriate moving averages — 86

Identify and discuss the significance of seasonal variation by inspecting time series graphs — 86

Draw a trend line based on moving averages (higher) — 89

Recognise seasonal effect at a given data point and average seasonal effect (higher) — 89

1.2.8 Estimation

Estimate population means and proportions from samples

Estimate population size based on the Petersen capture/recapture method (higher) — 18

Understand the effect of sample size on estimates and the variability of estimates **with a simple quantitative appreciation of appropriate sample size** — 99

1.2.9 Quality assurance

Plot sample means, medians and ranges over time on quality control charts that have target values, and action and warning limits (higher) — 114

Understand that in a process under control almost all of the means, medians or ranges fall inside the action limits, and only 1 in 20 fall outside the warning limits (higher) — 114

Know the action to be taken if a sample mean, median or range falls outside of each type of limit (higher) — 114

Skills in blue are higher tier skills; skills in grey or light blue are linked to controlled assessment or have otherwise been omitted from this book. They are included here for completeness.

1.3 Reasoning, interpreting and discussing results

1.3.1 Reasoning, interpreting and discussing results (combined)

[X] [?] [✓] Apply statistical reasoning, explain and justify inferences, deductions, arguments and solutions   57

[X] [?] [✓] Identify and examine relationships between variables   70

[X] [?] [✓] Know **and understand** the limitations of any assumptions

[X] [?] [✓] Be able to identify outliers using quartiles (higher)   57

[X] [?] [✓] Relate summarised data to any initial questions or observations

[X] [?] [✓] Check results for reasonableness and modify the approaches if necessary

[X] [?] [✓] Interpret correlation as a measure of the strength of the association between two variables, **including Spearman's rank correlation coefficient for ranked data**   70, 81

[X] [?] [✓] Compare or choose by eye between a line of best fit and a linear, quadratic or reciprocal model (higher)   79

1.4 Probability

1.4.1 Probability (combined)

[X] [?] [✓] Understand the meaning of the words event and outcome   92

[X] [?] [✓] Understand words such as impossible, certain, highly likely, likely, unlikely, possible, evens and present them on a likelihood scale   92

[X] [?] [✓] Put outcomes in order in terms of probability   92

[X] [?] [✓] Put probabilities in order on a probability scale   92

[X] [?] [✓] Understand the terms 'random' and 'equally likely'   94

[X] [?] [✓] Understand and use measures of probability from a theoretical perspective and from a limiting frequency or experimental approach   94, 99

[X] [?] [✓] Understand that in some cases the measure of probability based on limiting frequency is the only viable measure   99

[X] [?] [✓] Compare expected frequencies and actual frequencies   99

[X] [?] [✓] Use simple cases of the Binomial and discrete uniform distribution (higher)   109

[X] [?] [✓] Use simulation to estimate more complex probabilities (higher)   99

[X] [?] [✓] Use probability to assess risk   99

[X] [?] [✓] Produce, understand and use a sample space   94

[X] [?] [✓] Understand and use Venn diagrams and Cartesian grids (higher)   96

[X] [?] [✓] Understand the terms mutually exclusive and exhaustive   102

[X] [?] [✓] Know, for mutually exclusive outcomes, that the sum of the probabilities is one and in particular the probability of something not happening is one minus the probability of it happening   102

[X] [?] [✓] Draw and use tree diagrams and probability tree diagrams for independent events **and conditional cases**   104, 107

[X] [?] [✓] Understand, use and apply the addition law for mutually exclusive events **and the general addition law for independent events and conditional events and outcomes**   102

[X] [?] [✓] Understand, **use and apply** the multiplication law for independent events **and conditional events and outcomes**   102, 107

[X] [?] [✓] Understand the shape and simple properties of the normal distribution (higher)   111

1.1: Types of data

- ✓ Recognise the difference between quantitative and qualitative variables
- ✓ Recognise the difference between discrete and continuous data
- ✓ Recognise, understand and use scales of measurement
- ✓ Understand the effects of accuracy on measurements
- ✓ Understand the aspects of accuracy, reliability, relevance and bias in secondary data
- ✓ Categorise data through the use of well defined, precise definitions, intervals or class boundaries
- ✓ Understand the meaning of bivariate data

Need more help?
For more on this topic, see pages 1–7 of the main Edexcel textbook (ISBN 978-1-84690-454-7).

edexcel ⠿ key terms

bivariate data Data that involve two variables.
data Information that has been collected.
discrete data Data that can take only certain numerical values in a given range.
hypothesis An assumption made as the starting point of an investigation.
qualitative data Observations that do not have numerical values, e.g. colour.
quantitative data Observations that can take numerical values.
variable A quantity that can have different values.

Statistics

Statistics tries to answer questions. These questions are expressed as a **hypothesis**. For example, you might come up with a hypothesis like: 'The price of a second-hand car decreases as the car gets older'. You would then collect information such as the ages and prices of second-hand cars so that you can test this hypothesis.

The information you collect is known as **data**. Using the data you can decide whether or not the hypothesis is true. You can then reach a conclusion about the prices of second-hand cars.

Variables

The price of second-hand cars is called a variable because the price varies from car to car. Variables may be divided into two types:

1   Those that give **quantitative** data. These are variables that you can measure and give as a number, such as the age and price of a car.

2   Those that give **qualitative** data. These are variables that have to be described in words, e.g. the colour of a second-hand car might be described as 'red', 'white', 'blue' or some other colour.

Continuous and discrete numerical data

The number of doors a car has can take the value two, three, four or five. This is an example of numerical data, as it can be represented by a number, but it can only include whole numbers.

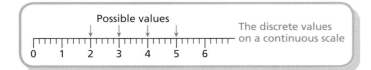

Data like this that can take only some values on a scale are known as **discrete** data.

The size of a car's engine is given by the volume of the cylinders, e.g. a two-litre engine has cylinders with a total volume of 2 litres. The volume of the cylinders can take any value on a continuous scale. For example, it could be 1.35 litres.

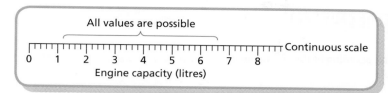

All values are possible

Continuous scale

0 1 2 3 4 5 6 7 8

Engine capacity (litres)

Data like this that can take any value on a **continuous** scale are called continuous data.

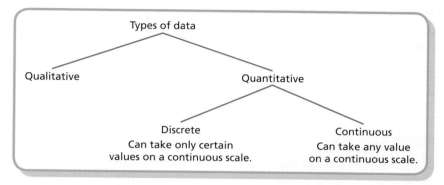

Types of data

Qualitative

Quantitative

Discrete
Can take only certain
values on a continuous scale.

Continuous
Can take any value
on a continuous scale.

Accuracy of continuous data

Continuous data are usually rounded to the nearest sensible unit. If the last number is a five or above, you round up. If the last number is less than five, you round down. So a measurement given to the nearest whole unit may be inaccurate by up to ± half a unit.

Sometimes data are rounded up or down to the whole number differently, e.g. someone 16 years, 11 months and 2 days old is usually said to be 16. The measurements can be up to +1 unit out in this case.

Test yourself

1 A manufacturer wants to know if customers prefer a new brand of toothpaste to the old one. Write down a hypothesis the company could use.

2 Which of the following are examples of qualitative data?
   A The number of people travelling on a train.
   B The weight of their luggage.
   C The colours of their tickets.
   D The type of book they bring to read on the train.

3 Which of the following are examples of continuous data?
   A The number of puppies born to a dog.   B The age of the mother.
   C The weight of a puppy.   D The colour of the puppies.

4 Which of the following is an example of discrete data?
   A The lengths of people's arms.
   B The numbers of brothers and sisters they have.
   C People's ages.
   D People's weights.

5 Joan is 163 cm to the nearest cm. What are the maximum and minimum heights Joan can be?

Results Plus
Exam tip

In an exam you often have to say whether data are qualitative or quantitative, and if quantitative whether the data are discrete or continuous. Make sure you can spell these terms correctly.

Remember, if data are quantitative, they measure the quantity of something and so must involve numbers.

Results Plus
Exam Question Report

Here is a list of words:
continuous   discrete   nominal
categorical   numerical   rank
Use two words from the list to complete the following sentence.
The weights of packets of flour are
_____ and _____ data. (2)

Answer: numerical; continuous.

How students answered
5% of students got no marks for this. Some students confused nominal with numerical and categorical with continuous.

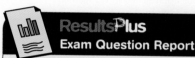

■   5% 0 marks

1 mark was given for each correct word. 35% of students only managed to get one of them right.

███████   35% 1 mark

60% of students got both these marks.

████████████   60% 2 marks

1.2: Populations and sampling

- ✓ Understand the meaning of the terms population, census, random, randomness and random sample
- ✓ Understand the reasons for sampling and that sample data are used to estimate values in the population
- ✓ Understand, design and use a sampling frame
- ✓ Be able to select a simple random or stratified sample by one category as a method of investigating a population
- ✓ Generate and use random numbers
- ✓ Be able to select a simple random or stratified sample by one category

Need more help?
For more on this topic, see pages 8–11 of the main Edexcel textbook (ISBN 978-1-84690-454-7).

edexcel ⊞ key terms

census data Information about every member of a population.
population Everybody or everything that could be involved in an investigation.
random sample A sample in which the people or items are chosen without making a conscious decision. Each person has an equal chance of being selected.
sample data Information about part of a population.
sampling frame A list of all the people or items in the population.
sampling units All the people or things in a population.

Populations and sampling

Anybody or anything that could be involved in an investigation is called the **population**. Sometimes the whole of the population is used in an investigation. This is called taking a **census**. For example, the British Government's National Census of the British population takes place every ten years.

If the population is large, only a small number of the population are usually included in the investigation. This is called a **sample**.

Advantages and disadvantages of using a sample or a census

	Advantages	Disadvantages
Census	Unbiased Accurate Takes the whole population into account	Time-consuming Expensive Difficult to ensure the whole population is used Lots of data to handle
Sample	Cheaper Less time-consuming Fewer data to be considered	Not completely representative May be biased

To represent the population accurately in a sample, the people or items should be chosen at random. If they are not chosen randomly they are said to be **biased**.

The people or units from which the sample is to be taken are called **sampling units**, and a list of these is called a **sampling frame**.

Watch out!

When asked to explain why you would use a sample rather than a census, make sure you state which you are describing:

'It is quicker' ✗

'Sampling is quicker' ✓

Simple random sampling

In simple random sampling each person or unit has an equal chance of being selected.

To take a simple random sample:

- Number the people or units on the sampling frame, starting with 0 for the first one (the 100th will be numbered 99).
- Obtain the required number of random numbers from a table, computer or calculator.
- Select the people or units from the sampling frame that have these numbers.

Stratified sampling

If there are factors that divide the population into sub-populations, such as gender (male/female), then these are known as strata (singular stratum). Each stratum should be represented in the same proportions in the sample as in the population.

For each stratum:

$$\text{number to be taken from stratum} = \frac{\text{number in stratum}}{\text{number in population}} \times \text{total number in sample}$$

For example, if you want to take a stratified sample of 30 people from 120 people (40 males and 80 females), you would select:

$$\frac{40}{120} \times 30 = 10 \text{ males}$$

Results Plus
Exam Question Report

There are 90 black cows and 10 brown cows in a herd of 100 cows.
The farmer wants to work out the average amount of milk produced by the herd of cows.
He will take a stratified sample of 10%.
Write down how he would do this. (2)

How students answered

⚠️ He would take 10% of 100 = 10 cows altogether.

$$\text{number to be taken from stratum} = \frac{\text{number in stratum}}{\text{number in population}} \times \text{total number in sample}$$

Black cows $= \frac{90}{100} \times 10 = 9$

Brown cows $= 10 - 9 = 1$ (1 mark)

Cows would be **randomly** selected from each strata. (1 mark)

🔵 Few students commented on how the cows would be chosen within the strata, so they only got one mark.

⬛ A common incorrect answer was five black and five brown cows.

Worked example: Random numbers

Here is a random number table.

5	2	2	9	4	3	0	4	3	9
6	2	0	4	9	3	1	1	5	4
5	1	9	4	9	0	7	6	6	5
6	7	8	2	1	5	6	6	7	3
9	2	1	2	2	7	0	6	0	9

Francis wants to take a random sample of six people from a list of 50 people. He starts from the top left of the table then works across the table row by row.

a   Write down the set of numbers Francis could use.

Answer: 29, 43, 04, 39, 11, 15.

Remember, because there are two digits in 50 you go across in twos. You work across the top line going from left to right, then you do the same on the second line, and so on. Omit repeat numbers (04 in this case) and numbers over 50 (52, 62, 93, 54, 51, 94, 90, 76, 65, 67 and 82 in this case).

b   Explain how Francis could use these numbers to obtain his sample.

Answer: Number the list of 50 people from 1 to 50 (or 0 to 49). Use those with the numbers in part **a** for the sample.

Mai wants to take a random sample of five of the 50 but he does not want to use a random number table.

c   Describe a way in which he can do this.

Answer: EITHER Put all the names in a hat and draw out five OR Number the people and then get random numbers from a calculator using the RAN button. Those with these numbers will be the sample.

ResultsPlus
Watch out!

Common errors would be to give the first six digits – in this case 5, 2, 9, 4, 3, 0 etc. – or 22, 29, 43, 30, 04.

Test yourself

1   Write down **two** advantages of using a sample rather than a census.

2   Name the sampling method that gives everybody or everything an equal chance of being selected.

3   Here is part of a random number table.
  86 13 84 10 07 30 05 39 97 12 88 07 37 21
  04 89 13 48 19 20 60 78 48 12 99 47 09 46

  a   Select five random numbers between 0 and 130 starting at the top left and going across the rows.
  b   Explain how you would use these to take a random sample of five from a population of 130.

4   A nursery school has 60 children. There are 36 boys and 24 girls.
  Work out how many boys should be included in a stratified sample of ten.

5   An investigation is being made into the types of career that students in Years 11 and 12 at a school wish to follow. A sample is to be taken.
  a   What are the sampling units in this case?
  b   What would be a suitable sampling frame?
  c   There are different numbers of boys and girls and their proportions are to be represented in the sample taken. Name a suitable sampling method.

1.3: Non-random sampling

- ✓ Understand and use systematic, quota and cluster sampling
- ✓ Have a basic idea of the concept of bias, how it might occur in a sampling procedure and how it might be minimised
- ✓ Collect or obtain data by convenience sampling
- ✓ Understand the strengths and weaknesses of various sampling methods, including bias, influences and convenience

Need more help?
For more on this topic, see pages 11–12 of the main Edexcel textbook (ISBN 978-1-84690-454-7).

Cluster sampling

This is a non-random sampling method that is used when the population splits naturally into groups, or clusters. A sample of the groups is selected randomly and observations are taken from each member of these groups.

For example, a county might contain a number of hospitals, and to question the whole population of nurses would take a long time and be expensive. Instead, a number of hospitals could be selected and every nurse in these hospitals could be questioned. Each hospital would be a cluster.

Quota sampling

A researcher is told to interview a number (quota) of people who have a certain combination of characteristics, e.g. 20 men over 20 years old, 20 women over 20 years old, 20 teenage boys and 20 teenage girls.

People may be classified in terms of age, sex, social class, etc.

Systematic sampling

A systematic sample takes every n^{th} person on a list. If there are N in the population and you want to take a sample of size n, then you would take every $\frac{N}{n}$ th on the sampling frame. A random number $\leq n$ is used in order to decide where on the list to start. A systematic sample is very convenient when the population is large.

To take a sample of 30 from a population of size 600, start at a random number between 0 and 29 and take every $\frac{600}{30}$ = 20th person or unit on the sampling frame.

Convenience sampling

Sometimes it is only possible to take a sample in one particular way, or time may be too short to use most sampling methods. When this happens any convenient sample may be used.

Higher tier

edexcel ⠿ key terms

cluster sampling A sample of the groups is selected randomly and observations are taken from each member of these groups.
quota sampling Pre-specified numbers of the population are taken with certain combinations of characteristics such as sex, age, etc.
systematic sampling Every n^{th} person or unit on an unordered list is selected, beginning at a random point.

ResultsPlus
Exam tip

Remember, when taking a systematic sample you must choose a starting point randomly. Many students forget to do this when answering questions.

Advantages and disadvantages of sampling methods

Each sampling method has its advantages and disadvantages:

Method	Advantages	Disadvantages
Simple random	Simple and cheap	Not suitable for large populations A sampling frame is needed
Stratified	Gives more accurate estimates where there are clear strata present	Within strata problems are the same as for simple random sampling If strata are not clear, overlap may occur
Cluster	Cheaper Suitable for large populations	Less precise than other methods Clusters have to be uniform in make-up
Quota	It enables field work to be done quickly with a small sample size	Not a random process Interviewer has to judge characteristics Interviewer can introduce bias
Systematic	Simple to use Suitable for large samples	It is only random if the list is truly random It can introduce bias

Test yourself

1 Give **one** advantage and **one** disadvantage of simple random sampling.

2 Describe how you would take a systematic sample of ten students from a population of 100 students.

3 A supermarket wishes to hand out a questionnaire to ten men between 20 and 40 years of age, ten women between 20 and 40 years of age, and ten people over 40 years of age. What is the name given to this method of sampling?

4 A sample of residents of Cumbria is to be taken. Describe a suitable sampling method.

5 A factory wants to get the views of its workforce on the provision of overalls. Write the name of the sampling method being used in each of the following cases.
  a Starting at a randomly selected point, they ask every tenth person on their list of employees.
  b They ask all the people in five of the ten departments in the factory.
  c They ask eight people chosen at random from each of the ten (equally sized) departments.

1.4: Collecting data

- Understand that data can be obtained from primary or secondary sources
- Collect or obtain data by observation, surveys, experiments, counting, data logging, questionnaires and measurement
- Understand the advantages and disadvantages of using interviews versus questionnaires
- Design and use efficient and effective data capture sheets and methods of recording data
- Understand the role, and use of, plot studies and pre-testing
- Understand and account for the problems of design, ambiguity of wording, leading and biased questions, definitions and obtaining truthful responses
- Understand the advantages and disadvantages of open and closed questions
- Understand problems related to identifying the appropriate population and to the distribution and collection of questionnaires and surveys
- Identify appropriate sources of secondary data

Need more help?
For more on this topic, see pages 15–18 of the main Edexcel textbook (ISBN 978-1-84690-454-7).

Primary and secondary data

Primary data are data collected by or for the person who is going to use it. For example, you could measure the heights of the students in your class.

Secondary data are data collected by someone else for their own use. Secondary data may be collected from: websites, magazines and newspapers, databases and research articles.

Both forms of data collection have advantages and disadvantages, as shown in the table:

Data	Advantages	Disadvantages
Primary	You know how the data were obtained You know the accuracy of the data	It is time-consuming It is expensive
Secondary	Easy to obtain Cheap	Method of collection unknown The data may be out of date May contain mistakes or be biased

edexcel ▦ key terms

closed question A question that has a set of answers to choose from.
leading question A question that leads the respondent to agree.
open question A question that gives no suggested answers.
pilot survey A small-scale replica of a survey done to find out if the main survey will work.
primary data Data collected by or for yourself.
secondary data Data collected by someone else for their own use.

Surveys

These may take the form of a questionnaire or a set of observations.

A **pilot survey** is conducted on a small sample so that any problems can be identified before the main survey takes place. It identifies any problems with wording, likely responses, etc.

Questionnaires

A questionnaire contains a number of questions designed to gather particular pieces of information. There are two types of question, open questions and closed questions.

An **open question** leaves the respondent to give their own answer. There may be many different answers given and this could make the answers difficult to analyse. An example of an open question is: 'What do you think of school uniforms?'

A **closed question** gives the respondent a set of answers to choose from. An example of a closed question is: 'Do you strongly agree, agree, disagree or strongly disagree with having a school uniform? Tick one box.'

Strongly agree ☐   Agree ☐   Disagree ☐   Strongly disagree ☐

Questions should:

- be short and only cover one topic
- use words and phrases that are easily understood
- avoid leading questions such as 'You do agree that there should not be school uniforms don't you?', which asks the respondent to say yes
- not have possible answers that overlap (for closed questions) – e.g. if you have age groups 10 to 25 and 20 to 30, where does someone of 23 put their tick?

ResultsPlus
Exam tip

Look out for biased questions. These often include words like 'agree', 'like' and 'think'. To use these words in an unbiased question you need to include the opposite as well, e.g. 'Do you agree or disagree…'

ResultsPlus
Exam Question Report

A manager decides to use a questionnaire to find out his workers' views on selling them overalls. Three of the questions are shown below.
Write down a criticism of each.
Q1: Give one reason why you support the idea of having overalls sold at the factory.
Q2: How much would you be willing to pay for overalls? Tick one box.

Less than £10 ☐   £10–£20 ☐
£15–£30 ☐   Over £30 ☐

Q3: What colour should the overalls be? (3)

Answer:

Q1: One mark for 'biased' or 'an open question' or 'a leading question'.

Q2: One mark for 'the possible answers overlap'.

Q3: One mark for either 'an open question' or 'boxes needed'.

How students answered

The question was answered badly and few students got three marks. Some students did not read the question properly and tried to answer the questions rather than criticise them!

44% 0–1 marks

36% of students got two out of the three marks.

36% 2 marks

Only 20% got all three marks.

20% 3 marks

Test yourself

1 Which of the following are primary data and which are secondary data?
   A Data from the Internet.
   B Data from a local factory's database.
   C Data you collect about the pocket money of students.

2 a What is a pilot survey?   b What are the advantages of a pilot survey?

3 What is meant by an open question?

4 What is meant by a closed question?

5 What is meant by a leading question?

6 What words in the following question make it biased?
   'Do you agree that it would be a good idea to build a new school?'

7 What is wrong with the following questions?
   a How often do you visit the supermarket each month?

   0–1 times ☐   2–3 times ☐   4–5 times ☐

   b Do you agree that it would be a good idea to have a new bowling alley in the town? Yes/No
   c What facilities would you like to see built on the new estate?
   d You do want to go to the fair don't you?

ResultsPlus

Exam tip

Remember to read the question carefully. In question 7 you are asked to write down what is wrong with the questions, NOT to answer them yourself.

Worked example: Decision making

A researcher is going to see how effective the drug 'Repanse' is at relieving the pain of arthritis. He intends to get information from a sample of the patients attending a clinic. He intends to use a stratified sample.

a Suggest strata he could use.

Answer: Males and females OR By age, e.g. under 30, 30 to 50, and over 50.

b Write down a hypothesis he might use.

Answer: Repanse does relieve the pain of arthritis OR Repanse has no effect on the pain of arthritis OR Males get more/the same/less relief than females OR Under 30s get more relief than over 30s OR converses OR other equivalents.

c Describe the data he needs to collect.

Answer: The data he is likely to require are: numbers who think it does relieve pain; numbers who think it does not relieve pain; and numbers who are not sure whether it relieves pain. He needs the data for different genders and/or different age groups.

d He finds that 58% of the patients think that it works well, 30% think that it has no effect and the rest are not sure. What sort of diagram could he use to show this information?

Answer: Pie chart OR Bar chart.

Worked example: Data collection

A market research company wants to find out the views of customers about a new DIY store that has just opened.

a Give **two** reasons why the company should take a sample rather than a census.

Answer: Any two from: A sample is cheaper OR A sample takes less time OR There are fewer data in a sample OR A sample is easier to do.

b Describe the sampling frame.

Answer: All the customers of the DIY store.

c Describe a sampling unit.

Answer: A single customer of the DIY store.

The market research company wants to take a sample of 50 customers. The sample is to be taken by asking predetermined numbers of customers of different ages and genders to fill in a questionnaire.

d Write down an example of a closed question that could be used on this questionnaire.

Answer: Do you like this store? Yes/No (Other answers possible.)

e Give **two** reasons why a pilot survey (pre-test) should be carried out.

Answer: Any two of: It identifies problems in answering questions OR It shows likely answers OR It checks the questions work OR It checks the questions are clear OR It gives an idea of response rate OR It checks the time it takes to do.

f One question on the questionnaire is 'Do you agree that the goods are well laid-out and easy to find?' Discuss whether this is a suitably worded question for the questionnaire.

Answer: This is not a good question. This question is biased. It asks two questions in one. It has no answer boxes.

Exam tip

Always make it clear whether you are talking about a sample or a census in this type of question.

Watch out!

Students often answer the question rather than criticise it.

Need more help?
For more on this topic, see pages 18–21 of the main Edexcel textbook (ISBN 978-1-84690-454-7).

edexcel ⋮⋮⋮ key terms

before and after experiment An experiment in which the situations before and after change are compared.
capture/recapture A way of estimating the size of a large population.
control group A randomly selected group that is not subject to any procedures being tested.
data logging Automatic recording of data at regular intervals.
matched pairs Two samples in which the members are matched, e.g. identical twins.

Exam tip

Care needs to be taken with telephone polls. They can be biased, particularly if the samples used are small.

Exam tip

Remember that a control group needs to be of a similar size to the group to be tested.

1.5: Other methods of collecting data

- ✓ Obtain primary data by questionnaires or experiment
- ✓ Understand the advantages and disadvantages of using interviews versus questionnaires
- ✓ Understand and account for the problems of design, ambiguity of wording, leading and biased questions, definitions and obtaining truthful responses
- ✓ Understand and account for the problems of question design with simplest form of random response in sensitive cases
- ✓ Design simple statistical experiments to obtain data
- ✓ Estimate population size based on the Petersen capture/recapture method

Interviews

These may be conducted in three ways:

- sending a questionnaire by post
- calling people on the telephone
- face to face interviews.

Method	Advantages	Disadvantages
Post	Cheap	Least likely to get a response
Telephone	Better response rate	More costly Interviewer may cause bias
Face to face	Suitable for more complex questions Interviewer can explain question	Most costly Could be embarrassing for respondent Greatest chance of interviewer bias

Investigations and experiments

Data can be collected by doing an experiment or by direct observation.

When doing experiments you often want to compare the effect of changing something with what happens if it is not changed. Here are three ways of doing this:

- **Before and after experiments** in which observations are made before change takes place and again after change has occurred. For example, the number of accidents on a stretch of road before and after a speed limit is imposed.

- **Control groups** in which one group is subject to the experiment and another group is used to act as a control for comparison. For example, a drug under test might be given to one group and a harmless substance given to the other group.

- **Matched pairs** in which each individual in one group is paired with an individual in the second group who has everything in common with them except the thing being studied. For example, identical twins brought up by different people could be studied to see if their upbringing has made any difference.

Data logging

This is when a mechanical or electrical device is used to automatically take readings at set time intervals, e.g. the pulse rate of a person in hospital.

Capture/recapture method

This is generally used for estimating numbers of fish, birds and animals. It estimates the size of a population that is too numerous to count.

M members of the population are captured and marked. They are returned to the population and then a sample of size n is taken and the number of marked individuals m in this sample are counted. The population estimate is given by:

$$N = \frac{Mn}{m}$$

Assumptions made in the capture/recapture method include:

- The population has not changed; no members are entering or leaving.

- The probability of being caught is the same for all individuals.

- Marks (or tags) are not lost and are easily recognised.

Results **Plus**

Exam Question Report

Mary wants to estimate the number of fish in a lake.
She catches 40 fish, marks them and puts them back in the lake.
Later she catches another 40 fish and finds that five of them are marked.
a   Work out an estimate of the number of fish in the lake. (2)
b   Write down one assumption you have made about the population of fish in the lake. (1)

How students answered

a   ▲ Let N be the estimate. Then $\dfrac{40}{N} = \dfrac{5}{40}$

$$1600 = 5N$$
$$N = 320$$

⬤ Some candidates gave $\dfrac{5}{40}$ as their answer – this received 1 mark.

⬛ Questions like these are often very badly done by students. 60% of students scored no marks on this question. Some did not realise that they needed to relate the ratio of marked fish in the sample to the ratio in the population. A common error was to add 35 onto 40 giving 75. Some students just answered that 'There are a lot of fish'.

b   ▲ 1 mark for any one of: 'The population does not change', 'The marks are permanent', or 'Every fish is equally likely to be caught'.

Worked example: Capture/recapture method of data collection

Jake wants to estimate the number of salmon in a fish farm holding pond.

He catches 30 salmon, marks them and puts them back in the pond.

Later he catches another 20 salmon and finds that three of them are marked.

a Work out an estimate for the number of salmon in the pond.

Answer:
Let N be the number of salmon in the pond. The ratio of marked salmon in the pond to total number of salmon in the pond is the same as the ratio of number of marked salmon in the second sample to the number of salmon in the second sample:

$$\frac{\text{total number of marked salmon}}{\text{number of salmon in pond}} = \frac{\text{number of marked salmon in second sample}}{\text{number of salmon in second sample}}$$

$$\frac{30}{N} = \frac{3}{20}$$

$3N = 30 \times 20$ so $N = 200$ salmon

b Write down **one** assumption you have made about the population of fish in the lake.

Answer: Any one of: The size of the population is unchanged OR The population is well mixed OR There is a constant population OR The marks are permanent.

Test yourself

1 Write down two ways in which data can be collected by interviewing.

2 A dentist wants to find out whether patients react better to a new anaesthetic he is trialling. Suggest a way in which he could do this.

3 A council wants to find out whether speed humps slow down traffic. Suggest a way that they can do this.

4 Write down **two** advantages and **two** disadvantages of using a face-to-face interview.

5 A company intends to do an opinion poll to find out what people think about the economic state of the country. They decide to use a telephone poll. They phone 50 people in each of ten towns in the south-east of England. One member of the company says that this is not a satisfactory sample. Do you agree with this view? Give a reason for your answer.

6 A zoo has a very large aviary full of various types of finches. The aviary keeper wants to work out an estimate for the number of finches in the aviary. He nets 50 finches and rings them. A week later he nets 80 finches and finds that five are ringed. Work out an estimate for the number of finches in the aviary.

2.1: Tallies, frequency tables and two-way tables

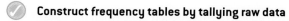

- ✓ Construct frequency tables by tallying raw data
- ✓ Tabulate using class intervals as appropriate
- ✓ Tabulate using open-ended classes and classes of varying width
- ✓ Read and interpret data presented in tabular or graphical form
- ✓ Design suitable tables, including summary tables; design and use appropriate two-way tables
- ✓ Convert raw data to summary statistics; design, construct and present summary tables

Need more help?
For more on this topic, see pages 30–41 of the main Edexcel textbook (ISBN 978-1-84690-454-7).

Tallies

A **tally** is used as a method of counting up items of data in fives. For example:

|||| is four items, and ||||| ||| is eight items.

Frequency tables

A **frequency table** is used to process raw data. A frequency table makes it easier to spot patterns.

The colour that had the highest frequency can be seen easily – it is blue with a frequency of 9.

Colour	Tally	Frequency
Red	|||	3
Blue	||||| ||||	9
Green	||||	4
Total		16

Grouping data

Sometimes when data are widely spread they are grouped into classes. For example, the table shows the scores made by 16 people during a game.

The total of the frequencies is the total number of observations.

Score	Frequency
8–10	3
11–13	8
14–16	5
Total	16

When there is an uneven spread of data, class intervals may vary in width and be open-ended. For example, the table shows the number of books read by a sample of 32 people in the course of a year. The last class is open-ended.

No. of books	Frequency
0–10	9
11–30	16
31+	7
Total	32

edexcel ░ key terms

class A group used for classifying the data.
cumulative frequency The total number of observations that are less than or equal to a certain value.
database An organised collection of data.
frequency table A way of presenting data showing the number of items, or the number of items in each group.
open-ended No finishing value or no starting value.
tally A way of counting items.
two-way table A way of showing two categories of data.

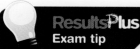

Results Plus
Exam tip

It is sensible to have a column for a tally – it helps to avoid errors. Using the 'five-bar gate' helps you to count the totals more accurately.

Higher tier

Cumulative frequencies

The **cumulative frequency** of a value is the total number of observations that are less than or equal to that value. The cumulative frequency of a value is the cumulative frequency for the previous value plus the frequency for that value.

A cumulative frequency column is often added to a frequency table when the data are quantitative. The following table shows the number of matches in each of 50 boxes.

Add the frequency of an item to the cumulative frequency for the previous item to get its cumulative frequency.

There are 3 boxes with 47 matches or fewer.

There are 3 + 10 = 13 boxes with 48 or fewer.

There are 13 + 18 = 31 boxes with 49 or fewer.

There are 31 + 12 = 43 boxes with 50 or fewer.

There are 43 + 7 = 50 boxes with 51 or fewer.

Number of matches	Frequency	Cumulative frequency
47	3	3
48	10	13
49	18	31
50	12	43
51	7	50

Two-way tables

These display frequencies for two categories of data.

You can read information from a **two-way table**.

The frequency for the number of females who like Games best is found at the intersection of the female column and the games row (9).

	Males	Females	Total
Maths	7	4	11
Games	8	9	17
Total	15	13	28

In this case, for example, there are a total of 28 in the class, 4 females like Maths best, and there are 15 males.

Worked example

The two-way table shows information about the gender and smoking habits of 100 people.

Complete the two-way table. [2]

Answer: This is an example of using a two-way table. Find the missing totals by adding the rows and columns in the table. Always double-check by adding your totals across and down to make sure they equal the final total.

You would get one mark for getting 27 and 73 in the bottom row and another mark for getting 50 and 50 in the last column.

	Smoker	Non-smoker	Total
Male	14	36	
Female	13	37	
Total			100

	Smoker	Non-smoker	Total
Male	14	36	50
Female	13	37	50
Total	27	73	100

Other tables

You can read information from other tables and databases in a similar way. Again, the data are found at the intersection of a row and a column. For example, consider the following table.

Food (100 g)	Protein (g)	Carbohydrate (g)	Fat (g)	Fibre (g)	Calories per 100 g
Dates	2	73	1	7	214
Grapes	1	16	1	1	69
Pears	1	15	0	2	61
Melon	1	5	0	1	21

The amount of carbohydrate in the pears is found at the intersection of the carbohydrate column and the pears row.

You can also see that melon has the least calories in 100 g, pears and melons both contain no fat and dates have 57 more grams of carbohydrate than grapes.

ResultsPlus
Watch out!

Sometimes data in tables are rounded. In this case it is rounded to the nearest whole number. Rounding can sometimes introduce anomalies. This often happens when a number of measurements are given and each is rounded so that the total does not equal the whole. For example, the number of acres on a farm might be 50 but when the different crop acreages are added up the total might come to 49.5, because the acreage for each crop is rounded to one decimal place.

Worked example: Cumulative frequency

For 100 days Saleem kept a record of the arrival times of the train he took to work. The table shows information about the amount of time the train was late.

Complete the cumulative frequency table. (2)

Answer: The cumulative frequencies are:

$0 \leq t \leq 1$: 23

$1 < t \leq 2$: $23 + 35 = 58$

$2 < t \leq 3$: $58 + 24 = 82$

$3 < t \leq 4$: $82 + 12 = 94$

$4 < t \leq 5$: $94 + 5 = 99$

$5 < t \leq 6$: $99 + 1 = 100$

Time late (t minutes)	Frequency	Cumulative frequency
$0 \leq t \leq 1$	23	
$1 < t \leq 2$	35	
$2 < t \leq 3$	24	
$3 < t \leq 4$	12	
$4 < t \leq 5$	5	
$5 < t \leq 6$	1	

If you got one cumulative frequency wrong, you would lose one mark.

If you got two or more cumulative frequencies wrong, you would not get any marks.

Test yourself

1 Here are the numbers of video games owned by each of a group of 30 children.

2	5	3	6	1	4	4	5	5	1
3	2	2	5	4	4	4	3	1	6
0	1	3	2	2	6	4	4	4	2

a Draw up a tally and frequency table for these data.
b Write down the most common frequency.

2 Here are the numbers of crisp packets sold by a corner shop each day for a period of 40 days.

14 7 10 12 8 3 10 9 7 4 21 17 15 11 4 6 16 14 24 23
19 10 12 5 16 23 20 16 8 9 15 2 18 14 14 12 20 14 7 9

a Draw up a grouped frequency table using classes 0–4, 5–9, 10–14, 15–19, and 20–24.
b What was the most common class?

3 Here is a partly completed two-way table showing the types of lunches eaten by a group of students.

	School dinner	Packed	Other	Total
Males	12	2	2	
Females	7	7	3	
Total				

a Copy and complete the table.
b How many students were in the group altogether?
c How many more males than females had a school dinner?

4 The numbers of sweets in 20 tubes of popular sweets were:

48 52 51 49 50 48 52 50 48 52 49 48 50 50 52 48 51 52 49 48

Draw a frequency table for these data, including a cumulative frequency column.

2.2: Pictograms, line graphs and bar charts

✓ Construct, use and understand pictograms for qualitative, quantitative and discrete data

✓ Construct, use and understand stick graphs for discrete data and bar charts for qualitative, quantitative and discrete data

✓ Label all forms of diagrams with correct and precise labelling

Pictograms

In a **pictogram** symbols or pictures are used to represent a certain number of items.

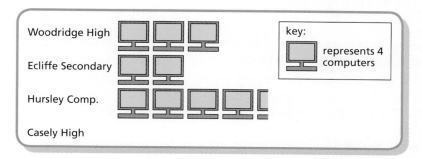
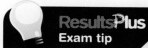

Woodridge High has $3 \times 4 = 12$ computers, and Hursley Comprehensive has $4\frac{1}{2} \times 4 = 18$ computers. Casely High has 14 computers so would require $\frac{14}{4} = 3\frac{1}{2}$ symbols.

Vertical/horizontal line (stick) graphs

In a **line graph** the frequency is represented by the length of a line. This line graph shows observations about the number of passengers per car.

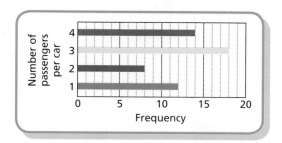

You can see immediately that there were 14 cars with four passengers in them. The total number of cars surveyed was $14 + 18 + 8 + 12 = 52$ cars.

Need more help?
For more on this topic, see pages 46–52 of the main Edexcel textbook (ISBN 978-1-84690-454-7).

edexcel :::: key terms

bar chart A chart in which the length of a bar (rectangle), drawn to scale, represents the frequency.
pictogram A diagram in which a number of symbols or pictures represent the frequency.
vertical/horizontal line diagram A diagram in which the length of a line, which is drawn to scale, represents frequency.

ResultsPlus
Exam tip

When drawing pictograms, make sure that:
- each picture is the same size
- the pictures can be divided easily to show different frequencies
- the spacing between pictures is the same
- you give a key.

ResultsPlus
Exam tip

Line diagrams can be used to represent discrete data. The lines may be horizontal or vertical.

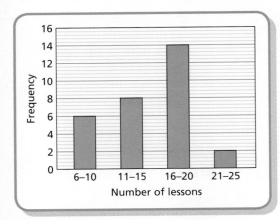

Bar charts

A **bar chart** is similar to a line graph but bars are used instead of lines. They are used to show qualitative data, discrete data or grouped discrete data.

This bar chart shows the number of driving lessons people had before passing their driving test.

There were 14 people who had between 16 and 20 lessons before passing their driving test.

Only two people needed between 21 and 25 lessons.

6 + 8 + 14 + 2 = 30 people were included in the sample.

ResultsPlus Exam tip

When drawing bar charts:
- draw bars of equal width for each category or group
- make sure the height or length of the bars represents the frequency
- make the gaps between the bars equal in width.

Test yourself

1 A pictogram is to be drawn to show the number of books on each of five shelves of a bookcase. For every six books a small picture of a book will be drawn.
   a Shelf 5 has 12 books. How many small pictures will be drawn to represent these?
   b Shelf 1 has 33 books. How many small pictures will be drawn to represent these?
   c Seven little books are used to represent the books on shelf 3. Write down the number of books on shelf 3.

2 A factory owner provides five buses in which their employees can travel to work. The buses are numbered 1 to 5. The manager checks the number of people on the buses on one Friday. The results are shown in the table.

Bus number	1	2	3	4	5
Number of people	12	15	8	10	18

   Draw a vertical line graph to represent these data.

3 The bar chart shows the number of islands in five island groups.

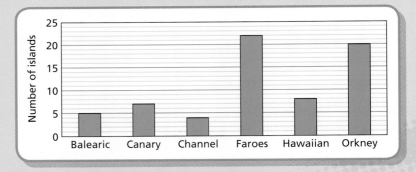

   a How many islands form the Orkney islands?
   b Which island group has the most islands?
   c Work out how many more islands the biggest group has than the smallest group.

ResultsPlus
Exam Question Report

The bar chart shows the number of repeat programmes shown by BBC1, BBC2 and ITV1 during one week.

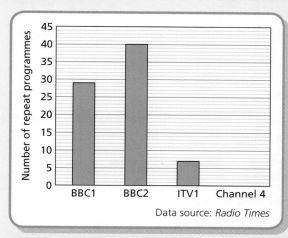

Data source: *Radio Times*

During the same week Channel 4 showed 39 repeat programmes.
a   Complete the bar chart to show this information. (1)
b   Work out the total number of repeat programmes shown during this week by BBC1, BBC2, ITV1 and Channel 4. (2)
c   Compare the numbers of repeat programmes. (2)

Answer:
a   A bar drawn going up to 39.
b   29 + 40 + 7 + 39 = 115
c   Any two from the following would get full marks: BBC has most repeats OR ITV has least repeats OR BBC2 had more repeats than BBC1, ITV or Channel 4 OR ITV has less repeats than BBC2 OR any other sensible **comparison**.

How students answered

a   Only 2% of students got part **a** wrong.

	2% 0 marks

Nearly all students managed to add the bar correctly for one mark.

	98% 1 mark

b   Only 4% of students got no marks for part **b**.

	4% 0 marks

Some candidates showed the addition of four reasonable (but not exactly right) figures – this got one mark.

	5% 1 mark

Most students picked up both the available marks.

	91% 2 marks

c   Just quoting figures got no marks. A common incorrect answer was ITV has 7, BBC1 has 29, BBC2 has 40 and Channel 4 has 39 – these are not comparisons.

	5% 0 marks

Some students lost a mark by only making one valid comparison.

	13% 1 mark

The key is that the question asks for comparisons, not just reading off the number.

	82% 2 marks

2.3: Stem and leaf diagrams and pie charts

Need more help?
For more on this topic, see pages 53–58 of the main Edexcel textbook (ISBN 978-1-84690-454-7).

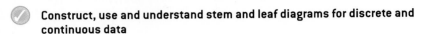 Construct, use and understand stem and leaf diagrams for discrete and continuous data

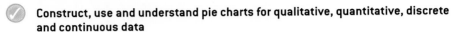 Construct, use and understand pie charts for qualitative, quantitative, discrete and continuous data

Stem and leaf diagrams

A **stem and leaf diagram** allows you to show the distribution of data without losing the details of the data. Each number in a sample is split into two parts:

- The first digit (or digits) of the number, which is called the **stem**.
- The last digits, which are called **leaves**.

The numbers in the stem are placed to the left of a vertical line and the ordered leaves are placed to the right.

This stem and leaf diagram shows the amount of rainfall, in cm, that fell over 31 days in December.

Stem	Leaves
0	0 0 0 0 0 4 7 8
1	0 1 1 2 2 6 7
2	1 1 2 2 7 8
3	0 1 2 3 5
4	3 5
5	2 2 6

key:
2 | 1
means 2.1 cm of rainfall

You can see from the stem and leaf diagram that 0.0 cm was the most common amount of rainfall, occurring on five days. There were six days on which the recorded rainfall was more than 2 cm but less than 3 cm.

Pie charts

A **pie chart** shows how something is shared or divided up. It uses area to represent frequency.

Sectors of a circle are used to represent shares. The angles of the sectors must add up to 360°.

The angle of a sector is given by:

$$\text{Angle} = \frac{\text{actual share}}{\text{total being shared}} \times 360°$$

This pie chart shows the types of housing in Showtown.

You can see that $\frac{1}{4}$ of the houses were detached.

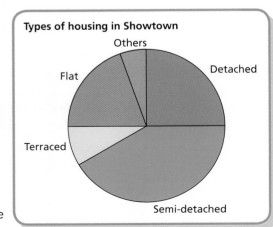
Types of housing in Showtown

edexcel ⋮⋮⋮ key terms

stem and leaf A diagram that shows the distribution of data. The stem is the first digit(s) and the leaves are the last digits.

pie chart A diagram showing how something is shared or divided up.

ResultsPlus Exam tip

Draw a stem and leaf diagram with the leaves out of order first. You can then draw an ordered stem and leaf using this by just ordering the leaves.

ResultsPlus Exam tip

You can use this formula in reverse to find a share given the angle:

$$\text{Share} = \frac{\text{Angle}}{360} \times \text{total being shared}$$

Test yourself

1 The stem and leaf diagram shows the numbers of spam e-mails received over a 20-day period.

Stem	Leaves
0	4 6
1	1 1 5
2	1 2 2 2 3 7 8
3	2 3 5 7 7 8
4	5 7

key:
2 | 1
means 21

  a Which number was most frequent?

  b Which were the highest and lowest numbers?

  c On how many days were there between 20 and 30 spam e-mails?

2 The pulse rates of 20 students were:

55 80 75 63 76 64 68 90 88 65 73 59 71 64 60 74 85 73 81 94

Draw a stem and leaf diagram to represent these data.

3 The pie chart shows the types of heating installed by a plumber in one year.

  a What type of heating did he install most of?

  b If there were 100 installations altogether, how many were oil-fired?

Pie chart: 45°, 135°, 90°, 90°

- Gas-fired
- Oil-fired
- Electric
- Solid fuel

4 The amount of crops grown on a farm were: wheat 45 hectares; barley 15 hectares; and oats 30 hectares. A pie chart is to be drawn for these data. What angle would oats have on the pie chart?

5 39 students were asked to read the same essay. The time taken, to the nearest minute, for each of 30 of the students is shown in the stem and leaf diagram.

Time   Key: 2 | 5 = 25

2	5	6	7	8	8	9						
3	2	2	2	3	4	4	4	4	5	6	7	7 7 9
4	0	0	1	1	1	2	2	3				
5	0	1										

The times for the other students are: 43 51 43 45 52 48 53 55 48

Complete the stem and leaf diagram.

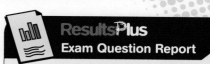

The pie chart shows information about the numbers of gold, silver and bronze medals won by Canada in the Paralympic Games in 2004.
Canada won a total of 72 medals.
Nineteen of these were silver.

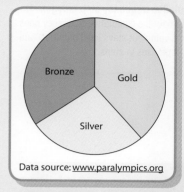

Bronze, Gold, Silver

Data source: www.paralympics.org

a Calculate the angle used for silver in the pie chart. (2)

The size of the angle used for gold in the pie chart is 140°.

b Work out the number of gold medals. (2)

Answer:

a $\frac{19}{72} \times 360° = 95°$ **b** $\frac{140°}{360°} \times 72° = 28°$

How students answered

a Some students got this wrong because they measured the angle on the diagram. You are given the total number of medals and the number of silver medals, so you can work out the size of the angle.

66% 0 marks

Some students lost 1 mark because they wrote down the calculation but did not work out the answer.

1% 1 mark

Only about one-third of students answered this question correctly.

33% 2 marks

b Some students lost 1 mark because they wrote down the calculation but did not work out the answer.

53% 1 mark

2.4: Cumulative frequency step polygons

Need more help?
For more on this topic, see pages 59–60 of the main Edexcel textbook (ISBN 978-1-84690-454-7).

edexcel ⠿ **key terms**

cumulative frequency step polygon This shows how the cumulative frequency goes up at each value but stays level between values. The graph rises in steps.

ResultsPlus
Exam tip

If you are asked to find values for a certain cumulative frequency in an exam, always draw in the lines on the graph.

✓ Construct, use and understand cumulative frequency step polygons

A **cumulative frequency step polygon** can be used when the data are discrete and not grouped.

As each number is reached, the cumulative frequency increases by the frequency of that number. It then remains at that level until the next number is reached.

This cumulative frequency table gives information about the numbers of matches in each of 50 boxes.

Number of matches	Frequency	Cumulative frequency
47	2	2
48	9	11
49	19	30
50	10	40
51	10	50

The cumulative frequency diagram shows how the cumulative frequency of the number of matches per box in a sample changes.

You can see that the 25th number was 49 (pink line).

The 10th number was 48 (green line).

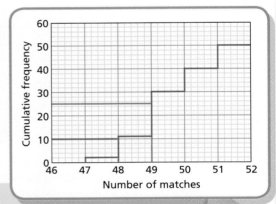

Test yourself

1 The step polygon shows the number of working days it took for some second-class letters to be delivered.

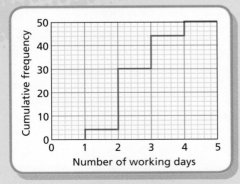

a How many letters were sent?
b How long did it take most letters to arrive?

c If the numbers of working days are arranged in order, from smallest to largest, how long did the 25th letter take to arrive?

2 The table shows the number of letters per word in a sentence taken from a child's first reading book.

Complete the table and draw a step polygon for these data.

Number of words	Frequency	Cumulative frequency
1	0	
2	1	
3	5	
4	6	
5	4	

2.5: Using bar charts to make comparisons

 Construct, use and understand multiple bar charts or composite bar charts for qualitative, quantitative and discrete data

Need more help?
For more on this topic, see pages 60–62 of the main Edexcel textbook (ISBN 978-1-84690-454-7).

Multiple bar charts

Multiple bar charts are used to compare two (or more) sets of data. For each class there will be two (or more) bars.

For example, this multiple bar chart shows the number of boy and girl students late for school during one week.

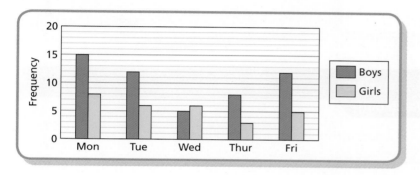

 **key terms**

composite bar chart A bar chart in which two (or usually more) bar charts are combined by putting the bars for each category one above the other in a single bar.
multiple bar chart Two (or more) bar charts combined so that for each class there are two (or more) bars.

ResultsPlus
Exam tip

You will be expected to make a comparison between the two (or more) classes in a multiple bar chart.

You can see from the graph that on each day except Wednesday there were more boys late than there were girls.

There were eight boys late on Thursday compared to three girls.

Composite bar charts

Composite bar charts show how the total frequency for each category is divided up between the separate component groups.

For example, this composite bar chart gives information about the number of computers and printers sold by a shop each year over a three-year period.

You can see that total sales increased each year, and that sales of laptops increased by a larger amount than sales of either of the other products.

In year 2 there were 1400 printers, 700 laptops and 100 desktops sold. The total sales were 2200 products sold.

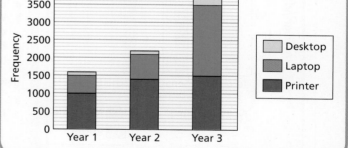

ResultsPlus
Exam tip

If the bars are done as percentages rather than frequencies, they will show 100% and will all be the same height.

Worked example

These composite bar charts show the percentages of GCSE grades gained by males and by females in England in 2001/2002.

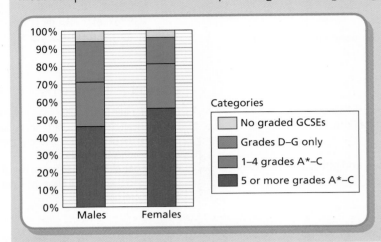

a Did males or females have the biggest percentage of five or more grades A*–C? (1)

Answer: Females.

b In which category did males and females gain the same percentage? (1)

Answer: 1–4 grades A*–C.

c Work out the percentage of males that gained grades D–G only. (1)

Answer: 23%

ResultsPlus
Watch out!

Be careful – many students misread the key in this type of question.

ResultsPlus
Exam Question Report

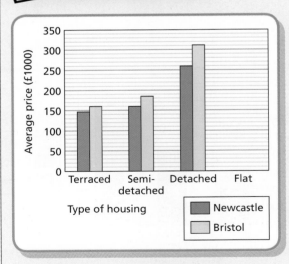

The multiple bar chart shows information about the average price, to the nearest £1000, of three different types of housing in Newcastle and Bristol in August 2005.

The average price of a flat in Newcastle in August 2005 was £130 000. The average price of a flat in Bristol in August 2005 was £160 000.

a Complete the multiple bar chart. (2)
b What does the multiple bar chart show you about the average price of detached houses? (1)
c If you had £150 000 to spend on housing in Newcastle, which type of housing were you most likely to buy? (1)

How students answered

a Two bars correctly drawn to the right height (left-hand bar £130 000, right-hand bar £160 000). 87% of students got both marks.

Students who drew one bar correctly got one mark.

b They are more expensive in Bristol than Newcastle. 83% of candidates got the mark.

A common incorrect answer was 'detached housing is expensive'.

c EITHER **Flat** or **terraced**.

Test yourself

1 The composite bar chart shows the number of newspapers sold by a newsagent's shop.

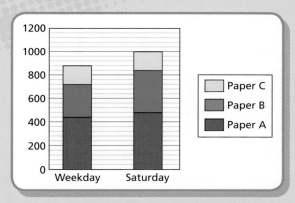

  a Altogether how many papers were sold on Saturday?

  b How many copies of Paper B were sold on Saturday?

  c Compare the sales of papers on Saturdays with the sales on weekdays.

  d On a Sunday 360 copies of Paper A are sold, 240 copies of Paper B and 80 copies of Paper C. Copy the multiple bar chart and add a bar for Sunday.

2 The multiple bar chart shows the ways in which boys and girls travelled to school.

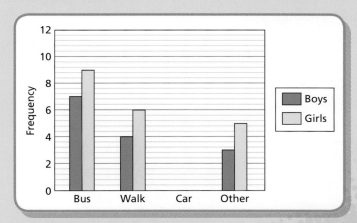

Eight boys and twelve girls travelled to school by car.

  a Copy and complete the multiple bar chart.

  b How many girls were there altogether?

  c How many boys travelled by bus?

Need more help?

For more on this topic, see pages 64–66 of the main Edexcel textbook (ISBN 978-1-84690-454-7).

2.6: Using pie charts to make comparisons

 Construct, use and understand pie charts and comparative pie charts with area proportional to frequency

edexcel key terms

comparative pie charts Two pie charts drawn so that their total areas are in the same proportions as their total frequencies.

pie chart A chart that shows how something is shared or divided up.

Comparative pie charts

Pie charts use areas to represent frequencies. The angle of a sector shows what proportion of the whole is represented by the sector and the area of the sector is a measure of the frequency.

If two pie charts are drawn that represent similar data, but in which the total frequencies differ, the areas of the two circles must be different.

The areas of the two pie charts must be in the same ratio as the two total frequencies.

If the frequencies are F_1 and F_2, and the radii r_1 and r_2, then:

$$\frac{F_2}{F_1} = \frac{\text{Area 2}}{\text{Area 1}} = \frac{\pi r_2^2}{\pi r_1^2}$$

or $\dfrac{r_2^2}{r_1^2} = \dfrac{F_2}{F_1}$ or $r_2 = \sqrt{\dfrac{F_2}{F_1}} \times r_1$

For example, the two pie charts below show the number of television sets per household in two villages – Orangeford and Appleville.

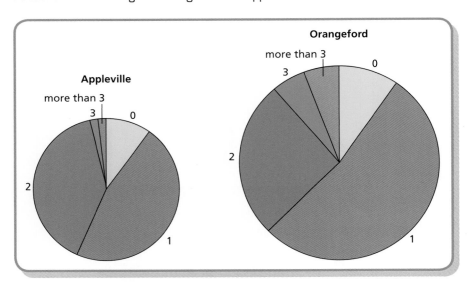

ResultsPlus
Exam tip

Remember that areas represent the frequencies, so the greater the area the greater the frequency.

The total number of households in Orangeford is greater because the circle for Orangeford has a larger area.

The frequency (number) of households with no television in Orangeford is greater than in Appleville, because although the angle is the same, the area is greater.

The frequency (number) of households with two televisions is a smaller proportion of the total in Orangeford than it is in Appleville (the angle is smaller) but is still greater in number than in Appleville (the area is larger).

ResultsPlus
Exam Question Report

The comparative pie charts show some information about the players at Seaton squash club in 1980 and in 1990. The three types of players at Seaton squash club are Senior male, Senior female and Junior. What has happened to the number of Senior male players at Seaton squash club between 1980 and 1990? Give a reason for your answer. (2)

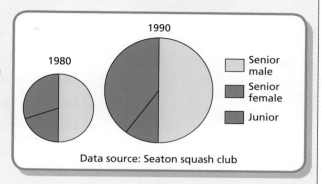

Data source: Seaton squash club

Answer: The number has increased. There is the same proportion but the area is larger.

How students answered

Few students got full marks. They did not seem to realise that the area of the pie chart is important. Common incorrect answers were:

'It is impossible to say because there are no numbers on the pie chart.'

'There was no change as half the pie chart was being used each year.'

42% 0 marks

Some students lost a mark by only mentioning what happened to the number but not saying *how* they knew the number had increased.

9% 1 mark

Less than half the students got both marks for this question.

49% 2 marks

Test yourself

1 The two pie charts show the methods of travel to school used by boy and girl students in a survey.

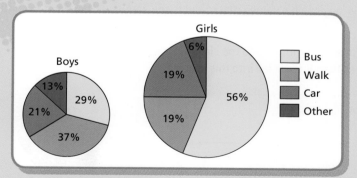

a Did more boys or more girls go to school by car? Give a reason for your answer.
b Was the proportion of boys walking to school bigger or smaller than the proportion of girls walking to school? Give a reason for your answer.
c Were there more boys or more girls in the survey?

2 The total number of boys in another survey was 25 and the number of girls was 16. If the circle for the boys is to have a radius of 5 cm, what should the radius for the girls' circle be?

3.1: Frequency tables for continuous data

- ✓ Understand, use and define situations for grouped and ungrouped data
- ✓ Tabulate using class intervals as appropriate
- ✓ Use open-ended classes and classes of varying width
- ✓ Tabulate using various forms of grouping the data
- ✓ Combine categories to simplify tables with an understanding of the problems of over-simplification, the effects on readability, the identification or masking of trends and the loss of detail

Need more help?
For more on this topic, see pages 79–80 of the main Edexcel textbook (ISBN 978-1-84690-454-7).

edexcel ⠿ key terms

class interval The range of values that is grouped together to form a class.
class width The maximum possible value that would be included in the class minus the minimum possible value.
continuous data Continuous data are data that can take any values in a given range.
frequency of continuous data The number of values that fall within a class interval.

Grouping continuous data

Continuous data can take any value on a continuous scale. **Class intervals** must cover the scale without the intervals overlapping. For example:

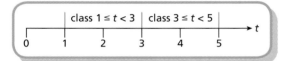

$1 \leq t < 3$ means that t can be any value greater than or equal to 1 and less than 3.

1 to 3 is the class interval and $3 - 1 = 2$ is the **class width**.

Dealing with rounded data

Often measurements are rounded to the nearest whole number. If this is the case, an additional rule is 'all possible values that round to the same number must be in the same class'.

If the numbers after rounding fit into the class $6 \leq t < 8$ then anything equal to or greater than 5.5 and less than 8.5 will fall into this group.

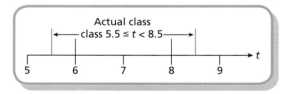

The true class interval in this case is 5.5 to 8.5 and the class width is $8.5 - 5.5 = 3$.

Frequency tables for continuous data

Continuous data can be sorted into a **frequency** table. For example, this table shows the times, in seconds, taken by 20 students to run a 400 m race.

In this example the intervals are of equal width.

Time (s)	Frequency
$50 < t \leq 60$	6
$60 < t \leq 70$	6
$70 < t \leq 80$	5
$80 < t \leq 90$	3

This need not always be the case. Use narrow intervals when the data are grouped together and wider intervals when the data are spread out.

If intervals are made too small the pattern becomes difficult to see. If the intervals are too large, important detail may be lost.

Test yourself

1 Peter records the amount of rainfall, *r* cm, each day in September.

The classes are $0 \leq r < 1$, $1 \leq r < 2$, $2 \leq r < 3$, $3 \leq r < 4$, etc.
   a Into which class will Peter put 2 cm of rainfall?
   b Into which class will he put 2.3 cm of rainfall?

2 Jamie recorded the length of 30 birds' eggs in centimetres. They were:

2.2   2.0   2.3   2.3   2.2   2.4   2.3   2.0   1.9   2.5
2.4   2.3   2.0   2.5   2.4   2.0   2.5   2.1   2.2   2.2
1.9   2.0   2.4   2.2   2.4   1.8   2.0   2.5   2.4   2.2

Copy and complete the frequency table for these data.

Length (cm)	Tally	Frequency
$1.8 \leq l < 2.0$		
$2.0 \leq l < 2.2$		
$2.2 \leq l < 2.4$		
$2.4 \leq l < 2.6$		

3 Here are the heights of 24 children rounded to the nearest centimetre.

136   143   139   156   160   155
165   148   149   150   146   154
152   160   137   167   156   159
148   160   156   162   156   149

   a What is the range of values that could be represented by the height 148 centimetres?
   b Jenny wants to use the class intervals $135 < h \leq 140$, $140 < h \leq 144$, $143 < h \leq 148$, etc. What is wrong with these intervals?
   c Draw up a grouped frequency table for these data using class intervals of 10 centimetres.

4 Jane and Mark were going to do an investigation into the times it took a telephonist to answer a call. The times were measured to the nearest tenth of a second. Here are the class intervals each decided to use.

Jane:

Time (s)	0–5	6–10	11–15	16–20	21–25

Mark:

Time *t* (s)	$0 < t \leq 5$	$5 < t \leq 10$	$10 < t \leq 15$	$15 < t \leq 20$	$20 < t \leq 25$

   a The first call took 5.5 seconds. Why did Jane have difficulty recording this in her table?
   b Which of the two tables is best? Explain the reasons for your answer.

Need more help?
For more on this topic, see pages 86–87 of the main Edexcel textbook (ISBN 978-1-84690-454-7).

3.2: Cumulative frequency diagrams for continuous data

 Construct, use and understand frequency diagrams and cumulative frequency diagrams for continuous data

edexcel key terms

cumulative frequency The number of values less than or equal to the upper class boundary.
cumulative frequency diagram A diagram showing how the cumulative frequency changes as the variable increases.

Cumulative frequency

The **cumulative frequency** is the sum of the frequencies up to and including the upper class boundary of the class interval being considered.

Each cumulative frequency can be found by adding the frequency for the class interval being considered to the cumulative frequency of the previous class interval. For example, the table shows the time, in seconds, for a number of mice to find their way through a maze.

Time (s)	Frequency	Cumulative frequency	
$8 \le t < 12$	8	8	
$12 \le t < 16$	14	22	8 + 14 = 22
$16 \le t < 20$	25	47	22 + 25 = 47
$20 \le t < 24$	8	55	
$24 \le t < 28$	5	60	

Cumulative frequency diagrams

A **cumulative frequency diagram** is drawn by plotting the cumulative frequencies against their corresponding upper class boundaries.

In the case of the mice, the diagram would look like this:

ResultsPlus
Exam tip

You can either join the points with a curve, as here, or with straight lines. In an exam straight lines are easier to draw and use.

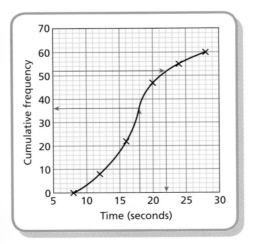

ResultsPlus
Exam tip

If you are asked to find values from the diagram, always draw in the lines to show how you got your answer.

A cumulative frequency diagram can be used to estimate or predict other values.

From the diagram:

- 52 mice are estimated to have completed the maze in 22 seconds or less (green lines).
- In 18 seconds or less, 36 mice are estimated to have completed the maze (red lines).

Exam Question Report

The table gives information about the typing speed, in words per minute, of a random sample of 60 typists at a typing agency.

a Use the information in the table above to complete the cumulative frequency table. (1)
b Draw a cumulative frequency diagram to represent this information. (3)
c Use your cumulative frequency diagram to find an estimate of the median (the typing speed of the 30th typist when they are arranged in order of typing speeds). (2)

Typing speed	Number of typists	Cumulative frequency
$30 < x \le 40$	10	10
$40 < x \le 50$	22	
$50 < x \le 60$	14	
$60 < x \le 70$	10	
$70 < x \le 80$	4	

How students answered

Few students gained full marks for this question. Part **c** was particularly badly done.

a ▲ Cumulative frequencies are 10, 32, 46, 56 and 60.

b ▲ Cumulative frequency diagram as shown. There was 1 mark for plotting points, 1 mark for joining points, and 1 mark for correct labels.

● The cumulative frequency diagram caused a lot of problems. Many students drew the axes correctly but then plotted the mid-points rather than the end-points. Most managed to produce a curve of some sort. This got 1 mark.

■ Common errors were: Many students did not label the axes. The scales were often written as group boundaries, such as 30 ≤ 40, 30 ≤ 50 etc., rather than individual typing speeds. Axes were sometimes drawn the wrong way round.

c ▲ 49 to 50 w.p.m. There was 1 mark for drawing the line on the graph, and 1 mark for the correct answer.

● If just a correct line was drawn on the graph then 1 mark was awarded.

■ A common error was for students to give their own opinion rather than an answer based on the statistics.

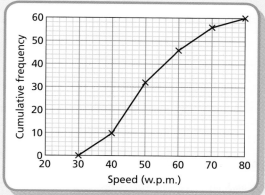

Test yourself

1 The diameters, in millimetres, of 60 pellets of lead shot are shown in the table.

Diameter	$1.0 < d \le 1.5$	$1.5 < d \le 2.0$	$2.0 < d \le 2.5$	$2.5 < d \le 3.0$	$3.0 < d \le 3.5$
Frequency	2	9	23	20	6
Cumulative frequency					

a Copy and complete the cumulative frequency table.
b Draw a cumulative frequency diagram for these data.
c Use your diagram to estimate how many pellets were less than 1.75 mm in diameter.
d Use your diagram to estimate how many pellets were between 1.7 and 2.7 mm in diameter.

2 The table gives some information about the height, in m, of 80 young people.

Height	$1.4 < d \le 1.5$	$1.5 < d \le 1.6$	$1.6 < d \le 1.7$	$1.7 < d \le 1.8$	$1.8 < d \le 1.9$
Frequency	6	14	28	20	12

a Draw a cumulative frequency diagram for these data.
b Use your diagram to estimate how many young people were less than 1.65 m tall.
c Use your diagram to estimate how many young people were between 1.5 and 1.75 m tall.

3.3: Histograms and frequency polygons

✓ Construct, use and understand histograms with equal class intervals for continuous data

✓ Understand the shape and simple properties of frequency distributions

✓ Understand symmetrical, positive and negative skew

Need more help?
For more on this topic, see pages 89–91 of the main Edexcel textbook (ISBN 978-1-84690-454-7).

Histograms

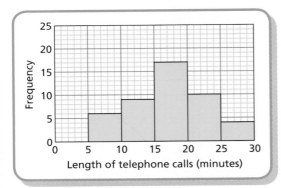

Length of telephone calls (minutes)

Histograms are similar to bar charts but because they represent continuous data there are no gaps between the bars. Each bar represents a single class interval.

The histogram on the left shows the lengths, in minutes, of telephone calls.

There were nine telephone calls that lasted between 10 and 15 minutes.

The greatest number of calls in any of the five-minute period groups was 17. These calls lasted between 15 and 20 minutes each.

A histogram shows how the data are distributed across the class intervals.

edexcel ⠿ key terms

frequency polygon A line joining the points plotted for the frequency and mid-points of the class intervals.
histogram Shows the distribution of continuous data. It has bars with no gaps between them.
skew Distributions that are not symmetrical are said to have skew.
symmetric Evenly distributed.

Frequency polygons

A **frequency polygon** joins the mid-points of the tops of the bars.

It is not necessary to draw a histogram in order to draw a frequency polygon. You can plot the actual frequencies against the middle points of the class intervals.

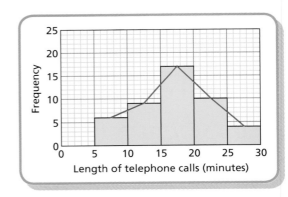

Length of telephone calls (minutes)

Skew

A distribution can be **symmetrical**, **positively skewed** or **negatively skewed**.

ResultsPlus
Exam tip

In negative skew the middle value is to the left of the highest point. In positive skew it is to the right.

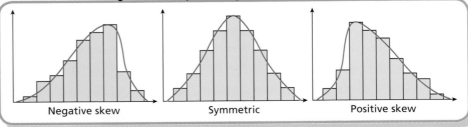

Negative skew   Symmetric   Positive skew

Exam Question Report

In an experiment a psychologist records the times, *x* seconds, for 50 people to complete a puzzle. The results are summarised in the table.

a Draw a histogram to represent the data in the table. (3)
b i Shade the region in your histogram that is within 40 to 80 seconds. (1)
ii Find the proportion of people represented by this region. (3)

How students answered

Many students found this difficult.

a ▲ 1 mark for correct axes, 1 mark for drawing the histogram, with no gaps between the bars, and 1 mark for correct heights.

■ Common errors were: Bar charts drawn instead of histograms. Scales written as class intervals.

b ▲ i 1 mark for correct shading.

ii 1 mark for correct frequencies, 1 mark for adding together and 1 mark for the correct answer: 9 + 12 = 21 people.

● 1 or 2 marks could be gained by getting the correct frequencies and/ or adding. Students who drew a bar graph in part **a** were still able to get a mark for shading in part **b i**.

x	Number of people (f)
$20 < x \le 40$	10
$40 < x \le 60$	9
$60 < x \le 80$	12
$80 < x \le 100$	9
$100 < x \le 120$	10

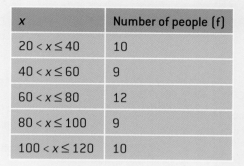

Test yourself

1 The table gives information about the widths of a sample of 100 leaves from a laurel bush.

Width (mm)	$30 \le w < 35$	$35 \le w < 40$	$40 \le w < 45$	$45 \le w < 50$	$50 \le w < 55$	$55 \le w < 60$
Frequency	5	25	25	20	15	10

a Draw a histogram for these data.
b Describe the skew of these data.

2 The frequency polygons to the right give information about the weights of 200 boys and 200 girls.

Compare the weights of the boys with the weights of the girls.

3 Describe the skew of each of the distributions below.

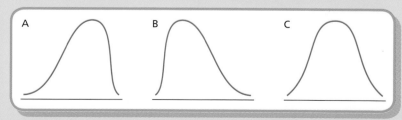

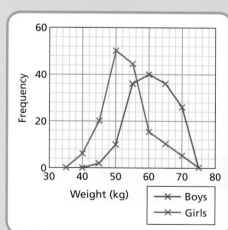

Need more help?
For more on this topic, see pages 94–95 of the main Edexcel textbook (ISBN 978-1-84690-454-7).

3.4: Histograms with unequal class intervals

 Construct, use and understand histograms with equal class intervals, histograms with unequal class intervals and the concept of frequency density, for continuous data

Histograms with unequal class intervals

If the class intervals are unequal you must use the area of a bar rather than its height to represent the frequency. This is done by introducing the idea of **frequency density**.

If area (= width of class interval × height) = frequency,

then height = $\dfrac{\text{frequency}}{\text{width of class interval}}$. We call this height the **frequency density**.

Here is an example.

The table shows the time, in minutes, spent by solicitors with clients at a first meeting:

Time	Frequency	Class width	Frequency density
$10 < t \le 20$	7	10	0.7
$20 < t \le 25$	17	5	3.4
$25 < t \le 30$	38	5	7.6
$30 < t \le 40$	30	10	3.0
$40 < t \le 60$	8	20	0.4

Class width = 20 − 10

Frequency density = $\frac{7}{10}$

edexcel ⦂ key terms

frequency density The frequency of a class interval divided by its width:

frequency density = $\dfrac{\text{frequency}}{\text{width of class interval}}$

unequal class intervals Intervals that have different class widths. Intervals are often narrower where the data are more numerous, and wider when they are less numerous.

ResultsPlus
Exam tip

To find the frequency between any two times, you find the area between them. Sometimes you are asked to find how many took a longer (or shorter) time than a given value. In this case you find the area above (or below) that value.

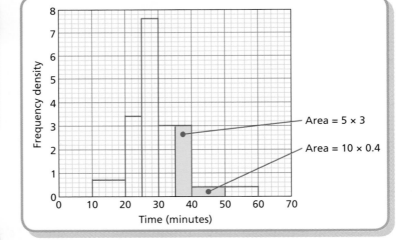

Area = 5 × 3

Area = 10 × 0.4

ResultsPlus
Watch out!

When you draw a histogram with unequal class intervals, remember to either label the vertical axis or give a key.

Make sure you know the difference between a histogram and a bar chart.

You can get information from a histogram that uses a frequency density scale.

The number of clients in the above example who took between 35 and 50 minutes is represented by the shaded area.

The number of people = (5 × 3) + (10 × 0.4) = 15 + 4 = 19 people.

The number of people who took more than 35 minutes would be 15 + (20 × 0.4) = 23 people.

ResultsPlus
Exam Question Report

Time t (minutes)	Frequency
$0 < t \leq 3$	9
$3 < t \leq 5$	47
$5 < t \leq 6$	38
$6 < t \leq 8$	60
$8 < t \leq 12$	46

(Data source: Supa store December 2004)

The manager of a supermarket records the times taken, t minutes, to serve 200 customers. The results are summarised in the frequency table.

a   **Draw a histogram for this information. (3)**
b   **Calculate an estimate for the median time to serve these customers. (2)**

How students answered

a   ▲ Students got the full three marks for frequency density bars with correct heights and widths and no gaps. Heights: 3, 23.5, 38, 30, 11.5.

   ● One mark was awarded for frequency densities, one mark for scales and one mark for correctly plotted bars (no gaps). Some students lost one or two marks here.

   ■ Many students got this wrong – some drew a bar chart and a common error was not to use frequency density correctly.

b   ▲ $6 + \dfrac{6}{60} \times 2 = 6.2$

   ● Many students scored one mark for realising that they were required to find the 100th (or 100.5th) value of the data.

   ■ Very few students got this right. Many students simply drew a bar chart with class intervals for scales.

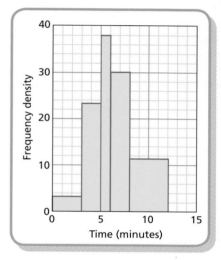

Test yourself

1   The table gives information about the lifetime, in hours, of 70 light bulbs.

Lifetime (hrs)	Frequency	Class width	Frequency density
$20 < l \leq 24$	14		
$24 < l \leq 26$	36		
$26 < l \leq 28$	10		
$28 < l \leq 30$	10		

a   Complete the table.
b   Draw a histogram for these data.

2   The histogram shows the distribution of times taken to complete a race.

   a   How many people took between 25 and 40 minutes to finish the race?

   b   How many people took longer than 42 minutes to finish the race?

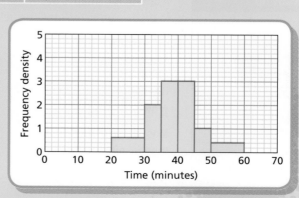

3.5: Population pyramids and choropleth maps

✅ Construct, use and understand population pyramids for continuous data

✅ Construct, use and understand choropleth maps (shading)

Need more help?
For more on this topic, see pages 101–105 of the main Edexcel textbook (ISBN 978-1-84690-454-7).

edexcel ⠿ key terms

choropleth map A map that shows the density or frequency of a statistic in regions of a country (or area).
population pyramid A diagram that shows the distribution of various age groups in two strata (usually males and females) of a population.

Population pyramids

A **population pyramid** shows the distribution of various age groups in a population, which normally forms the shape of a pyramid.

It typically consists of two back-to-back bar graphs, with the population plotted on the horizontal axis and age on the vertical axis, one showing the number of males and one showing females. The number of males and females may be shown as a raw number or as a percentage of the total population.

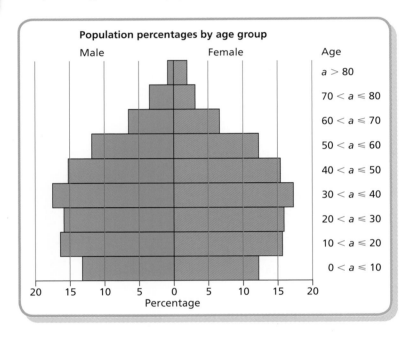

The diagram tells you that the highest percentage of males and females is in the 30 to 40 age group.

ResultsPlus
Exam tip

In an exam you **cannot** use colour or shading since everything has to be in black and white. A system of hatching will be used, for example:

Choropleth maps

A **choropleth map** is used to show regions of a country (or area). The regions are shaded in proportion to the statistic being displayed on the map, e.g. population density. A key is given to the shading.

The map on the right gives information about the number of daisy plants growing in a field.

Most daisy plants were in the top left squares.

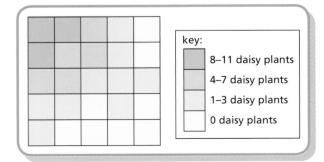

Exam Question Report

A bird reserve is divided into 16 regions of equal size. The number of swans' nests in each region is counted. The results are shown in the diagram on the right .

0	0	3	3
1	2	4	3
2	1	4	6
3	5	7	8

a Use the information in the diagram to complete this choropleth map.
12 regions have already been shaded. (1)

Number of swans' nests
0–2
3–5
6–8

| 5 | means 5 swans' nests in this region |

b Describe how the swans' nests are spread across the bird reserve. (2)

How students answered

a 91% of students got this mark by shading in the boxes as shown below.

b Uneven spread (1 mark). More swans at bottom right (1 mark).

Most candidates got one mark for a description of the uneven spread of nests in the bird reserve, such as 'more in the bottom right' or 'more in the south-east'. Very few described the spread so they did not get the second mark.

The most common mistake was a description of the number of nests in each individual section rather than a comment on the overall spread.

Test yourself

1 The population pyramids give information about the ages of people in a country.
  a Are males or females likely to live longer in this country?
  b In which age group were there most men?
  c In which age group were there least women?

2 The diagram below shows the position of cows in a field.

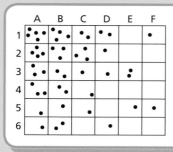

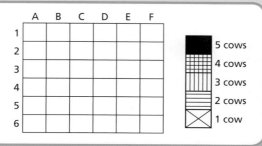

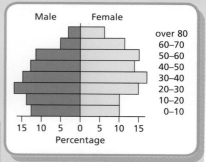

a Copy and complete the choropleth map.
b There is a feeding trough in the field. Suggest the square in which it is situated. Give a reason for your answer.

3.6: Misleading diagrams

✓ Understand the distinction between well presented and poorly presented data

✓ Understand the potential for visual misuse, by omission or misrepresentation

Need more help?

For more on this topic, see pages 107–108 of the main Edexcel textbook (ISBN 978-1-84690-454-7).

Misleading diagrams

Diagrams represent the magnitude or frequency of data by using the lengths of lines (or bars), or by the use of areas, together with scales. If any of these are hard to understand or are missing then the diagram is poorly presented.

Scales

Scales should normally begin at zero, be continuous and be uniform.

This histogram has a vertical scale that does not start at zero, is non-uniform (i.e. goes up in ones then by two and then by three) and is not labelled. The consequence is that the areas of the bars do not represent the size of the data.

The frequency from two to three seconds looks twice that from one to two seconds, but this is misleading.

The frequency from three to four seconds looks 1.5 times that for two to three seconds, but again this is incorrect.

Areas

Areas may be distorted by making things look three dimensional.

This pie chart is 3D (three dimensional), so sectors at the front and back look bigger than those at the sides. You cannot measure the angles correctly, and no key is given. A sector has been taken out and moved to the front, making it difficult to compare it with the other sectors. The colour black on the cut-out sector makes it more prominent than the paler colours of the other sectors.

This bar chart has no labels, and because it is 3D bar 4 shows a larger area than the other bars. The actual value of bar 4 is twice that of bar 3.

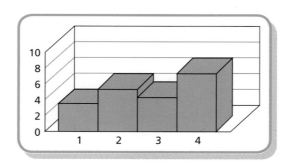

Exam Question Report

This graph appeared in a national newspaper. The graph is supposed to give information about the price, in pence, of buying a share in The Carphone Warehouse. The paper said 'Shares in The Carphone Warehouse have increased a lot over the year 2003'.

a Write down one feature of the graph that makes the increase look greater than it was. (1)

b Write down one other misleading feature of this graph. (1)

How students answered

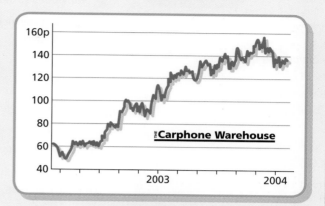

a ▲ Vertical scale does not start at zero.

■ Many candidates realised that the thick line and shading was misleading but this was not a suitable answer. The question asks about the increase looking bigger than it was. An answer referring to the scale or pence was required.

b ▲ Any one of the following answers would get the mark:

No proper labels on the axes.

The line is very thick.

The horizontal axis scale is poor.

It is not clear where years start.

■ Most students did not appreciate that the 2003 on the horizontal axis was badly placed. Students answered this question incorrectly by saying such things as 'the line is wiggly'.

Test yourself

1 This graph shows how the price of a product has increased over time.

The price seems to have gone up a lot. Explain what misleading features make this a poor graph.

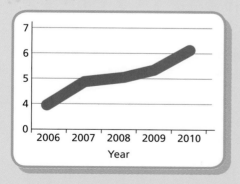

2 This pictogram shows the same information as question 1.

What features make this a poor diagram?

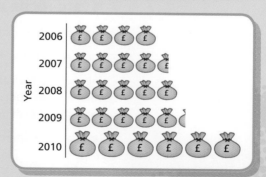

4.1: Averages

 Work out and use the mean, mode and median of raw data presented as a list

 Work out the mean, mode and median for discrete data presented as a frequency distribution

Need more help?
For more on this topic, see pages 117–120 of the main Edexcel textbook (ISBN 978-1-84690-454-7).

edexcel key terms

mode Most common.
median The middle value.
mean $= \bar{x} = \frac{\Sigma x}{n}$ where n is the number of items.
modal class The class with the highest frequency.
median for a frequency table The $\frac{n+1}{2}$ th value.
mean for a frequency table $\frac{\Sigma fx}{\Sigma f}$
estimated mean for a grouped frequency table Can be found by interpolating from the table: $\frac{\Sigma f \times midpoint}{\Sigma f}$

Averages

An average is a single value used to describe a set of data. The mean, mode and median are all averages.

The **mode** is the value that occurs most.

The **median** is the middle number in a list after they have been put in order. If there are two middle numbers, the median is midway between the two.

If the number of values, n, is large, you can find which is the median using:

median is the $\frac{n+1}{2}$ th value.

If n is an odd number this will be a whole number. If n is an even number it will not be a whole number and you take the mid-point of the two whole numbers either side of the number.

The **mean** is worked out by adding up the numbers then dividing by how many numbers there are:

$$mean = \frac{\Sigma x}{n}$$

For example, the ages of members of a youth club are:
14, 14, 14, 15, 15, 15, 16, 16, 17, 17, 17, 17, 17, 18, 18.

Mode = 17; median = 16; mean = 240/15 = 16.

Mean, mode and median of discrete data in a frequency table

The mode is the class with the highest frequency.

The median is the middle value: $\frac{n}{2}$.

The mean of the variables, x, is often written as $\bar{x}$. It is found by multiplying each value x by its frequency f and dividing the sum of the $(f \times x)$ by the total number of values (= sum of the f).

This can be written:

$$mean = \frac{\Sigma fx}{\Sigma f}$$

No. of Books x	Frequency f	fx
10	11	110
11	7	77
12	7	84
Total	25	271

For example, for the table on the left.

The mode is 10 books (it has the highest frequency).

The median is the 13th value, which is 11.

The mean is $\frac{271}{25}$ which is 10.84.

Exam Question Report

The table shows the monthly rainfall in mm for Braemar in Scotland in 2005.

Month	Jan	Feb	Mar	Apr	May	Jun	Jul	Aug	Sep	Oct	Nov	Dec
Rainfall	93	59	59	51	65	55	58	76	73	87	86	96

(Data source: *Braemar Weather Station*)

a   Write down the mode of the monthly rainfall. (1)
b   Work out the median of the monthly rainfall. (2)
c   Work out the mean of the monthly rainfall. (2)

How students answered

Students usually got the mode correct but often the median and mean were muddled and put the wrong way round.

a   ▲   The mode was **59**. Students usually got this correct.

b   ▲   Put in order: 51, 55, 58, 59, 59, 65, 73, 76, 86, 87, 93, 96 (1 mark). The middle value is **69** (1 mark). (An answer of 69 with no working gets 2 marks.) 46% of candidates got both marks.

c   ▲   858 (or their sum) ÷ 12 (1 mark). You could get this mark if you tried to add all the values but made a small error and did not get 858. The answer is **71.5** (1 mark). (71.5 with no working gets 2 marks.)

■   Students who used a calculator and rounded the answer to 71 got no marks. It is always worth putting in the working. Some students who were unsure which was median and which was the mean hedged their bets by putting two arrows between parts **b** and **c** to suggest the marker should choose which one was correct. These students got no marks for either part.

Test yourself

1   Here is a list of the ages of some children at a birthday party.

   7   8   6   5   6   8   9   6

   a   How many children were there at the birthday party?
   b   Write down the mode for these data.
   c   Work out the median for these data.
   d   Calculate the mean of these data.

2   The table gives some information about the numbers of puppies in 20 litters.

Number of puppies x	4	5	6	7	8	9
Number of litters f	1	6	8	3	1	1
fx						

   a   Write down the modal class.
   b   Work out the median number of puppies in a litter.
   c   Calculate the mean number of puppies in a litter.

3   A researcher counts the number of wild flower plants in each of 30 metre-square plots. The results are shown in the table on the right.

   a   Write down the modal class.
   b   Work out an estimate of the median number of plants in a plot.
   c   Calculate an estimate of the mean number of plants in a plot.

Exam tip

Always put in and complete a row or column for *fx* to help you with the calculation when working out the mean for a frequency distribution table.

No. of plants x	No. of plots f
2–4	2
5–7	6
8–10	10
11–13	8
14–16	4

4.2: Averages of grouped data

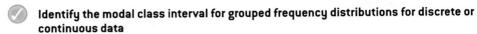

✓ Identify the modal class interval for grouped frequency distributions for discrete or continuous data

✓ Work out and use estimates for the mean and median of grouped frequency distributions for discrete or continuous data

Need more help?
For more on this topic, see pages 120–128 of the main Edexcel textbook (ISBN 978-1-84690-454-7).

edexcel :::: key terms

modal class The class with the highest frequency.

estimated mean for a grouped frequency table Can be found by interpolating from the table: $\dfrac{\sum f \times \text{mid-point}}{\sum f}$

estimated median for a grouped frequency table This is the middle value.

Modal class and mean of data in a grouped frequency table

The **modal class** is the class that has the highest frequency.

To find the mean of grouped data we assume that the values are equally spread across the class interval and their average value is equal to the mid-point of the class interval.

An estimate for the mean is given by:

estimated mean $= \dfrac{\sum fx}{\sum f}$ where x is the mid-value of the class intervals and f is the frequency.

For this table:

No. of minutes x	No. of boys f	Mid-point x	$f \times x$
$1 < x \le 2$	5	1.5	7.5
$2 < x \le 3$	4	2.5	10.0
$3 < x \le 4$	6	3.5	21.0
Total	15		38.5

Modal class is $3 < x \le 4$.

Estimate of the mean is $\dfrac{38.5}{15} = 2.57$.

Median of data in a grouped frequency table

No of minutes x	No. of boys f
$1 < x \le 2$	5
$2 < x \le 3$	4
$3 < x \le 4$	6
Total	15

This will be the middle value: $\dfrac{n+1}{2}$. It will be an estimate. For the table on the left:

There are 15 boys so the median one is the $\dfrac{15+1}{2} = $ 8th boy. The 8th boy is three into the $2 < x \le 3$ class interval.

We assume that the values are equally spread so we need to go $\dfrac{3}{4}$ into the $2 < x \le 3$ class interval.

This will be 2 minutes $+ \dfrac{3}{4}$ of one minute $= 2.75$ minutes.

An estimate of the median for a grouped frequency table can also be worked out using a cumulative frequency diagram (see Section 4.4).

Also see the worked example in Section 4.6.

Exam Question Report

Stephanie recorded the time she took to travel to work on each of 50 days. The table shows the information about these times.

Calculate an estimate of the mean time Stephanie took to travel to work. (3)

Answer: Mean $= \frac{2099}{50} = 41.98$ minutes

Time (minutes) x	Frequency f	Mid-time	Mid-time $\times f$
$20 < x \le 30$	4	25	100
$30 < x \le 38$	9	34	306
$38 < x \le 42$	12	40	480
$42 < x \le 50$	18	46	828
$50 < x \le 60$	7	55	385
Total	50		2099

The first mark was given for showing the mid-times, all within the given interval and with at least two correct. One mark was given for totalling (mid-time × f) and dividing by 50. An error on the addition was allowed providing the first mark had been gained.

The last mark was given for getting 41.98. Giving 41.98 with no working got all three marks.

How students answered

Many students found this difficult. Many did not use the mid-points – they used either the upper or lower boundary for each class. Other students divided by 5 instead of 50.

29% 0 marks

20% of students got the final answer wrong but still picked up marks for showing some correct working.

20% 1–2 marks

Only about half the candidates got all three marks.

51% 3 marks

Test yourself

1 A survey of the speeds of 60 cars was done on a motorway during one 15-minute period in November. The data collected are shown in the table.

   a Copy and complete the table.
   b Write down the modal class.
   c Work out an estimate for the median speed using the table.
   d Work out an estimate for the mean speed. Use the table to help you.

Speed (mph) x	Frequency f	Mid-point	$f \times$ mid-point
$30 < x \le 40$	9		
$40 < x \le 50$	14		
$50 < x \le 60$	15		
$60 < x \le 70$	20		
$70 < x \le 80$	2		
Total			

2 The number of hours of sunshine per day during June at a seaside resort are shown in the table.

   a Write down the modal class.
   b Work out an estimate for the median number of hours of sunshine using the table.
   c Work out an estimate for the mean number of hours of sunshine. Use the table to help you.

Hours of sunshine s	Frequency f
$s < 2$	2
$2 \le s < 4$	5
$4 \le s < 8$	10
$8 \le s < 10$	8
$10 \le s < 12$	5
$s > 12$	0

Exam tip

In an exam always add extra columns for the mid-point and for frequency × mid-point. Also add a total row for totals. This makes the question much easier to do.

Need more help?
For more on this topic, see pages 130–133 of the main Edexcel textbook (ISBN 978-1-84690-454-7).

edexcel ⠿ key terms

transformation of data This means simplifying the data to make them easier to use.

weighted mean This is given by: $\bar{x} = \dfrac{\sum wx}{\sum w}$

where w is the weighting given to each variable x.

4.3: Deciding which average to use, transforming data and weighted means

✓ Understand the appropriateness, advantages and disadvantages of each of the three measures of central tendency

✓ Be able to make a reasoned choice of a measure of central tendency appropriate to a particular line of enquiry

✓ Be able to make a reasoned choice of a measure of central tendency appropriate to the nature of the data and purpose of the analysis

✓ Understand the effects of transformations of the data on the mean, mode and median

✓ Understand the effect on the mean, mode and median of changes in the data including the addition or withdrawal of a population or sample member

✓ Calculate and use a weighted mean

Averages

The mean, mode and median are all averages. It is important to know when each should be used. The advantages and disadvantages of each are summarised in the table.

Average	Advantages	Disadvantages
Mode	Easy to find. Can be used with any type of data. Unaffected by open-ended or extreme values. The mode will be a data value.	Mathematical properties are not useful (e.g. it cannot be used to calculate other information about the distribution of the data). There is not always a mode or sometimes there is more than one.
Median	Easy to calculate. Unaffected by extreme values.	Mathematical properties are not useful (e.g. it cannot be used to calculate other information about the distribution of the data).
Mean	Uses all the data. Mathematical properties are well known and useful (e.g. it can be used in the calculation of a measure of spread).	Always affected by extreme values. Can be distorted by open-ended classes.

Higher tier

ResultsPlus
Exam tip

Remember to reverse the *order* of operations, as well as the arithmetic operations themselves.

Transforming data

Sometimes finding a mean can be made easier by changing the figures. Small figures are easier to deal with than large figures. You can subtract, add, multiply or divide by a number. You can do more than one of these procedures at once if you wish. Then to get back to the mean of the original data, reverse the process.

For example, if the ages of five pensioners are 73, 82, 79, 85 and 76:

- First **subtract 70** from each age giving 3, 12, 9, 15 and 6.
- **Divide by 3** giving 1, 4, 3, 5 and 2. The mean of these numbers is 15/5 = 3.
- Now reverse the process: $(3 \times 3) + 70 = 79$ (the reverse process is **multiply by 3** and **add 70**).
- 79 is the mean age.

Weighted mean

The formula to use is: $\bar{x} = \dfrac{\sum wx}{\sum w}$ (w is the weighting and x is the variable).

For example, in a Statistics examination the final percentage is worked out using a weighted mean. Paper 1 has a weighting of 80 and paper 2 has a weighting of 20.

If Jahed gets 68% on paper 1 and 54% on paper 2, his final percentage would be:

$$\frac{(80 \times 68) + (20 \times 54)}{80 + 20} = 65.2\%$$

ResultsPlus
Exam tip

The weights do not always add up to 100. Weighted means are commonly used with costs of commodities.

ResultsPlus
Exam Question Report

The table shows the monthly rainfall in mm for Braemar in Scotland in 2005.

Month	Jan	Feb	Mar	Apr	May	Jun	Jul	Aug	Sep	Oct	Nov	Dec
Rainfall	93	59	59	51	65	55	58	76	73	87	86	96

(Data source: *Braemar Weather Station*)

Braemar Weather Station wishes to compare the rainfall for 2005 with the rainfall for each of the previous 25 years. Which average, mean, mode or median, should they use to see if the amount of rainfall shows a pattern of increase? (1)

How students answered

Students found this quite difficult.

 The mean.

 Any other answer got no marks.

There might not be a mode or the mode might be the lowest value so this is not a good measure in this case. The median is only going to give a value for one particular month. The mean is best because it uses all the data.

ResultsPlus
Exam tip

Remember, transformation means making the numbers much simpler. In question 2 below you can add and divide to get very small numbers.

Test yourself

1 In each of the following cases write down whether the mean, mode or median would be the best measure of average to be used to represent the data:
   a The ages of children in an after school club are: 9, 7, 7, 9, 7, 7, 8, 8, 6
   b The cost of dresses in a shop are: £14, £98, £16, £17, £16, £17
   c The daily sunshine (hours) one week: 2, 7, 3, 9, 1, 8, 1

2 The number of modules made by factory workers on each of five days in a week in March were:

   527   572   545   581   518

   Work out the mean number of modules using a method of transformation.

3 The table gives the basic weekly wage of three categories of factory workers.
   Find a weighted weekly mean wage.

Worker type	Number of workers	Basic weekly wage
unskilled	25	£280
semi-skilled	50	£400
skilled	100	£600

4.4: Ranges and quartiles

✓ Work out and use the range for data presented in a list or frequency distribution

✓ Work out the quartiles, interquartile range and percentiles for discrete and continuous data presented as a list, a frequency table or a grouped frequency table

✓ Work out the quartiles, percentiles, deciles and interquartile and interpercentile ranges for discrete data presented as a list, frequency table or distribution or grouped frequency distribution

Need more help?
For more on this topic, see pages 133–139 of the main Edexcel textbook (ISBN 978-1-84690-454-7).

edexcel key terms

range Highest − lowest.
median Q_2 is the median.
quartiles for discrete data

$Q_1 = $ the $\frac{n+1}{4}$ th value

$Q_2 = $ the $\frac{n+1}{2}$ th value

$Q_3 = $ the $\frac{3(n+1)}{4}$ th value

$IQR = (Q_3 - Q_1)$

quartiles for continuous data

$Q_1 = $ the $\frac{n}{4}$ th value

$Q_2 = $ the $\frac{n}{2}$ th value

$Q_3 = $ the $\frac{3n}{4}$ th value

$IQR = (Q_3 - Q_1)$

percentiles These are used to divide data into 100 equal-sized groups.
deciles These are used to divide data into ten equal-sized groups.

Range

The **range** is a crude measure of spread.

The range of a data set = the highest value − the lowest value.

Quartiles for discrete data

There are three quartiles. They divide the data set into four equal parts.

- The **lower quartile (Q_1)** is the value that 25% (one-quarter) of the data are less than or equal to.
- The **middle quartile (Q_2)** is also the median. It is the value that 50% (one half) of the data are less than or equal to.
- The **upper quartile (Q_3)** is the value that 75% (three-quarters) of the data are less than or equal to.

For discrete data:

$Q_1 = $ the $\frac{n+1}{4}$ th value $\qquad$ $Q_2 = $ the $\frac{n+1}{2}$ th value $\qquad$ $Q_3 = $ the $\frac{3(n+1)}{4}$ th value

The **interquartile range** (IQR) is the upper quartile minus the lower quartile ($Q_3 - Q_1$).

For example, for the set of numbers 2, 4, 3, 6, 7, 8, 8, 5, 6, 8, 9:

Putting the numbers in order gives 2, 3, 4, 5, 6, 6, 7, 8, 8, 8, 9.

Range = 9 − 2 = 7

$Q_1 = \frac{12}{4} = $ 3rd value = 4 $\qquad$ $Q_2 = $ median = 6th value = 6

$Q_3 = \frac{12 \times 3}{4} = $ 9th value = 8 $\qquad$ $IQR = Q_3 - Q_1 = 8 - 4 = 4$

Quartiles for data in a frequency table

These can be found using the formulae but can also be found using a step polygon.

Quartiles for continuous data in a grouped frequency table

For continuous data:

$Q_1 = $ the $\frac{n}{4}$ th value $\qquad$ $Q_2 = $ the $\frac{n}{2}$ th value $\qquad$ $Q_3 = $ the $\frac{3n}{4}$ th value

Percentiles (P)

If data are divided into 100 equal parts, each part is a percentile.

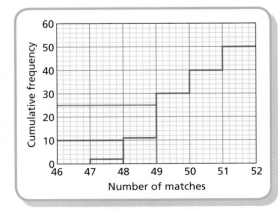

The pink line shows the median. The green line shows the 20th percentile.

Deciles (D)

If data are divided into ten equal parts, each part is a decile.

Using cumulative frequency diagrams

It is easiest to find quartiles, percentiles and **deciles** using a cumulative frequency diagram. In this diagram:

- The three quartiles, Q_1, Q_2 and Q_3, are shown in red.
- The 15th percentile P15 is in green.
- The 9th decile D9 is shown in yellow.

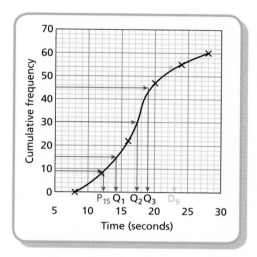

Interpolation

Quartiles for continuous data can also be found by using interpolation.

No. of minutes x	No. of boys f
$1 < x \le 2$	5
$2 < x \le 3$	4
$3 < x \le 4$	3
Total	12

For example, for the data in the table, Q_1 is the $\dfrac{12}{4}$ th value.

This is the 3rd value. This is in the $1 < x \le 2$ class interval.

So it is $\dfrac{3}{5} = 0.6$ into the 1 minute interval, i.e. $Q_1 = 1.6$ minutes.

 Results **Plus**
Exam Question Report

The weights, to the nearest kilogram, of 19 pigs were:

36	38	30	31	38	43	55	38	37	30
48	41	33	25	34	43	37	40	36	

Find the interquartile range of the weights. (2)

How students answered

△ 25 30 30 31 33 34 36 36 37 37 38 38 38 40 41 43 43 48 55

$Q_1 = \dfrac{19 + 1}{4}$ th value = 5th value = 33

Q_3 = 15th value = 41

Therefore IQR is $41 - 33 = 8$

The correct answer is 8 and that, even with no working, would give 2 marks.

⬤ Many students knew how to set about finding the quartiles and ordered the data. Most attempted to then find the quartiles, thus getting the first mark. Some could not complete the process. The answer $41 - 33$ gave only 1 mark.

■ Putting in no working is a risky strategy. If you are wrong you get no marks.

Test yourself

1 A village shop recorded the number of orders it took per day for 15 days.

12 10 8 14 17 9 12 14

15 13 16 15 17 8 10

  a Find the range.

  b Work out the quartiles.

  c Calculate the interquartile range.

2 The table shows information about the number of times each of the students in year 13 was late during a term.

Times late	0	1	2	3	4	5	6	7
Frequency	4	16	8	9	12	5	4	2
Cumulative frequency								

  a Copy and complete the table.

  b Draw a step polygon for these data.

  c Use the polygon to find the quartiles for these data.

  d Work out the range and IQR for these data.

3 The table gives information about the speed of cars on a motorway in England.

Speed mph	$20 < x \le 30$	$30 < x \le 40$	$40 < x \le 50$	$50 < x \le 60$	$60 < x \le 70$	$70 < x \le 80$	$80 < x \le 90$
Frequency	2	10	18	34	24	8	4
Cum. freq.							

  a Copy and complete the table.

  b Draw a cumulative frequency graph for these data.

  c Use your cumulative frequency graph to find estimates for Q_1, Q_2, Q_3 and the IQR.

  d Use your cumulative frequency graph to find estimates for the 45th percentile (P45) and the 3rd decile (D3).

4 The table gives information about the speeds of cars on a highway in America.

Using interpolation find:

  a The lower quartile.

  b The upper quartile.

  c The median.

Speed (mph) x	Frequency f
$30 < x \le 40$	9
$40 < x \le 50$	14
$50 < x \le 60$	15
$60 < x \le 70$	20
$70 < x \le 80$	2

4.5: Box plots

- Construct, interpret and use box plots
- Understand symmetrical, positive and negative skew
- Be able to identify outliers using quartiles
- Understand how to look for and discover errors in data and recognise data that do not fit a general trend or pattern, including outliers
- Apply statistical reasoning and explain and justify inferences, deductions, arguments and solutions

Need more help?
For more on this topic, see pages 142–143 of the main Edexcel textbook (ISBN 978-1-84690-454-7).

Box plots

Box plots show the distribution of a data set. They show the maximum and minimum values, the median and the upper and lower quartiles.

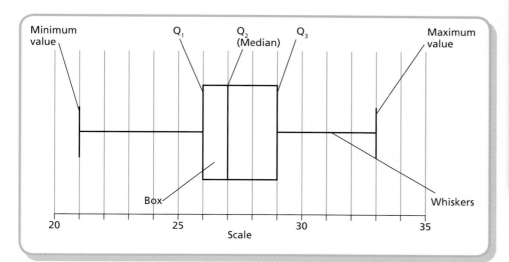

edexcel ⠿ key terms

box plots Diagrams that show the maximum, minimum, median and upper and lower quartiles of a data set.
negative skew The median is closer to the upper quartile than the lower quartile.
outliers These are data values that are anomalies. They are any piece of data that is more than 1.5 IQR above the upper quartile or 1.5 IQR below the lower quartile.
positive skew The median is closer to the lower quartile than the upper quartile.
skew This describes the shape of the distribution.
symmetrical The median is equidistant from the upper and lower quartiles.

A box plot shows whether a distribution is skewed. If the median is closer to the upper quartile than it is to the lower quartile, the data are negatively skewed. If the median is closer to the lower quartile than it is to the upper quartile, the data are positively skewed. If the median is equidistant from both the upper and lower quartiles, the data are symmetrical.

Negatively skewed, positively skewed and symetrical box plots.

Worked example: Box plots with interpretation

The table shows some summary statistics for the weights of two types of apple.

	Smallest	Lower Quartile	Median	Upper Quartile	Largest
Bramley weight (g)	218	226	238	245	254
Granny Smith weight (g)	204	214	228	240	252

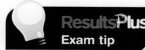
ResultsPlus
Exam tip

Remember that the average used in a box plot is the median, NOT the mean.

a Draw box plots for comparison of each type of apple.

Answer:

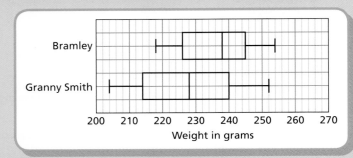

b Work out the interquartile range for the Bramley apples.

Answer: 245 − 226 = 19

Note: Full marks would be given for 19. If you do not work out the answer and leave it as 245 − 226 you are likely to lose a mark.

c Work out the range for the Granny Smith apples.

Answer: 252 − 204 = 48

Again you need to give the worked out answer of 48 to get full marks.

d Compare the distributions for the Bramley and the Granny Smith apples.

Answer: The Bramleys have a higher **median** weight. The Granny Smiths have a bigger **interquartile range**. Both have negative **skew**.

Note: To compare box plot distributions you must compare medians, IQR and skew.

e Write down which one of these distributions has the smallest variation in weight. Give a reason for your answer.

Answer: Bramley apples because the range is smaller.

ResultsPlus
Exam tip

NEVER compare upper quartiles, lower quartiles or end-points when comparing distributions. Remember to always use correct statistical words. Do NOT use spread or average. Use median, IQR, range or skew.

Higher tier

Outliers

An outlier is an extreme value. It is defined as any value that is more than 1.5 times the interquartile range below the lower quartile and more than 1.5 times the interquartile range above the upper quartile.

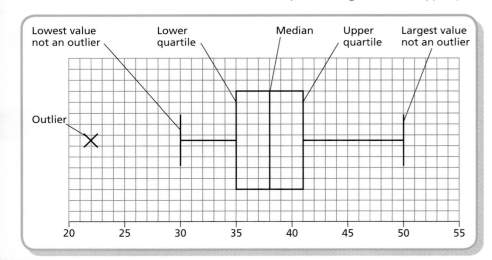

For example, the scores gained in a test by a group of 15 students were:

22	30	32	35	36	37
37	38	39	40	40	41
42	44	50			

$Q_1 = 35$ and $Q_3 = 41$, so the IQR = 41 − 35 = 6

Now 1.5 × 6 = 9

Outliers are greater than 41 + 9 = 50 and smaller than 35 − 9 = 26.

So the only outlier is 22.

Outliers are marked on the box plot as a cross.

Exam Question Report

Karl collected information about the Paralympic World Cup 2007. He collected the times for 31 male swimmers in the 50 m freestyle event. The stem and leaf diagram shows this information. The times are given to the nearest second.

Male swimmers' times

```
2 | 8 8 8 8 9 9
3 | 0 2 2 2 2 2 3 3 3 3 4 4 4 6 6 6 9 9
4 | 0 1 1 2 7
5 | 4 8
```

key:
5 | 4 = 54 seconds

Lowest value	
Lower quartile	32
Median	
Upper quartile	39
Highest value	

a Use the information in the stem and leaf diagram to complete the table on the left. (3)
b Identify any outliers for the times of the male swimmers. (3)
c Draw a box plot to show the distribution of the male swimmers. (3)

How students answered

▲ Most candidates (88%) got the answer to **a** correct – 28, 33, 58 – and got all three marks.

● Part **b** was done badly by many candidates. In this part marks were given for working, so seeing the correct answer of 54 and 58 with no working only got 1 mark, since this was probably a good guess.

■ In part **c** the correct answer of 47, 54, 58 with no working got no marks. Many candidates incorrectly used the median +/− (1.5 × IQR). Only 29% of candidates earned all three of the available marks here.

Watch out!

Many candidates make the mistake of saying the outliers are 1.5 × IQR either side of the mean.

Test yourself

1 The data show the number of absentees from a Statistics class over 11 days:

1 2 2 3 4 5 7 7 8 8 8

  a Write down the values of the upper and lower quartile and the median.
  b Draw a box plot for these data.
  c Describe the skew of these data.

2 The table gives some summary statistics about the weights (in kg) of male and female collie dogs at an obedience class.

	Minimum	Lower quartile	Median	Upper quartile	Maximum
Male	20	26	28	31	32
Female	15	17	20	22	26

  a On the same graph paper and using the same scale, draw box plots for the male and female collies.
  b Describe the skew of the male collies.
  c Describe the skew of the female collies.
  d Compare the ranges.

3 The lower quartile for a data set is 14. The upper quartile is 22. Work out the limits for the outliers.

4 A dairy farm records the milk yield (litres) for 19 of their pedigree cows. The yields for one day were as follows:

26 40 34 39 35 23 15 35 5 33
34 25 42 19 41 24 35 25 28

  a Find the median and quartiles.   b Work out the outliers.
  c Draw a box plot for these data.   d Describe the skew of these data.

Need more help?
For more on this topic, see pages 145–148 of the main Edexcel textbook (ISBN 978-1-84690-454-7).

4.6: Variance and standard deviation

- Calculate and use variance and standard deviation
- Understand the advantages and disadvantages of the following measures of dispersion: range, quartiles, interquartile range, percentiles
- Understand the advantages and disadvantages of the following measures of dispersion: deciles, interpercentile range, variance and standard deviation

Higher tier

edexcel key terms

standard deviation (for a set of numbers)

$$\sqrt{\frac{\sum(x - \bar{x})^2}{n}} \quad \text{or} \quad \sqrt{\left(\frac{\sum x^2}{n} - (\bar{x})^2\right)}$$

$$\text{or} \quad \sqrt{\left(\frac{\sum x^2}{n} - \left(\frac{\sum x^2}{n}\right)^2\right)}$$

standard deviation (for a discrete frequency distribution)

$$\sqrt{\left(\frac{\sum fx^2}{\sum f} - \left(\frac{\sum fx}{\sum f}\right)^2\right)} \quad \text{or} \quad \sqrt{\frac{\sum f(x - \bar{x})^2}{\sum f}}$$

variance A measure of dispersion or spread:

$$\frac{\sum(x - \bar{x})^2}{n} \quad \text{or} \quad \frac{\sum x^2}{n} - (\bar{x})^2$$

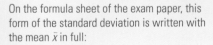

ResultsPlus
Exam tip

The symbol σ (sigma) is used for standard deviation.

ResultsPlus
Exam tip

On the formula sheet of the exam paper, this form of the standard deviation is written with the mean $\bar{x}$ in full:

$$\sqrt{\left(\frac{\sum x^2}{n} - \left(\frac{\sum x}{n}\right)^2\right)}$$

Variance and standard deviation

The variance is a measure of dispersion or spread. The standard deviation is the square root of the variance.

The variance $= \dfrac{\sum(x - \bar{x})^2}{n}$ and the standard deviation is $\sqrt{\dfrac{\sum(x - \bar{x})^2}{n}}$

Or an easier formula to use is:

Variance $= \dfrac{\sum x^2}{n} - \bar{x}^2$ and standard deviation $= \sqrt{\left(\dfrac{\sum x^2}{n} - \bar{x}^2\right)}$

For example, given the data 4 6 4 5 8 9:

Method 1:

$\bar{x} = \text{mean} = \dfrac{36}{6} = 6$

$\sum(x - \bar{x})^2 = (4) + (0) + (4) + (1) + (4) + (9) = 22$

Variance $= \dfrac{22}{6} = 3.6666$

Standard deviation $= \sqrt{3.6666} = 1.9$

Method 2 (using the easier formula):

$\bar{x} = \text{mean} = \dfrac{36}{6} = 6$

$\sum x^2 = 16 + 36 + 16 + 25 + 64 + 81 = 238$

Variance $= \dfrac{238}{6} - 36 = 3.6666$

Standard deviation $= \sqrt{3.6666} = 1.9$

If your data are in the form of a grouped frequency table you need to use the formula:

Standard deviation $= \sqrt{\left(\dfrac{\sum fx^2}{\sum f} - \left(\dfrac{\sum fx}{\sum f}\right)^2\right)}$ or $\sqrt{\left(\dfrac{\sum f(x - \bar{x})^2}{\sum f}\right)}$

Advantages and disadvantages of measures of dispersion

Measure	Advantages	Disadvantages
Range	A reasonably good indicator.	Badly affected by extreme values.
Interquartile range	Not affected by extreme values. Often used with skewed data.	Does not tell you what happens beyond quartiles.
Variance	Good measure. All values used. Used when data are fairly symmetrical.	Mathematical properties not useful (use the standard deviation in preference). Not so good if data are strongly skewed.
Standard deviation	Good measure. All values used. Used when data are fairly symmetrical. Can be used in mathematical calculations of other statistics.	Not so good if data are strongly skewed.

ResultsPlus
Exam Question Report

Stephanie recorded the time (x) she took to travel to work on each of 50 days in a grouped frequency table. The mean time Stephanie took to travel to work was 41.98 minutes. Calculate an estimate of the standard deviation of her times given that $\Sigma fx^2 = 91\,367$. (2)

Answer: As this data comes from a frequency table we use the formula:

$$\text{Estimated standard deviation} = \sqrt{\left(\frac{\Sigma fx^2}{\Sigma f} - \left(\frac{\Sigma fx}{\Sigma f}\right)^2\right)} = \sqrt{\left(\frac{\Sigma 91367}{50} - 41.98^2\right)} \text{ (1 mark)}$$

$$= 8.06 \text{ (1 mark)}$$

How students answered

Few students knew which formula to use and many forgot that formulae are at the front of the exam paper. This question followed on from a part that asked candidates to find the mean (41.98). Most did not realise that they could use this answer to help find the standard deviation.

67% 0 marks

Some students rounded the answer to 8. If there was no sign that they had got 8.06 in the working they lost the second mark.

8% 1 mark

Only a quarter of students got both marks for this question.

25% 2 marks

Higher tier

ResultsPlus
Exam tip

Remember this formula is at the beginning of the exam paper!

ResultsPlus
Exam tip

Remember to give your answer to at least two decimal places unless told otherwise.

Test yourself

1 Police recorded the speed of traffic on a motorway. The range was 50 mph and the interquartile range was 15 mph. Write down the advantages and disadvantages of using these two measures of spread in this situation.

2 Use the formula $\sqrt{\dfrac{\Sigma(x - \bar{x})^2}{n}}$ to find the standard deviation of the following numbers: 1 3 4 4 5 6 6 6 7

Worked example: Averages/standard deviation from grouped frequency tables

Zoe recorded the time it took her to do the newspaper crossword on each of 25 days. The table shows this information.

Time t (minutes)	Frequency f	Mid t	$f \times$ mid t
$10 < t \le 14$	10	12	120
$14 < t \le 18$	3	16	48
$18 < t \le 24$	6	21	126
$24 < t \le 26$	4	25	100
$26 < t \le 28$	2	27	54
Totals	$\sum f = 25$		$\sum ft = 448$

a Write down the modal class.

Answer: $10 < t \le 14$ (one with highest frequency).

b Write down the class into which the median falls.

Answer: $14 < t \le 18$ (mid-value of 25 is the 13th value).

c Work out an estimate of the mean time.

Answer: mean $= \dfrac{\sum ft}{\sum f} = \dfrac{448}{25} = 17.92$.

d Calculate the standard deviation of these times. You may use $\sum ft^2 = 8812$.

Answer: The best formula to use is $\sigma = \sqrt{\left(\dfrac{\sum fx^2}{\sum f} - \left(\dfrac{\sum fx}{\sum f} \right)^2 \right)}$.

In this case we have t instead of x so it becomes $= \sqrt{\left(\dfrac{\sum ft^2}{\sum f} - \left(\dfrac{\sum ft}{\sum f} \right)^2 \right)}$

Remember, $\dfrac{\sum ft}{\sum f}$ is the mean so $\sigma = \sqrt{\left(\dfrac{8812}{25} - \left(17.92 \right)^2 \right)} = 5.6$

Test yourself

3 A child did a mental arithmetic test at school every day for two weeks. The table shows the marks gained.

Day	1	2	3	4	5	6	7	8	9	10
Mark	7	4	8	7	5	8	8	4	9	10

Find the mean mark, the variance and the standard deviation.

4 The frequency table shows the ages of brides under 21 that were recorded at a registry office over a year.

Age x	16	17	18	19	20
Frequency f	3	6	10	18	23

Use the equation $\sqrt{\left(\dfrac{\sum fx^2}{\sum f} - \left(\dfrac{\sum fx}{\sum f} \right)^2 \right)}$ to find the standard deviation of the ages.

5 The 5 scores (x) in a game were recorded. The mean score was found to be 9 and the $\sum x^2 = 495$. Find the standard deviation of the scores.

6 Write down **two** advantages and **one** disadvantage of using the standard deviation as a measure of spread.

4.7: Comparing data sets and standardised scores

✓ Use an appropriate measure of central tendency together with range, quartiles, interquartile range and percentiles to compare distributions of data

✓ Use an appropriate measure of central tendency together with deciles, interpercentile range, variance and standard deviation to compare distributions of data

✓ Calculate, interpret and use standardised scores to compare values from different frequency distributions

Comparing data sets

To compare data sets, the minimum comparisons that must be made are:

- central tendency (mean, mode or median)
- spread (range, interquartile range or standard deviation).

Another comparison that can be made is that of skew (positive, negative and symmetrical).

Comparisons can be made using diagrams. The diagrams must always be drawn close to each other and to the same scale.

Histograms with equal intervals allow you to compare the modes, ranges and skew.

Box plots can be used to compare medians, ranges, interquartile ranges and skew.

Standardised scores

These are used to compare two individual results. They are very useful in comparing exam marks in two different subjects.

Standardised score $= \dfrac{\text{score} - \text{mean}}{\text{standard deviation}}$

If the score is below the mean, the standardised score will be negative.

If the aim is to score high then the higher the standardised score the better, e.g. exam mark. If the aim is to score low then the lower the standardised score the better, e.g. time taken to do a task.

Here is an example. Class 7 did a number puzzle and a crossword puzzle and recorded their times in minutes. The table shows some summary data and the times taken by Jason and Marco.

	Jason's time	Marco's time	Mean time for group	Standard deviation
Number puzzle	3.6	4.5	5	0.7
Crossword puzzle	8.5	7.5	8	0.5

Need more help?
For more on this topic, see pages 150–152 of the main Edexcel textbook (ISBN 978-1-84690-454-7).

edexcel ::: key terms

standardised score A way of comparing two individual results. Standardised score $= \dfrac{\text{score} - \text{mean}}{\text{standard deviation}}$

ResultsPlus
Watch out!

With box plots you must remember that you are comparing medians. In exam questions a large percentage of students get the name of the average wrong.

Higher tier

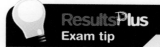
ResultsPlus
Exam tip

It is very important to decide at the beginning whether a low or a high standardised score is best.

Jason's standardised scores:

Number puzzle = $\dfrac{3.6 - 5}{0.7} = -2$ 　　　 Crossword puzzle = $\dfrac{8.5 - 8}{0.5} = +1$

Marco's standardised scores:

Number puzzle = $\dfrac{4.65 - 5}{0.7} = -0.5$ 　　　 Crossword puzzle = $\dfrac{7.5 - 8}{0.5} = -1$

The aim here is to get a low time so the lower the standardised score the better.

Jason did better in the number puzzle than in the crossword puzzle as his standardised score was lower in this. Marco did better in the crossword puzzle as his standardised score was lower in this. Marco did better than the rest of the group as both his scores were below zero. Jason had one standardised score above zero. He did not do well in the crossword puzzle.

Test yourself

1 A group of hospitals recorded the weights, in kg, of newborn babies who were premature and those who were born at full term. The summary data are shown in the table.

	Minimum	Lower quartile	Median	Upper quartile	Maximum
Premature	1	1.2	1.6	2.2	2.8
Full term	1.4	1.7	2.2	2.8	3.6

a Draw comparative box plots for these data.
b Compare the two distributions of the weights.

2 The histograms on the left show the times taken by a group of boys and a group of girls to run a measured distance.

Compare the two distributions.

3 The table shows some data about the marks Charles got in his French and Spanish exams.

	Charles's mark	Mean mark of class	Standard deviation
French	56	60	2
Spanish	68	60	6

a Calculate Charles' standardised scores for each subject.
b Write down the subject in which Charles did best. Give a reason for your answer.

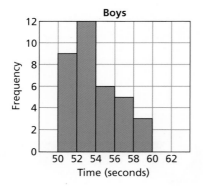

Boys
Frequency vs Time (seconds)

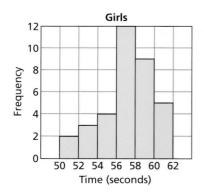

Girls
Frequency vs Time (seconds)

Exam Question Report

The box plot shows information about the times it took female swimmers to swim 50 m freestyle.

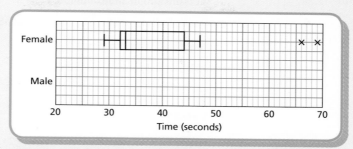

The table shows the times of the male swimmers.

	Min.	Lower quartile	Median	Upper quartile	Max.	Outliers
male	28	32	33	39	49	54 and 58

a   On the grid draw a box plot to show the times of the male swimmers. (3)
b   Compare the distributions of the times of the female swimmers and the times of the male swimmers. (3)

Answer:

a

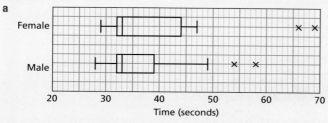

b   A comment on range or IQR, e.g. The IQR/range for females is greater than that for males (or the converse). (1 mark)

Both have positive skew. (1 mark)

Both have the same median. (1 mark)

How students answered

a   Only 6% of students lost two or more marks on part **a**. Some got only one mark if they had drawn a box plot but the median and quartiles were incorrect.

■ 6% 0–1 marks

A common error was to leave out the outliers, which lost a mark.

▬ 65% 2 marks

Less than a third of students got all the available marks for part **a**.

▬ 29% 3 marks

b   Part **b** was done badly. In comparing box plots you need to consider an average, a measure of spread, and skew. No marks were given for comparing individual quartiles. A common error was to comment about the mean rather than the median.

▬ 34% 0 marks

Many students wrote about spread but did not use the correct statistical expressions of range or interquartile range. Many students said they had the same skew but to get the mark it needed to be identified as positive.

▬ 61% 1–2 marks

Only 5% of candidates got full marks for part **b**.

▮ 5% 3 marks

4.8: Index numbers

- ✓ Understand simple index numbers
- ✓ Use and understand chain base index numbers
- ✓ Use weighted index numbers
- ✓ Understand the retail price index (RPI)

Simple index numbers

These are used to see how the prices of things vary over time. There is always a starting year from which you consider the change in prices. This is called the **base year**. The base year has the index number 100. The simple index number tells you the percentage change since the base year.

For example, if the base year was 2002 (index 100) and the simple index number for 2005 is 107, then there has been a rise of 7% between 2002 and 2005, making a total of 107% of what it originally was.

Similarly if the simple index number for 2008 is 94 then there has been a drop of 6% between 2002 and 2008 and it is 94% of what it was.

To find the simple index number for a particular year you use:

$$\text{Simple index number} = \frac{\text{current price}}{\text{base year price}} \times 100$$

Worked example: Index numbers

The table gives information about the mean price, to the nearest £1000, of terraced houses in the north-west in March 2005 and in March 2008.

Year	2005	2008
Price (£)	80 000	95 000

a Using 2005 as the base year, work out the index number for the mean price of terraced houses in the north-west in 2008. Give your answer to the nearest whole number.

Answer: $\frac{95\,000}{80\,000} \times 100 = 118.75$, so the answer is 119.

b Using 2005 as the base year, the index number of the mean price of terraced houses for March 2009 was 110.

   i By what percentage has the mean price of terraced houses changed between 2005 and 2009?

Answer: 10%

   ii Work out the mean price of terraced houses in 2009.

Answer: £80 000 + (10% of 80 000) = £80 000 + £8000 = £88 000

c Describe in words what has happened to house prices over the years between 2005 and 2009.

Answer: We know that prices increased between 2005 and 2008 but they dropped in 2009.

Need more help?
For more on this topic, see pages 154–157 of the main Edexcel textbook (ISBN 978-1-84690-454-7).

edexcel ⋮⋮⋮ key terms

chain base index number

$$\frac{\text{current price}}{\text{previous year's price}} \times 100$$

RPI A weighted index number showing the change in price of a basket of goods.

simple index number

$$\frac{\text{current price}}{\text{base year price}} \times 100$$

weighted index number

$$\frac{\Sigma(\text{index number} \times \text{weight})}{\Sigma \text{ weights}}$$

Results**Plus**
Exam Question Report

The following table shows the total sales of wrapping paper, in £s, in a gift shop in 2002 and 2003.

Year	2002	2003
Sales (£)	75	87

a Taking 2002 as the base year, work out the index number for the sales in 2003. (2)

b The sales of wrapping paper decreased in the gift shop by 5% between 2004 and 2005. Taking 2004 as the base year, complete the table to show the index numbers for the sales in 2004 and 2005. (2)

Year	2004	2005
Index number		

How students answered

a △ $\frac{87}{75} \times 100$ (1 mark) = 116 (1 mark)

■ Many candidates got this wrong. A lot of these forgot to multiply by 100. The commonest incorrect answer was 12 (87 − 75).

b △ The base year has an index number of 100 (1 mark). The increase is 5% so the index number for 2005 is 100 + 5 = 105 (1 mark).

■ Hardly any students got this right. There seemed to be no understanding of how to deal with the 5%.

Chain base index numbers

These are used to see how the price each year compares with the previous year.

To find the chain base index number for a particular year you use:

$$\text{Chain base index number} = \frac{\text{current price}}{\text{previous year's price}} \times 100$$

For example, the table shows the price of a camera over four years.

Year	2006	2007	2008	2009
Price	£150	£175	£200	£180

The chain based index numbers for 2008 and 2009 are:

Chain based index no. for 2008 $= \frac{200}{175} \times 100 = 114.3$ and for 2009 $= \frac{180}{200} \times 100 = 90$.

The price between 2007 and 2008 went up by 14.3%.

The price between 2008 and 2009 went down by $100 - 90 = 10\%$.

Weighted index numbers

These are a way of comparing weighted means.

$$\text{Weighted index number} = \frac{\text{sum of (index numbers} \times \text{weights)}}{\text{sum of weights}}$$

The $\sum$ index number × weight of a bag of groceries in 2009 was 140×100.

The $\sum$ weights for the same bag of groceries in 2007 was 125.

The weighted index number for the price of this bag of groceries in 2009, taking 2007 as the base year, is $\frac{140}{125} \times 100 = 112$.

The price has gone up 12%.

Retail prices index (RPI)

This is a weighted index that shows how the price of a basket of goods changes from year to year.

Watch out!

Many students forget to multiply by 100.

Exam tip

The current year means the price in the particular year for which you want to find the index number.

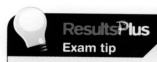

Exam tip

If an exam question mentions an index number then a simple index number is required. If any other type is required it will be clearly stated.

Higher tier

Worked example: Index numbers

Jackson Engineering makes stainless steel. Stainless steel contains steel, chromium and nickel. A stainless steel is made with 74% steel, 18% chromium and 8% nickel.

The table shows the price, in pounds per ton, for chromium and nickel in the years 2005 and 2008.

a Taking 2005 as the base year, calculate the index numbers for the price of chromium and nickel in 2008 and put them in the table.

Metal prices	Year	
	2005	2008
Chromium (£/ton)	81 500	93 575
Nickel (£/ton)	20 000	21 240

Answer: Chromium $\frac{93\,575}{81\,500} \times 100 = 114.8$ (1dp)

Nickel $\frac{21\,240}{20\,000} \times 100 = 106.2$

The index number for the price of steel in 2008 was 102. Jackson Engineering wants to find out the weighted index number for the price of the raw materials for stainless steel.

Metal	Index 2005	Index 2008
Steel	100	102
Chromium	100	114.8
Nickel	100	106.2

b Calculate this number.

Answer: 74% of 102 + 18% of 114.8 + 8% of 106.2 = 75.48 + 20.67 + 8.49 = 104.6. So the index number for the price of steel in 2008 based on 2005 is 104.6.

c Write down the percentage by which the price of raw materials for stainless steel went up between 2005 and 2008.

Answer: 4.6%

The table shows the price of a particular amount of steel in three consecutive years.

Year	2007	2008	2009
Price (£)	8500	10 700	10 000

d Taking 2007 as the base year, work out the chain base index numbers for 2008 and 2009.

Answer: 2008 is $\frac{10\,700}{8500} \times 100 = 125.9$

2009 is $\frac{10\,000}{10\,700} \times 100 = 93.5$

ResultsPlus
Exam tip

Unless told otherwise, one decimal place is adequate for index number questions.

Exam Question Report

The table shows the number of registered vehicles for each of the years 2001 to 2005. Calculate the chain base index numbers for 2002, 2003, 2004 and 2005.

Give your answer to one decimal place. (3)

	2001	2002	2003	2004	2005
Number of registered vehicles (thousands)	29 747	30 557	31 207	32 259	32 897

Answer: 102.7, 102.1, 103.4, 102.0

How students answered

The most common errors were:

- not multiplying by 100 and getting incorrect answers in the region of 1.02, 1.03, 1.03, 1.02

- not giving the answers to one decimal place

- working out simple index numbers using 2001 as the base year.

53% 0 marks

One mark was given for an attempt to find one or more chain base index numbers, e.g. $\frac{30557}{29747} \times 100$ or $\frac{31207}{30557} \times 100$.

Another mark was given for getting two correct chain base numbers.

22% 1–2 marks

Only a quarter of candidates achieved the full three marks.

25% 3 marks

Test yourself

1 In 2008 the price of a certain computer was £350. In 2009 the price of the same computer was £300. Work out the simple index number for the price of the computer in 2009 using 2008 as the base year.

2 The simple index number for the price of a camera in January 2009 was 114 based on January 2007. Write down the percentage increase in the price between January 2007 and January 2009.

3 The simple index numbers for the price of milk are shown in the table – base year 2006.

Describe exactly what has happened to the price of milk between 2006 and 2009.

Year	2006	2007	2008	2009
Simple index number	100	102	95	103

4 The table shows the second-hand value of a saloon car over a period of four years.

Work out the chain base index numbers for each of the years 2008, 2009 and 2010.

Year	2007	2008	2009	2010
Value	£6500	£4800	£3000	£1500

5 The table shows the chain base index numbers for the price of a certain television for sale in a store over four years.

Describe exactly what has happened to the price of this television over the four years.

Year	2007	2008	2009	2010
Chain base index number	100	105	98	110

6 The weighted mean of a bag of items was £20 in 2007 and £18 in 2009.

a Work out the weighted index number for the price of these items in 2009 using 2007 as the base year.

b By what percentage did the price of these items change between 2007 and 2009?

5.1: Scatter diagrams

✓ Plot data as points on a scatter diagram

✓ Construct, use and understand scatter diagrams for bivariate data

✓ Recognise positive, negative and zero linear correlation by inspection

✓ Understand the distinction between correlation, causality and a non-linear relationship

✓ Draw a line of best fit passing through the mean of the points on a scatter diagram

✓ Identify and examine relationships between variables

✓ Interpret correlation as a measure of the strength of the association between two variables

Need more help?
For more on this topic, see pages 170–181 of the main Edexcel textbook (ISBN 978-1-84690-454-7).

edexcel ⠿ key terms

associated Two variables are associated if knowing the value of one variable tells you something about the likely value of the other one.

causal relationship This is when a change in one variable directly causes a change in another variable.

correlation A measure of the strength of the linear association between two variables.

scatter diagram A diagram that shows the association between two data sets.

ResultsPlus
Exam tip

You will be told when to draw the line of best fit through the mean point.

Scatter diagrams

These are used to show whether two sets of data are **associated** in some way.

If the points on a **scatter diagram** lie in approximately a straight line then the data sets are said to be linearly related. A line of best fit can be drawn on a scatter diagram if the points look as though they are linearly related. A line of best fit is a straight line drawn so that the plotted points are evenly scattered on either side of the line. It can be drawn by eye but it is best if it goes through the mean point $(\bar{x}, \bar{y})$.

The diagram shows a scatter diagram with a line of best fit for the weekly wages of seven young people:

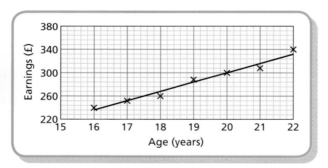

Correlation

This is a measure of the strength of the linear association between two variables.

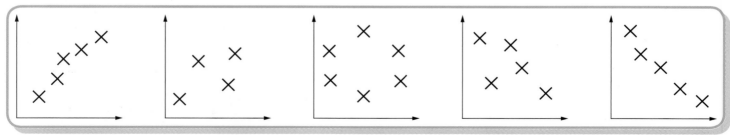

Strong positive linear correlation (e.g. the weight on a wire and how much it stretches).

Weak positive linear correlation (e.g. the height and weight of people).

No correlation (e.g. a student's height and maths test mark).

Weak negative linear correlation (e.g. the speed of a car and its petrol consumption).

Strong negative linear correlation (e.g. the weight on top of a spring and its length).

The scatter diagram on the last page shows strong positive correlation. The older a young person is, the greater the weekly wage they receive.

Causal relationship

This is when a change in one variable directly causes a change in another variable, e.g. the age of a car and its value. Age causes a decrease in value. This is a **causal relationship**.

Results Plus
Exam tip

Association is not always linear. Sometimes it shows a curve. For the purposes of the work in this section we are only concerned with linear correlation.

Results Plus
Exam tip

Correlation does not always imply a causal relationship. Sometimes each of the variables are affected by the same third variable. For example, an increase in sales of mobile phones will not give an increase in sales of washing machines, but both might increase because of improvements in technology.

Results Plus
Exam Question Report

An Internet company wants to know if its advertising works. The table shows the amount of money it spent, per quarter, on advertising over five quarters. It also shows the amount of money customers spent using the company's Internet site.

Money spent on advertising (£1000)	1.2	2.0	3.4	3.9	5.0
Money spent by customers on the Internet site (£1000)	12	20	25	35	38

a   On the graph paper below, draw a scatter diagram for the data. (2)

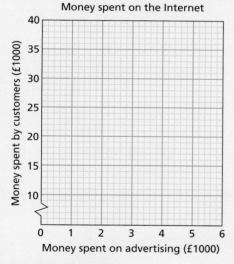

b   Draw a line of best fit. (1)
c   Write down the effect advertising appears to have on the amount spent on the Internet. (2)

How students answered

a   ▲ Two marks if all points plotted correctly. Students generally answered this quite well.

⬤ Three points plotted correctly got 1 mark.

b   ▲ Sensible line with a positive gradient.

◼ A common incorrect answer was to draw a line going through the origin.

c   ▲ This shows positive correlation. Increasing money spent on advertising increases the money spent by customers.

⬤ Only giving one of these answers got 1 mark.

◼ A common error was to refer to a particular point. This got no marks.

Test yourself

1 The table shows the population density and the distance from the centre of the town for each of eight towns.

Distance from centre (km)	0.6	1	1.5	1.8	2.0	3.0	3.5	4.0
Density (people per hectare)	50	40	45	30	30	20	10	8

a Draw a scatter diagram for these data.
b Draw in a line of best fit by eye.
c Describe the correlation.
d What does the correlation tell you about the relationship between these two variables?

2 A river was restocked with fish. For the eight years after the restocking, the local angling club recorded the number of fish caught on a particular stretch of river. The table shows this information.

Year after restocking	1	2	3	4	5	6	7	8
Number of fish caught	200	190	170	154	136	130	120	100

a Draw a scatter diagram for these data.
b Draw in a line of best fit through the mean point (4.5, 150).
c Describe the correlation.
d What does the correlation tell you about the relationship between these two variables?

3 The table shows the marks gained by seven students in a Maths exam and in an English exam.

Maths	50	45	35	25	20	15	5
English	40	35	30	25	25	20	10

a Draw a scatter diagram for these data.
b Work out the co-ordinates of the mid-point to one decimal place.
c Draw in a line of best fit through the mean point.
d Describe the correlation.
e What does the correlation tell you about the relationship between the marks?

5.2: Using a line of best fit

✓ Use interpolation and extrapolation and understand the pitfalls

✓ Interpret data presented in the form of a scatter diagram

Using a line of best fit

Lines of best fit can be used to estimate other values from a graph.

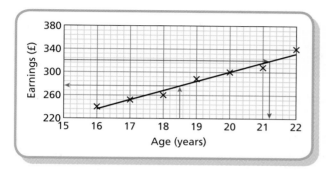

Need more help?
For more on this topic, see pages 182–185 of the main Edexcel textbook (ISBN 978-1-84690-454-7).

edexcel ⣿ key terms

extrapolation This is when the data point you need lies outside the range of the given data values.

interpolation This is when the data point you need lies within the range of the given data values.

We can estimate the earnings of an 18.5-year-old by drawing a line from 18.5 on the horizontal axis to the line of best fit, and then to the vertical axis (as shown by the red line). We find that the estimate of earnings is approximately £280.

We can also estimate the age of the young person who gets £320 by drawing a line from £320 on the vertical axis to the line of best fit and then to the horizontal axis (as shown by the blue line). We find that the age is approximately 21.2 years.

This is called **interpolation** because we are working within the limits of the given data. This gives fairly reliable estimates.

If we want to estimate outside the given data, either above or below, we have to extend the line of best fit. Such estimates are often very unreliable.

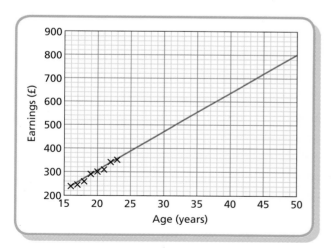

In the case above, wages would keep rising as you age. The extended line of best fit (red) suggests that at 50 the weekly wage will be £800, which is unlikely. Most people reach a point at which they are on maximum wages. Also, wages do not necessarily continue to rise at the same rate.

Estimating outside the limits of the given data is called **extrapolation**. Extrapolation is unreliable.

Exam Question Report

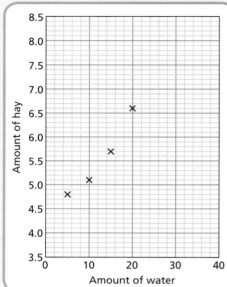

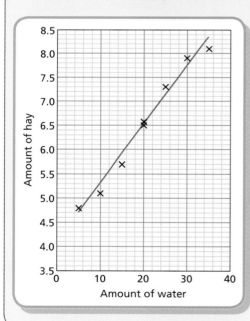

Sprinklers are used to water similar plots of land on an experimental farm. The table shows the amount of water applied, in cm, and the amount of hay grown, in tonnes per acre, on each of seven plots of land.

Amount of water (x cm)	5	10	15	20	25	30	35
Amount of hay (y tonnes/acre)	4.8	5.1	5.7	6.6	7.3	7.9	8.1

a Plot the last three points from the table to complete the scatter diagram for these data. (1)
b Describe the correlation between the amount of water applied and the amount of hay grown per acre. (2)
c On the scatter diagram:
  i plot the mid-point (20, 6.5)
  ii draw the line of best fit. (2)
d Estimate the amount of hay grown when 32 cm of water is applied by the sprinklers to another one of these plots. (2)
e Extend your line of best fit to find the amount of hay grown when no water is applied by the sprinklers. Discuss this answer. (2)

How students answered

a ▲ Last three points plotted correctly.

b ▲ The correlation is positive AND the more water the more hay (2 marks).

⬤ Either the correlation is positive OR the more water the more hay (1 mark).

■ A common error was to write 'one goes up as the other goes up'. This is not a satisfactory contextual interpretation. The variables must be clearly stated.

c i ▲ Point plotted correctly (see diagram in part **a**).

■ A common error was to plot the point at (6.5, 20).

ii ▲ Line of best fit drawn passing through (20, 6.5) – (see diagram in part **a**).

■ Common incorrect answers: Line not passing through the point (20, 6.5); or line passing through (0, 3.5).

d ▲ Any figure in the range 7.9 to 8.1.

⬤ Line from 32 to line of best fit gets 1 mark.

e ▲ Figure between 4.1 and 4.4 (1 mark). Plus either: This is the amount of hay produced due to rain only OR Extrapolation (extending beyond the line) is not reliable.

⬤ Either just the figure or just the explanation got 1 mark.

■ A common incorrect answer was 'If there is no water there is no hay'.

Test yourself

1 What is the difference between extrapolation and interpolation?

2 The scatter diagram gives information about the distance from a bank and the depth of a dyke.

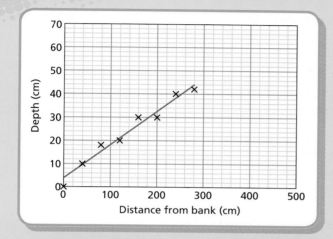

a Use the line of best fit to estimate the depth when the distance is 150 cm.
b Use the line of best fit to estimate the distance when the depth is 15 cm.
c Why would it be unwise to use the line of best fit to find the depth at a distance of 450 cm?

3 The data table gives the marks in French and History gained by nine students in an exam.

| French | 25 | 55 | 45 | 70 | 60 | 30 | 35 | 60 | 65 | 55 |
| History | 40 | 55 | 50 | 65 | 60 | 40 | 45 | 55 | 60 | 60 |

a Draw a scatter diagram for these data.
b Draw a line of best fit on your diagram.
c i Use your line of best fit to estimate the French mark of a student who got 62 in History.
ii Does your answer to i involve interpolation or extrapolation?
d i Use your line of best fit to estimate the History mark of a student who got 85 in French.
ii Does your answer to i involve interpolation or extrapolation?

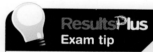

ResultsPlus
Exam tip

Take care to use a sensible scale. Look for the highest and lowest number for each variable to help decide starting and ending values. Then go up in sensible intervals – one, five or ten usually work well.

Need more help?

For more on this topic, see pages 187–190 of the main Edexcel textbook (ISBN 978-1-84690-454-7).

5.3: Equations of lines of best fit

 Find the equation of a line of best fit in the form $y = ax + b$ and a practical interpretation of a and b in context

Equation of a line of best fit

The **equation of the line of best fit** is of the form $y = ax + b$,

where a is the gradient of the line of best fit, so $a = \dfrac{\text{change in } y}{\text{change in } x}$

and b is the value of y where the line of best fit intercepts with the y axis (i.e. when $x = 0$).

If b cannot be read from the graph, put the value of a in the equation, pick a point on the line and put the values of x and y into the equation as well, and then solve the equation to get b.

For example, the scatter graph shows foreleg length and tail length of an animal.

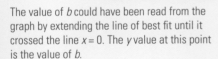

edexcel ⦚ key terms

equation of line of best fit $y = ax + b$

a This is the gradient: $\dfrac{\text{change in } y}{\text{change in } x}$

b This is the value of y when $x = 0$

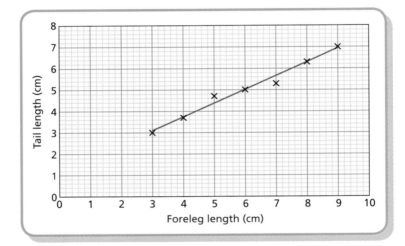

Two points on the line are $(4, 3.7)$ and $(8, 6.3)$, so $a = \dfrac{6.3 - 3.7}{8 - 4} = \dfrac{2.6}{4} = 0.65$

So $y = 0.65x + b$.

Now $x = 4$ when $y = 3.7$, so we can write $3.7 = (0.65 \times 4) + b$ and so $b = 1.1$.

The equation is $y = 0.65x + 1.1$.

ResultsPlus
Exam tip

The value of b could have been read from the graph by extending the line of best fit until it crossed the line $x = 0$. The y value at this point is the value of b.

Using a line of best fit

The equation of a line of best fit can be used to make predictions.

Using the equation for the line of best fit above, you can predict the tail length at any foreleg length. For example, when the foreleg length is 3.5 cm the tail length $y = (0.65 \times 3.5) + 1.1 = 3.375$ cm.

You can also predict the foreleg length when you know the tail length.

For example, when the tail length is 6 cm then $6 = 0.65x + 1.1$, so the foreleg length $x = 7.54$ cm.

ResultsPlus
Exam tip

Remember, predictions made for values outside the data range involve extrapolation and are unreliable.

Interpreting the gradient, *a*, and the *y* value at the intercept *b*

The gradient should always be interpreted in context. Always start by writing the gradient as a fraction. If it is a whole number, write the whole number over 1.

If the above equation was $y = \frac{2}{3}x + \frac{1}{2}$, the gradient *a* is $\frac{2}{3}$. This means that for every three across there is a rise of two. This should be written in context as 'For every increase of 3 cm in the foreleg there is an increase of 2 cm in the tail length'.

The interpretation of *b* is that 'The tail length, when the foreleg is 0 cm, is half a centimetre'. This is obviously impossible and is an example of the danger of extrapolation.

The gradient will not always be positive. If *x* (years) is the age of a car and *y* is the value (£100s) then the gradient is negative. Suppose the gradient is $-\frac{1}{20}$, then the interpretation will be that for every year the car increases in age, the value decreases by 20 (£100s).

ResultsPlus
Exam tip

Don't interpret a gradient as so much across and so much up. Always look at the axes labels and interpret in context.

Test yourself

1 Two points on a line of best fit are (4, 9) and (6, 12). Work out the equation of the line in the form **y = ax + b**.

2 The equation of the line of best fit drawn on a scatter diagram showing the relationship between the English mark (*x*) and the Maths mark (*y*) of a group of students is $y = \frac{1}{2}x + 12$. Use the equation to:
   a Predict the Maths mark of a student who got a mark of 64 in English.
   b Predict the English mark of a student who got a mark of 58 in Maths.

3 The height (*x* cm) of a broad bean was measured over a period of time (*y* weeks). A scatter diagram with a line of best fit was drawn for these data. The equation of the line of best fit was $y = 3x$. Interpret the gradient of this line.

4 The temperature (*y*°C) of the boiling point of water was measured at different heights (*x* metres) above sea level. A scatter diagram with a line of best fit was drawn for these data. The equation of the line of best fit was
   $y = -\frac{1}{300}x + 100$.

   For this equation, interpret in context the values:
   a $-\frac{1}{300}$ b 100.

5 The table gives information about the age and hours spent on homework each week by a group of students.

Age (years)	12	13	14	15	16	17	18
Hours	6	7	8.2	9	9.7	11	12

   a Draw a scatter diagram for these data.
   b Work out the co-ordinates of the mean point.
   c Draw a line of best fit through the mean point.
   d Work out the equation of the line of best fit in the form $y = ax + b$.
   e Interpret in context the values of *a* and *b* in this equation.
   f Why would it not be a good idea to use this equation to find the number of hours of homework done by an eight-year-old?

ResultsPlus
Exam Question Report

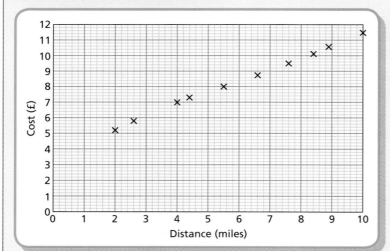

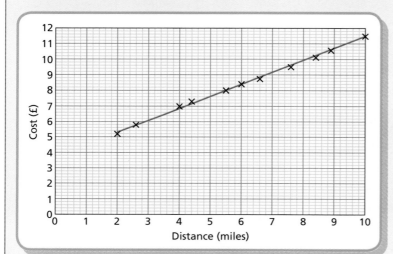

The scatter diagram shows the distance (*x* miles) and the cost (£*y*) of each of ten taxi journeys in Huddersgate.

a On the scatter diagram:
 i plot the mean point (6, 8.4). (1)
 ii draw the line of best fit. (1)

The equation of the line of best fit has the form $y = ax + b$.

b Using your line of best fit, find the value of *a* and the value of *b*. (3)

c Explain what the value of *a* and the value of *b* represent in this context. (2)

d Give a reason why the equation $y = ax + b$ may not be used reliably to predict the cost of a journey of 100 miles. (1)

How students answered

a ⚠ 1 mark for mean point and 1 mark for line of best fit through the mean point. This was quite well done by candidates.

b ⚠ *a* = between 0.67 and 0.87 (1 mark). *b* = 4 (or read off your graph). There was also 1 mark for an effort at working out a gradient.

⬤ 1 mark or 2 marks dependent on how many of gradient $= \frac{\text{diff. in } y}{\text{diff. in } x}$, *a* and *b* were correct. Many candidates could write down the value of *b* in the equation for the line of best fit but they could not manage to find the gradient.

⬛ A common error was to use $\frac{\text{diff. in } x}{\text{diff. in } y}$ to find the gradient.

c ⚠ *a* represents cost per mile and *b* represents the amount that is paid to hire the taxi/the amount paid to travel 0 miles.

⬤ 1 mark for interpreting either *a* or *b* correctly.

⬛ This wasn't well answered by most candidates. A common error was to describe *a* and *b* as the gradient and intercept of the line. Marks were only given for in context interpretation.

d ⚠ Linear model may not be appropriate for distances greater than 10 miles. OR Cannot extrapolate. OR The trend might not continue.

⬛ Only about a third of the candidates could give a valid **statistical** explanation based on the uncertainty of extrapolation.

5.4: Fitting a line of best fit to a non-linear model

 Recognise positive, negative and zero linear and non-linear correlation by inspection

 Fit non-linear models

 Compare or choose by eye between a line of best fit and a linear, quadratic or reciprocal model

Non-linear models

Sometimes a straight line is not the best fit for an association between two variables.

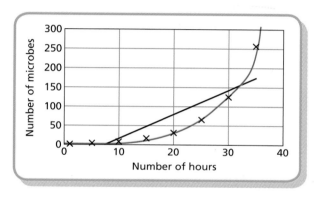

The graph shows the growth of microbes in a Petri dish over a number of hours. The straight line of best fit is not a good model. The curve is much better.

Equations of non-linear curves of the form $y = ka^x$

Where we are looking at the way things decay and grow, we usually get what is called an **exponential** function. This is one of the form $y = ka^x$. The curve on the graph above is of the form $y = ka^x$ ($a > 1$) since it models the growth of the microbes.

Equations of non-linear curves of the form $y = ax^n + b$

Other equations you need to recognise are those of the form $y = ax^n + b$, where $n = 2, -1$ or $\frac{1}{2}$.

- For $n = 2$ the equation is $y = ax^2 + b$.

- For $n = -1$ the equation is $y = \frac{a}{x} + b$.

- For $n = \frac{1}{2}$ the equation is $y = a\sqrt{x} + b$.

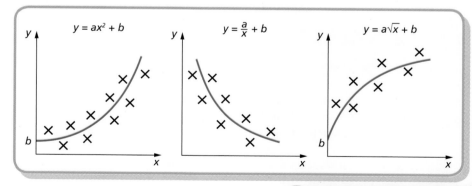

edexcel ⠿ key terms

equations of other non-linear models:

- $y = ax^2 + b$
- $y = \frac{a}{x} + b$
- $y = a\sqrt{x} + b$

exponential function One that models the way things grow or decay.
exponential model equation $y = ka^x$.
non-linear model One that does not follow a straight line.

Need more help?
For more on this topic, see pages 192–194 of the main Edexcel textbook (ISBN 978-1-84690-454-7).

ResultsPlus
Exam tip

You do need to recognise these models and their equations.

ResultsPlus
Exam Question Report

The wingspans and weights of eight common birds are shown in the scatter diagram.
Which of the following laws is the best model for these data? (1)

A: $y = ax^2$ B: $y = \dfrac{a}{x}$
C: $y = a\sqrt{x}$

How students answered

Students found this very difficult.

 A (1 mark).

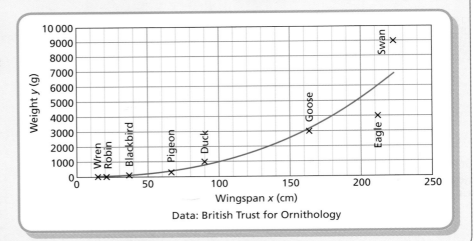

Data: British Trust for Ornithology

Test yourself

1 Suggest an equation for each of the following:

2 A scatter diagram of the following data suggests that an equation of the form $y = ax^2 + b$ would be a suitable model.

x	1	2	3	4	5	6	7
y	2	5	10	17	26	37	50

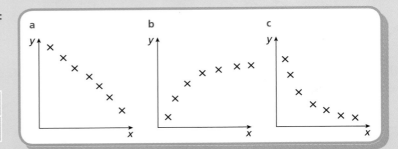

a Draw a scatter diagram for these data.
b On your graph draw a line of best fit and a curve of best fit.
c State which is the better fit.

3 The table gives some information about the increase in the number of aphids on a lupin plant.

Time (hours)	2	4	6	8	10	12
Number of aphids	4	8	16	32	64	128

a Draw a scatter diagram for these data.
b Draw a curve of best fit on the diagram.
c Suggest a suitable model for the relationship between these variables.

5.5: Spearman's rank correlation

- ✓ Calculate Spearman's rank correlation coefficient
- ✓ Use Spearman's rank correlation coefficient as a measure of agreement or for comparisons of the degree of correlation
- ✓ Interpret correlation as a measure of the strength of the association between two variables, including Spearman's rank correlation coefficient for ranked data

Need more help?
For more on this topic, see pages 195–200 of the main Edexcel textbook (ISBN 978-1-84690-454-7).

Ranking

Ranking means giving the largest value the rank one and the next largest the rank two and so on, until all observations are ranked.

Spearman's rank correlation coefficient

Correlation is a measure of the strength of the linear association between two variables. Spearman's rank correlation coefficient (r_s) is a numerical measure of the strength of the association.

It is given by: $r_s = 1 - \dfrac{6\sum d^2}{n(n^2 - 1)}$, where d is the difference in the ranks and n is the number of observations.

For example, the table shows the marks given by two judges who were judging a competition.

Judge 1	24	35	18	19	26
Judge 2	36	40	26	20	16
Rank 1	3	1	5	4	2
Rank 2	2	1	3	4	5
d	1	0	2	0	-3
d^2	1	0	4	0	9

$\sum d^2 = 14$ so $1 - \dfrac{6\sum d^2}{n(n^2 - 1)} = 1 - \dfrac{6 \times 14}{5(25 - 1)} = 1 - \dfrac{84}{120} = 1 - 0.7 = 0.3$

So the Spearman's rank correlation coefficient for these data is 0.3.

Interpreting Spearman's rank correlation coefficients

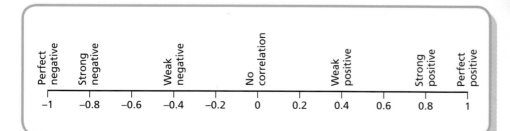

edexcel ⠿ key terms

interpretation −1 is perfect negative correlation; 0 is no correlation; +1 is perfect positive correlation.
negative correlation In context this means as one variable increases the other decreases.
positive correlation In context this means as one variable increases the other also increases.
ranking Giving the largest value the rank one and the next largest the rank two and so on, until all observations are ranked.
Spearman's rank correlation coefficient
$r_s = 1 - \dfrac{6\sum d^2}{n(n^2 - 1)}$

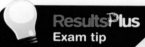
ResultsPlus
Exam tip

Always remember to rank in the same direction. If you always start with the highest value being rank one, you will not make a mistake.

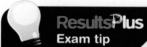
ResultsPlus
Exam tip

This formula is at the front of every exam paper on the formulae page.

ResultsPlus
Exam tip

Remember, if the difference is negative, when you square it, it will be positive.

As well as interpreting whether it is **positive correlation** or **negative correlation**, you also need to interpret in context. A coefficient of 0.7 can be interpreted as fairly strong positive correlation.

If you got a coefficient of −0.9 for the relationship between car age and price, the interpretation would be that this is strong negative correlation. As age increases, price decreases.

If you got a coefficient of 0.4 for the relationship between car engine size and car running costs, the interpretation would be that this is weak positive correlation. There is some evidence that as engine size increases so running costs increase.

Test yourself

1 Two judges give ranks to five entries for a knitting competition. The $\sum d^2 = 31$. Work out Spearman's rank correlation for these data and interpret your answer.

2 The table gives the number of goals and the league position for six school teams.

Goals	28	24	42	33	27	20
League position	1	2	3	4	5	6
Rank goals						
d						
d^2						

a Copy and complete the table.
b Work out Spearman's rank correlation coefficient.
c Interpret your answer to part b.

3 The table shows some information about the number of years five people have smoked and the damage to their lungs.

Number of years smoked	15	25	28	31	42
Lung damage grade	30	55	35	42	56

a Work out Spearman's rank correlation coefficient.
b Interpret your answer to part a.

ResultsPlus
Exam Question Report

Table 1 shows seven countries selected at random, their HDI (Human Development Index – a measure of their quality of life) and their GNP (Gross National Product per person – a measure of their wealth).

Table 1

Country	Niger	Rwanda	India	Oman	China	Cuba	UK
HDI	0.116	0.304	0.439	0.535	0.716	0.877	0.970
GNP	20	26	25	93	22	66	113

Table 2 shows the countries ranked in descending order for their HDI.

Table 2

Country	Niger	Rwanda	India	Oman	China	Cuba	UK
HDI rank	7	6	5	4	3	2	1
GNP rank							
Difference in ranks (d)							
d^2							

a   Complete Table 2. (2)
b   Use the information in Table 2 to calculate Spearman's rank correlation coefficient for this data. Give your answer to three decimal places. (2)
c   Interpret your answer to part b. (2)

How students answered

a   ▲ 7, 4, 5, 2, 6, 3, 1 (1 mark) and d^2 row: 0, 4, 0, 4, 9, 1, 0 (1 mark). Most students got this right.

   ● Some students used a reverse order (1, 4, 3, 6, 2, 5, 7) and so lost the first mark, but they could still get 1 mark for a d^2 row of 36, 4, 4, 4, 1, 9, 36.

b   ▲ An answer of 0.679 got 2 marks.

   ● Some students lost a mark because they did not give their answer to three decimal places as requested. The following got 1 mark: Either 0.6/0.67/0.68 or $1 - \dfrac{6 \times 18}{7 \, (7^2 - 1)}$

   ■ Some students wrote the formula down incorrectly. This should not happen as it is at the front of the exam paper. Common errors were to forget the 1 or to put it on top of the fraction. Some students managed to write down the formula but had no idea what n referred to.

c   ▲ It is positive PLUS EITHER: The higher the HDI the higher the GNP. OR: The lower the HDI the lower the GNP.

   ● Just one of the above got 1 mark. Many students lost a mark here as they gave no contextual answer.

   ■ Comments about strength without the direction (positive) got no mark. A common incorrect effort at contextual interpretation was 'They are associated'.

6.1: Time series

✓ Construct, use and understand line graphs and time series

✓ Plot points as a time series

Need more help?
For more on this topic, see pages 212–214 of the main Edexcel textbook (ISBN 978-1-84690-454-7).

edexcel ▦ key terms

time series A set of observations taken at intervals over time.
time series graph A graph showing how the variable alters over time.
trend The trend may be increasing, decreasing or level.
trend line A line drawn through the points on a time series graph to show the trend.

Time series

A **time series** is a set of observations of a variable taken at intervals (usually regular intervals) over time.

A **graph** can be plotted of a time series. The time is plotted horizontally and the variable is plotted vertically.

This is an example of a time series graph. It shows how much money Jack has in his savings account over eight weeks.

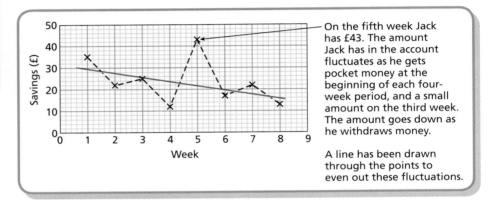

On the fifth week Jack has £43. The amount Jack has in the account fluctuates as he gets pocket money at the beginning of each four-week period, and a small amount on the third week. The amount goes down as he withdraws money.

A line has been drawn through the points to even out these fluctuations.

The line is called a **trend line**. It shows that the **trend** is for the amount in the account to fall. Over the eight weeks Jack is spending more than he is putting in.

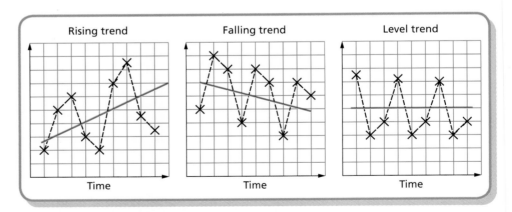

A **trend line** may show a tendency to rise, to fall or to stay level.

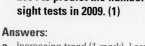

Exam Question Report

The time series graph shows information about the number of sight tests in England each year from 1995 to 2004.

a   Explain what the time series graph shows about the number of sight tests from 1995 to 2004. (2)

b   Use the information in the time series graph from 2000 to 2004 to predict the number of sight tests in 2009. (1)

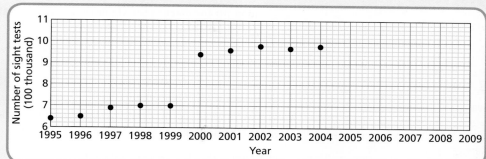

Answers:

a   Increasing trend (1 mark). Large increase in 2000 (1 mark).

b   1 000 000 to 1 100 000 OR 10 to 11.

How students answered

a   The most common incorrect answer was to say there was no trend.

| | 3% 0 marks |

A lot of students got one mark by mentioning one of the answers.

| | 49% 1 mark |

Less than half of the candidates got both marks.

| | 48% 2 marks |

b   Common incorrect answers were 1000, 12 and 100 000.

| | 51% 0 marks |

This question was not very well done – less than half the candidates got the mark.

| | 49% 1 mark |

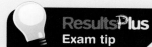

Exam tip

To get the figure for part b, draw in a trend line for these years.

Test yourself

1   The table gives information about the number of people, in 100s, attending a performance of an opera.

Day	Mon	Tues	Wed	Thu	Fri	Sat	Sun
Week 1	9	10	9	13	14	22	20
Week 2	7	8	6	13	14	20	17

Draw a time series graph for these data.

2   The time series graph shows the wind speed at a weather recording station.

a   Which trend line best describes the trend of the points?

b   Describe the trend shown by line A.

c   Describe the trend shown by line C.

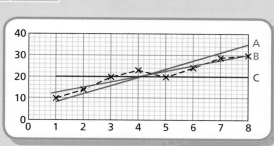

6.2: Moving averages

✓ **Calculate and use appropriate moving averages**

✓ **Draw a trend line by eye and use it to make a prediction**

✓ **Identify and discuss the significance of seasonal variation by inspecting time series graphs**

Need more help?
For more on this topic, see pages 219–223 of the main Edexcel textbook (ISBN 978-1-84690-454-7).

edexcel ::: key terms

moving average An average worked out over successive observations. The number of points of observation should cover one cycle. Moving averages are plotted at the mid-point of the time interval they cover.

seasonal variation A pattern of variations either side of the general trend that repeats itself in cycles.

Seasonal variations

A time series graph may show a general trend and variations either side of the trend line that show a repeating pattern. The variations either side of the trend are called **seasonal variations**.

This graph shows the sales of ice cream.

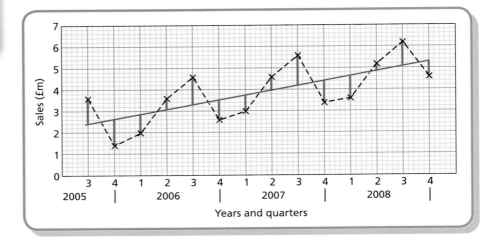

The seasonal variations are shown as green lines, e.g. the seasonal variation for 2005 Q4 is −£1.2m. This pattern corresponds with the fourth season of the year and repeats every fourth reading.

Not all patterns correspond with the four seasons. You could for example have television viewings that relate to the days of the week. You would then have a seven-season variation that corresponds to the seven days of the week.

Moving averages

A moving average is an average worked out over a given number of successive observations. The number of points in each moving average should cover one complete cycle of variations. If there are four seasons you would use a four-point moving average. If there are seven seasons you would use a seven-point moving average.

Moving averages can be plotted on a time series graph. They are plotted at the mid-point of the time interval they cover.

A trend line can be drawn through the moving averages.

The mean hours of sunshine per day in each quarter of the year for two consecutive years are shown.

ResultsPlus
Exam tip

Foundation students are expected to deal with up to five-point moving averages and Higher students up to seven-point moving averages.

The first moving average $= \dfrac{2.6 + 6 + 4.6 + 2}{4} = 3.8$

Quarter	Q1	Q2	Q3	Q4
Year 1	2.6	6	4.6	2
Year 2	2.5	6	4.8	2

The mid-point of the time interval is Q2.5.

The second moving average $= \dfrac{6 + 4.6 + 2 + 2.5}{4} = 3.78$

The mid-point is Q3.5.

All the moving averages are shown plotted on the diagram with a trend line drawn through them.

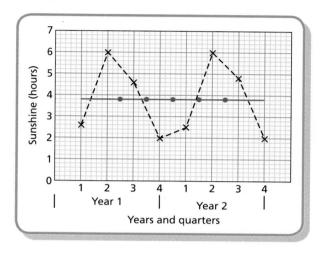

The trend line is level. There has been little change in the amount of sunshine.

The equation of a trend line

The equation of the trend line may be found as in Section 5.3.

Test yourself

1 The table gives information about the sales (£1000s) of a magazine.

	2007	2008	2009
Q1	60	65	65
Q2	62	67	70
Q3	70	75	78
Q4	70	71	72

a Draw a time series graph for these data.
b Calculate the four-point moving averages and plot these on the graph.
c Draw a trend line through the moving averages.

ResultsPlus
Exam Question Report

The table shows the quarterly takings, in £100s, at a swimming pool for each quarter of two successive years.

a **Complete the table to show the remaining four-point moving averages. (2)**

b **On the graph below, plot the four-point moving averages. (2)**

Year	Quarter	Takings	Four-point moving average
1	1	36	
	2	47	
			$(36 + 47 + 65 + 40) \div 4 = 47$
	3	65	
	4	40	
2	1	24	
	2	39	
	3	57	
	4	32	

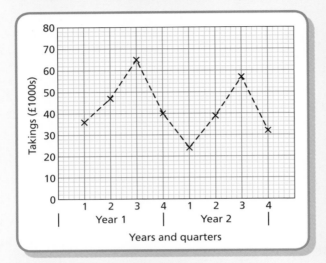

c **On the graph, draw a trend line for the moving averages. (2)**

d **Using your trend line, decide whether the takings at the swimming pool are increasing or decreasing over time. Explain your answer. (2)**

The swimming pool employs extra staff at busy times of year.

e i **In which quarter are they most likely to employ extra staff? (1)**

   ii **Give one reason why you think that this quarter is the busiest. (1)**

How students answered

a ▲ 44, 42, 40, 38

   ● One wrong got only 1 mark.

b ▲ Plot points at (2.5, 44), (3.5, 42), (4.5, 40), (5.5, 38).

   ● One point incorrect got 1 mark.

   ■ Many students were unable to plot the moving averages correctly. A common incorrect answer was to plot the points at (2, 44) (3, 42) etc.

c ▲ Correct trend line as shown.

   ■ A trend line outside sensible limits got 0 marks.

d ▲ Decreasing (1 mark) plus 'The trend line is sloping downwards' (or equivalent) (1 mark).

   ● One of the above got 1 mark.

e i ▲ Quarter 3 (1 mark).

      ■ A common incorrect answer was 'Year 1, Quarter 3'.

   ii ▲ Any one of: Hot weather, summer visitors or equivalent.

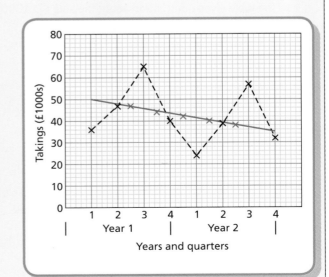

6.3: Average seasonal variation

✓ Draw a trend line based on moving averages

✓ Recognise seasonal effect at a given data point and average seasonal effect

Need more help?
For more on this topic, see pages 225–233 of the main Edexcel textbook (ISBN 978-1-84690-454-7).

Average seasonal variations

The **seasonal variation** at a point = actual value at that point − value as shown by the trend line.

The **average seasonal variation** is the mean value of all the seasonal variations for that season, e.g. the mean of the seasonal variations for the first quarter of each year.

The time series graph below shows the seasonal variations of the sales of ice cream.

edexcel ⠿ key terms

average seasonal variation The mean of all the seasonal variations for that season.
predicted value The projected trend line value + the mean seasonal value.
seasonal variation The actual value − trend line value.

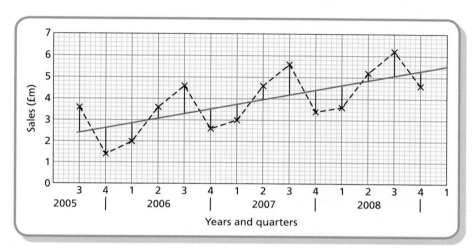

The seasonal variations as read from the graph are shown in the table.

The estimated means will be

Q1 estimated mean $= \dfrac{-2.5}{3} = -0.83$ Q2 estimated mean $= \dfrac{1.5}{3} = 0.5$

Q3 estimated mean $= \dfrac{5.1}{4} = 1.28$ Q4 estimated mean $= \dfrac{-3.8}{4} = -0.95$

Making predictions

A trend line and an estimated mean seasonal variation can be used to make predictions.

Predicted value = predicted trend line value (from trend line on graph) + estimated mean seasonal variation for the season being estimated.

On the graph above the trend line value for Q1 of 2009 is 5.6 and the mean seasonal variation for Q1 is −0.83, so the estimated value for Q1 of 2009 is:

estimated value = trend line value + mean seasonal variation = 5.6 + (−0.83) = £4.77 million.

Year	Quarter			
	1	2	3	4
2005			1.2	−1.2
2006	−0.8	0.5	1.3	−0.9
2007	−0.7	0.6	1.4	−1.0
2008	−1.0	0.4	1.2	−0.7
Total	−2.5	1.5	5.1	−3.8

	Quarter			
Year	1	2	3	4
2002	80	115	120	90
2003	95	120	125	100
2004	105	130	135	105

Exam Question Report

The table on the left shows the number of cooling fans sold by Breeze Engineering each quarter, for the years 2002 to 2004.
The data has been plotted as a time series. The four-point moving averages are also shown.

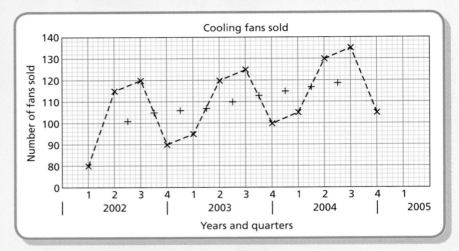

a   Draw a trend line on the diagram for this data. (1)
b   Write down what the trend line shows about the number of cooling fans sold between the years 2002 and 2004. (1)

The graph shows that the season of the year affects the number of fans sold.
c   Write down a reason why. (1)

The value of the average seasonal effect for the first quarter is −13.8.
d   Calculate the predicted sales for the first quarter of 2005. (2)
e   i   Write down two assumptions you made when predicting the sales for the first quarter of 2005.
    ii How reasonable are these assumptions?

How students answered

a   ⚠ Trend line drawn as shown.

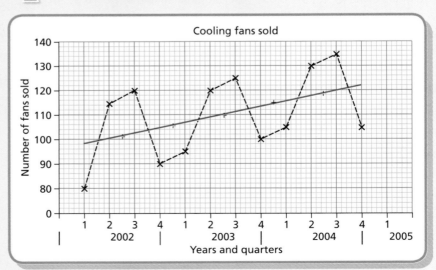

◾ Some students plotted all the points to one side of the line or drew a line that went through the middle point with the points to the left above the line and those to the right below. Given that the points were nearly in a straight line this was rather surprising.

b ▲ Sales rising. It was exceptional for marks to be lost in this part.

c ▲ It is hotter in summer than winter or equivalent. Most students were able to say something sensible here.

d ▲ 110.7 (answers in the range 108.2–113.2 were accepted). 110 with no working got 1 mark only.

● 124.5 (values in the range 122–127 were accepted) – 13.8 got 1 mark.

◾ Many students tried to use the last value of 105 (from the table: 2004 Q4), either adding (or subtracting) the seasonal value from this, or adding 5 to it on the grounds that it had gone up 5 the previous year.

e **i** ▲ Trend and seasonal pattern continue.

ii ▲ Very reasonable.

● Even those that got part **d** right had difficulty in coming up with the 'textbook' answers of continuing trend and seasonal effect. In **ii**, the answer depended on getting part **i** correct.

ResultsPlus
Exam tip

It is important to always show your working.

Test yourself

1 The table shows the seasonal variations in the price of lettuce.

	Seasonal variation (pence)			
Year	Q1	Q2	Q3	Q4
1	0.0	−6	8	4
2	2.2	−4	6	2

Work out the mean seasonal variations.

2 This table gives information about the quarterly profits, in £1000s, of a small factory.

	Quarter			
Year	1	2	3	4
2007	30	50	60	40
2008	35	55	65	45
2009	40	60	70	50

a Draw a time series graph for these data.
b Work out the moving averages for these data and plot them on the graph.
c Draw a trend line on the graph.
d Find the mean seasonal variation for Q1.
e Predict the profit for Q1 of 2010.

7.1: Events, outcomes and probability

- ✓ Understand the meaning of the words event and outcome
- ✓ Understand words such as impossible, certain, highly likely, likely, unlikely, possible, evens and present them on a likelihood scale
- ✓ Put outcomes in order in terms of probability
- ✓ Put probabilities in order on a probability scale

Need more help?
For more on this topic, see pages 242–247 of the main Edexcel textbook (ISBN 978-1-84690-454-7).

edexcel ⋮⋮⋮ key terms

equally likely outcomes When outcomes have the same chance of happening.
event A set of one or more successful outcomes.
outcome The possible results of a trial.
probability A numerical measure of the chance of an event happening.
probability scale A scale that goes from 0 for impossible to 1 for certain to happen.
trial The act of testing or doing something.

Trials, outcomes and events

If you throw a six-sided die, the act of throwing it is called a **trial**. When the die is thrown you may get any one of the numbers one to six. The possible results of the trial are called the **outcomes**. If when throwing a die you need a number greater than three, then four, five and six would be successful outcomes. A set of successful outcomes like this is called an **event**.

A likelihood scale

Not all events are equally likely to happen. The scale below shows some words used to describe how likely a particular event is to happen.

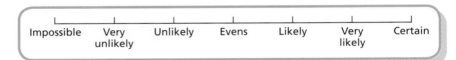

Probability

A numerical measure of the likelihood of an event happening is known as its **probability**.

If an event is impossible the probability of it happening is zero. If it is certain to happen the probability of it happening is one. Here is a **probability scale**:

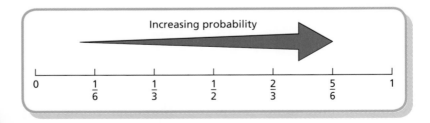

ResultsPlus
Exam tip

When asked to mark probabilities such as $\frac{2}{7}$ on a line, measure the line and work out what $\frac{2}{7}$ of the length is. If the line is 14 cm long it would be $\frac{2}{7} \times 14 = 4$ cm from the zero.

If an event B has a probability of $\frac{1}{3}$ it is likely to happen once in every three trials. The probability of the event is written $P(B) = \frac{1}{3}$.

Probabilities may be written as fractions, decimals or percentages.

Equally likely outcomes

When a six-sided die is rolled, each of the numbers one to six is equally likely to be the result. These outcomes are said to be **equally likely**.

Exam Question Report

A magician puts a set of ten numbered counters in a hat. The counters are numbered one to ten. A woman takes a counter at random from the hat. The events *A*, *B* and *C* are:

> **A** She takes the number ten.
> **B** She takes an odd number.
> **C** She takes a number greater than six.

a Mark the events *A*, *B* and *C* on the probability scale below. **(2)**

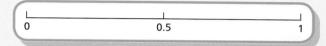

b For this set of counters, suggest a different event that has the same probability as event *B*. **(1)**

How students answered

Most students were able to score some marks.

a

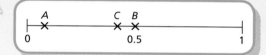

$0 < A < 0.25$, $0.25 < C < 0.5$, $B = 0.5$

◖ B was usually placed correctly, but a significant minority placed C to the right of B.

b ▲ She selects an even number. Most students stated that an even number should be taken. Other correct answers included 'greater than 5' or 'less than 6'.

■ Some of the weaker students either confused the figures by stating 'less than 5', or gave an example that did not include the counters in the question.

Test yourself

1 List the possible outcomes for these trials.
   a A penny is flipped.
   b The results of a football match your team is playing tomorrow.

2 Write down the most suitable word to describe the probability of each of the following events.
   a A fair coin will fall with tails uppermost when tossed.
   b There will be snowfall in July this year in England.
   c On your next birthday you will be one year older.

3 Draw a numerical probability scale and mark the probability of each of these events on it.
   a The next person you meet will have been born on a Monday.
   b The News will be on television today.
   c You will win the lottery this week.

Need more help?
For more on this topic, see pages 246–249 and 256–258 of the main Edexcel textbook (ISBN 978-1-84690-454-7).

7.2: Probability of an event and sample spaces

- ✓ Understand the terms 'random' and 'equally likely'
- ✓ Understand and use measures of probability from a theoretical perspective and from a limiting frequency or experimental approach
- ✓ Produce, understand and use a sample space

edexcel ⠿ key terms

probability of an event If all outcomes are equally likely $= \dfrac{\text{number of successful outcomes}}{\text{total number of outcomes}}$

sample space A list of all possible outcomes.

The probability of an event

If all possible outcomes are equally likely, the **probability of an event** is given by:

$$\text{probability} = \frac{\text{number of successful outcomes}}{\text{total number of outcomes}}$$

For example, if you throw a fair die there are six possible outcomes, each equally likely. If you want to know the probability of the event 'throwing a number greater than four', then there are two successful outcomes (five or six).

The probability of the event is $\dfrac{2}{6} = \dfrac{1}{3}$.

Sometimes the information is given in a two-way table.

This two-way table shows the numbers of males and females in a year of 50 students who do or do not wear glasses.

	Male	Female	Total
Wears glasses	3	7	10
Does not wear glasses	27	13	40
Total	30	20	50

If one student is chosen at random the probability of the event 'it is a girl who wears glasses' is readily found. There are seven successful outcomes and 50 outcomes in total. The probability is therefore $\dfrac{7}{50}$.

Sample spaces

A list of all possible outcomes is called a **sample space**.

For example, if you throw two fair dice the possible outcomes of the sum of the two dice can be shown in a table.

The probability of getting a total greater than eight is $\dfrac{10}{36} = \dfrac{5}{18}$

There are ten outcomes greater than eight and 36 possible outcomes altogether.

ResultsPlus
Exam tip

Remember that a two on die 1 followed by a three on die 2 is not the same as a three on die 1 followed by a two on die 2.

		Die 1					
		1	2	3	4	5	6
Die 2	1	2	3	4	5	6	7
	2	3	4	5	6	7	8
	3	4	5	6	7	8	9
	4	5	6	7	8	9	10
	5	6	7	8	9	10	11
	6	7	8	9	10	11	12

ResultsPlus
Exam Question Report

A farmer wants to find out if a vaccine can stop his sheep getting foot rot. He uses a sample of 100 sheep that do not have foot rot. He vaccinates 60 of these sheep. The two-way table below shows the results after a period of time.
He chooses one of the 100 sheep at random.

	No. with foot rot	No. with no foot rot	Total
Vaccinated	10	50	60
Not vaccinated	20	20	40
Total	30	70	100

a Write down the probability that the sheep:
  i does not have foot rot
  ii had been vaccinated and has foot rot. (2)
b Did the vaccine help to stop foot rot? Write down the reason for your answer. (2)

The farmer did not give the vaccine to all of the 100 sheep.
c Explain why. (1)

How students answered

a i ▲ $\frac{70}{100}$ ii ▲ $\frac{10}{100}$

■ Some students gave their answer out of 60 rather than 100.

b ▲ Yes (1 mark). A larger proportion of those vaccinated did not get foot rot (1 mark).

● Most students gained a mark for stating that it did reduce the foot rot but some candidates did not say 'yes'.

■ Many students lost a mark because they referred to the numbers getting foot rot rather than to the proportions.

c ▲ 'Control group' or 'To compare the vaccinated sheep with the non-vaccinated sheep'.

■ It was uncertain whether many of the students had a clear idea of why the vaccine was not given to all the sheep. Some suggested it might be because of the possible side-effects, or that it was too expensive to give to all the sheep. Many referred to the need to give it to just one group of sheep, but did not earn the mark as they did not mention some comparison with the other group.

Test yourself

1 A fair six-sided die is numbered one to six. Work out:
  a the probability of getting an odd number
  b the probability of getting a one
  c the probability of getting a number less than five.

2 The two-way table shows the number of court cards (Jack, Queen or King) and the number of other cards in a pack.
  If one card is drawn at random, work out the probability of getting:

	Court card	Non-court card	Total
Red cards	6	20	26
Black cards	6	20	26
Total	12	40	52

  a a black card   b a red court card   c a non-court card.

3 Three fair coins are flipped.
  a Write down the sample space.
  b Work out the probability of getting exactly two tails.
  c Work out the probability of getting three tails.

7.3: Venn diagrams

 Understand and use Venn diagrams

Need more help?
For more on this topic, see pages 260–266 of the main Edexcel textbook (ISBN 978-1-84690-454-7).

edexcel ⠿ key terms

Venn diagram A way of representing a sample space.

ResultsPlus
Exam tip

All the separate regions (including S) must add up to the total number involved. The numbers in set A (P and Q) must add up to the total number in set A. The numbers in set B (R and Q) must add up to the total number in set B.

ResultsPlus
Exam tip

Always remember to draw the rectangle around the circles, and do not forget those that are in neither set.

Venn diagrams

A Venn diagram is a way of representing a sample space. Each region of the diagram represents the number of a different set of data.

P represents the data in set A but **not** in set B.
Q represents the data in set A **and** in set B.
R represents the data in set B but **not** in set A.
S represents data that are not in set A and not in set B.

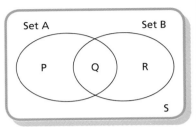

For example, the Venn diagram below shows the number of students who:

A have an MP3 player
B have a mobile phone.

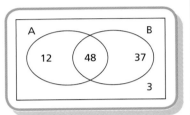

12 students have an MP3 player but do not have a mobile phone.
48 students have both.
37 have a mobile phone but no MP3 player.
3 have neither.

The total number of students is 12 + 48 + 37 + 3 = 100.

Venn diagrams showing probabilities

Instead of showing numbers a Venn diagram can show the probability of an item picked at random being in that region. The Venn diagram above would look like this:

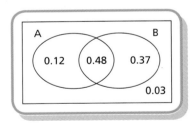

The probability of a student having an MP3 player but not a mobile phone is 0.12.
The probability of a student having an MP3 player and a mobile phone is 0.48.
The probability of a student having a mobile phone but not an MP3 player is 0.37.
The probability of a student having neither is 0.03.

The total of all the probabilities is always one.

ResultsPlus
Exam Question Report

A health trust does a survey to see how many of its hospital beds have access to a radio and/or a television. It finds that 21% have access to televisions only, 12% have access to radios only, and 2% have access to neither.

a **Complete the Venn diagram. (2)**

b **Find the probability that a bed chosen at random will have access to a radio or a television but not both. (1)**

c **Find the probability that a bed chosen at random will not have access to a television. (1)**

d **Given that a patient is in a bed with access to a radio, what is the probability that the bed also has access to a television? (2)**

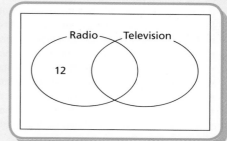

How students answered

a ▲ All values correct got 2 marks.

● The most common error was to omit '65'.

b ▲ 12 + 21 = 33% (or 0.33).

■ Some students worked out an answer of 0.33, but then corrected this to $\frac{1}{3}$ on the answer line.

c ▲ 12 + 2 = 14% (or 0.14).

d ▲ $\frac{65 \,(f.t.)}{65 \,(f.t.) + 12} = \frac{65}{77}$ (= 0.84)

■ Most students ignored the conditionality of the probability and simply wrote $\frac{65}{100}$.

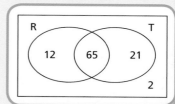

Test yourself

1 On a fairground stall you have two attempts at hitting a target. If you hit the target on both attempts you win a prize.

20 people hit the target on the first attempt only.

30 people hit the target on the second attempt only.

10 people hit the target on both attempts.

40 people missed on both attempts.

a Draw a Venn diagram to represent these data.

b How many people tried to win a prize?

c If one person is selected at random, what is the probability that they won a prize?

2 A group of people were asked if they played the guitar, the piano or drums.

The probability of a person playing all three instruments was 0.15.

The probability of a person playing the guitar only was 0.2.

The probability of a person playing the piano only was 0.25.

The probability of a person playing drums only was 0.15.

The probability of a person playing guitar and piano was 0.1.

The probability of a person playing guitar and drums was 0.05.

The probability of a person playing piano and drums was 0.01.

a Draw a Venn diagram for these data.

b Work out the probability that a person played none of the instruments.

ResultsPlus
Exam Question Report

A travel agent organises several different tours to the continent. The tours offer travellers the chance to visit Germany, France and Switzerland. Each tour visits one, two or three of these countries. 200 travellers book one of these tours.

- 130 travellers book a tour that visits Germany.
- 131 travellers book a tour that visits France.
- 122 travellers book a tour that visits Switzerland.
- 74 travellers book a tour that visits Switzerland and France.
- 84 travellers book a tour that visits France and Germany.
- 75 travellers book a tour that visits Germany and Switzerland.
- 50 travellers book a tour that visits all three countries.

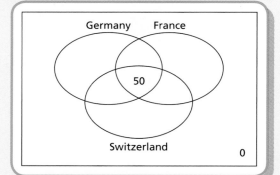

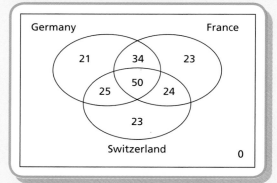

a Complete the Venn diagram for this information. (3)

A traveller is chosen at random from the 200 travellers.

b Write down the probability that the traveller has booked a tour that visits all three countries. (1)

c Write down the probability that the traveller has booked a tour that does not visit France. (2)

d Work out the probability that the traveller has booked a tour that visits Switzerland given that the traveller visits France. (2)

Answers:

a 34, 24, 25, 21, 23 and 23 all in the correct places got 3 marks.

Method: Always work out from the middle.
Overlaps of: France/Germany = 84 − 50 = 34;
Germany/Switzerland = 75 − 50 = 25;
Switzerland/France = 74 − 50 = 24;
Germany only = 130 − (25 + 50 + 34) = 21;
France only = 131 − (34 + 50 + 24) = 23;
Switzerland only = 122 − (25 + 50 + 24) = 23.

34, 24, 25 in correct places got 1 mark and 21, 23, 23 in correct places got 1 mark.

b $\frac{50}{200}$ or $\frac{1}{4}$ or 0.25 got 1 mark (as 50 out of the 200 visited all three countries).

c $\frac{69}{200}$ or 0.345 got 2 marks. (200 − 131) = 69 got 1 mark.

d $\frac{74}{131}$ got 2 marks. 50 + 24 = 74 got 1 mark.

How students answered

This question was generally done very badly. Few students understood how to fill in the Venn diagram. Students did not seem to realise that they should have checked the Venn diagram was correct by adding all the figures together to see if they came to the correct figure of 200. A common incorrect answer for part **a** was to just put in the figures given in the question.

60% 0–2 marks

A number of students got **b** correct. Some students managed to get marks for **b**, **c** and **d** despite getting no marks for the Venn diagram.

9% 3–4 marks

Less than a third of students got five or more of the eight marks available.

31% 5–8 marks

7.4: Experimental probability

✓ Understand and use measures of probability from a theoretical perspective and from a limiting frequency or experimental approach

✓ Understand that in some cases the measure of probability based on limiting frequency is the only viable measure

✓ Compare expected frequencies and actual frequencies

✓ Understand the effect of sample size on estimates and the variability of estimates

✓ Obtain primary data by simulations

✓ Use simulation to estimate more complex probabilities

✓ Use probability to assess risk

Need more help?
For more on this topic, see pages 250–253 of the main Edexcel textbook (ISBN 978-1-84690-454-7).

edexcel ⠿ key terms

cost of insurance The amount being insured × the probability of an accident.
limiting value The estimated probability based on a large number of trials.
simulation The imitation of a situation by doing a theoretical study.
trial An experiment or survey.

Experimental probability

The probability of an event cannot always be worked out theoretically. For example, you could not work out theoretically the probability that a person would be cured by taking a certain medicine. In such cases you need to carry out an experiment or survey to estimate the probability. Each of these is called a **trial**.

$$\text{The estimated probability that an event might happen} = \frac{\text{number of successful outcomes}}{\text{total number of trials}}$$

That is to say, if an event E happens m times in n trials then estimated $P(E) = \frac{m}{n}$

Limiting frequency

As the number of trials in experiments and surveys increases, the estimate (taken over all the trials) gets nearer to the true value.

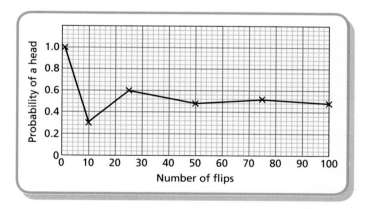

The graph shows how the probability of heads when a coin is flipped gets close to the true value as the number of tosses increases.

You can compare the **limiting value** of 0.49 with the expected value of 0.5. This is a fair coin.

If the limiting value was 0.6, say, you might conclude that the coin was biased.

Using probability to assess risk

The insurance industry uses estimates of probability based on limited frequency to assess risk. The probability of you having an accident would be found by looking at the number of people like you who have had accidents compared to the total number at risk. The cost of insurance is based upon this probability.

Cost of insurance = amount being insured × probability of an accident.

The actual cost would be greater than this because of the profit the company hopes to make and the cost of their overheads such as salaries etc.

Higher tier

Simulation

Simulation is the imitation of a situation by doing a theoretical study. For example, it is known that a certain commuter train arrives late 30% of the time, early 10% of the time and on time 60% of the time. You could simulate the next ten arrivals by using random digits. You let the digits 0, 1 and 2 mean a train is late, the digit 3 mean that it is early and the digits 4, 5, 6, 7, 8 and 9 that it is on time. The digits 0 9 4 4 3 5 7 8 1 6 would then give the first train late, the next three on time, the next one early etc.

Test yourself

1 In an experiment it was found that out of a total of 100 bicycles checked, 35 had some fault to the tyres or brakes. Find the probability that a bicycle chosen at random had a fault.

2 Using past records an insurance company finds that over the past year exactly two houses in a certain area had claimed for house subsidence. There are 300 houses in the area.
   a Work out the probability that a house chosen at random in the area would make a claim for subsidence.
   b Jemima has a house worth £300 000 in this area. Work out the cost of subsidence insurance for Jemima's house, excluding any overheads and profits.

3 In a works canteen the four meals offered are a salad, a roast, pasta or vegetarian. Over a period of time it was found that out of every ten workers, two chose salad, three chose a roast, four chose pasta and one chose vegetarian. Each lunchtime they serve 30 workers.
   a Explain how you would allocate random digits so that a simulation of a mealtime could be run. It is thought that the actual choices vary from day to day.
   b Explain why repeated simulations would give the chef information about the maximum number of each type of meal he would get asked for on any given day.

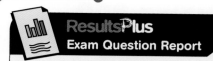

Exam Question Report

Peter is a supporter of Valley United football club. Valley United have played 40 games. The table shows the number of games won, lost and drawn.

Result	Won	Lost	Drawn
No. of games	20	14	6

Peter wants to simulate the results of Valley United's next ten games. He uses random numbers between 00 and 99. The table below shows the numbers he gives to each result.

Result	Won	Lost	Drawn
Numbers given	00–49	50–84	85–99

a Explain why he gives the numbers 00–49 to the games won. (1)

Peter uses the following random numbers to simulate the results of the ten games:
55 06 80 67 91 64 79 52 33 89
b Complete the table to show the results of the simulation. (1)

Result	Won	Lost	Drawn
Numbers given			

c i How does Peter's simulated result compare with the expectation based on the first 40 games? (1)

ii How could Peter improve his simulation? (1)

How students answered

a ▲ 50% of games were won, and 00–49 is 50% of the possibilities.

● Some students lost a mark by being vague, e.g. referring to 'most' games having been won.

■ Some students thought that 00–49 included only 49 numbers, so demonstrating a lack of familiarity with simulation.

b ▲ W = 2, L = 6, D = 2.

c i ▲ Not well – the team won 50% of the first 40 games but would only win 20% according to the simulation.

● Some students lost a mark by giving vague answers such as 'badly' or 'they don't'.

ii ▲ More simulations give a better estimate OR More random numbers give a better estimate.

■ Many candidates were unable to express themselves clearly, making vague references to 'more random numbers' or 'better numbers' and giving the impression that they meant the range of numbers allocated, rather than doing more simulations. Others thought that the numbers allocated to winning, losing and drawing should be reallocated so that the probability of winning was increased.

Need more help?

For more on this topic, see pages 266–274 of the main Edexcel textbook (ISBN 978-1-84690-454-7).

edexcel ⊞ key terms

addition law $P(A \text{ or } B) = P(A) + P(B)$

exhaustive A set of events is exhaustive if it contains all possible outcomes.

independent Two events are independent if the outcome of one does not affect the outcome of the other one. If events are independent they can both happen at once.

multiplication law $P(A \text{ and } B) = P(A) \times P(B)$ OR (if not mutually exclusive) $P(A \text{ or } B) = P(A) + P(B) - P(A \text{ and } B)$.

mutually exclusive Events are mutually exclusive if they cannot happen at the same time.

7.5: Mutually exclusive and exhaustive events

- ✓ Understand the terms mutually exclusive and exhaustive

- ✓ Know, for mutually exclusive outcomes, that the sum of the probabilities is one and in particular the probability of something not happening is one minus the probability of it happening

- ✓ Understand, use and apply the addition law for mutually exclusive events

- ✓ Understand, use and apply the general addition law for independent events and conditional events and outcomes

- ✓ Understand the multiplication law for independent events

- ✓ Understand, use and apply the multiplication law for conditional events and outcomes

Mutually exclusive events

Events are mutually exclusive if they cannot happen at the same time. A penny that is flipped cannot come down heads and tails at the same time so the events 'a head' and 'a tail' are mutually exclusive.

If two events A and B are mutually exclusive, $P(A \text{ or } B) = P(A) + P(B)$. This is called the **addition law** for mutually exclusive events.

For example, if the probability of A hitting a six off the last ball of a cricket match is 0.03 and the probability of B hitting or running a four off the last ball is 0.08, and four runs are needed to win the game, the probability of winning $= P(A) + P(B) = 0.03 + 0.08 = 0.11$.

Higher tier

The law may be extended to three or more events: $P(A \text{ or } B \text{ or } C) = P(A) + P(B) + P(C)$.

Exhaustive events

A set of events is **exhaustive** if the set contains all possible outcomes.

For a set of exhaustive events, the sum of the probabilities is one $(\sum p = 1)$.

In particular, the probability of an event happening + the probability of it not happening $= 1$. We write this as $(P(A) + P(\text{not } A) = 1)$.

For example, if a bag contains red, yellow and green balls, and the probability of getting a red ball is 0.4, the probability of getting a yellow or green ball $= P(\text{not red}) = 1 - 0.4 = 0.6$.

Results Plus
Exam tip

It is very easy to mix up the addition and multiplication rules. Remember, OR means add, AND means multiply.

Independent events and the multiplication law

Two events are **independent** if the outcome of one event does not affect the outcome of the other.

For two independent events, A and B, the $P(A \text{ and } B) = P(A) \times P(B)$. This is called the **multiplication law** for independent events.

If the events are not mutually exclusive, P(A or B) = P(A) + P(B) − P(A and B). This is the addition law for events that are not mutually exclusive.

For example, in a group of people there are five men and five women. Three of the men have red hair and one woman has red hair. If M stands for man and R for red hair:

P(M) = 0.5; P(R) = 4/10 = 0.4; P(M and R) = 3/10 = 0.3

The probability of a person picked at random being a man or having red hair = P(M or R)
= P(M) + P(R) − P(M and R) = 0.5 + (0.4 − 0.3) = 0.6

ResultsPlus
Exam Question Report

There are 800 children living in Finton. 500 of the children have had chickenpox. One of the 800 children is chosen at random.
a Write down the probability that this child has had chickenpox, *C*. (1)

Some of the 800 children have had measles, *M*. A child is chosen at random. The probability that this child has had measles is $\frac{1}{10}$.
b Write down the probability that a child selected at random has not had measles. (1)

Having had measles is independent of having had chickenpox.
c (Higher tier) Work out the probability that a child has had chickenpox or measles or both. (2)

How students answered

a ▲ $P(C) = \frac{500}{800} = 0.625$

b ▲ $P(\text{not } M) = 1 - \frac{1}{10} = 0.9$

   ▬ Many candidates put $\frac{1}{10}$ as an answer.

c ▲ $P(C \text{ or } M) = P(C) + P(M) - P(M \text{ and } C) = 0.625 + 0.1 - (0.625 \times 0.1) = 0.6625$

   ▬ Many students who knew they should multiply the fractions lost marks because they could not do the multiplication correctly.

Test yourself

1 *A*, *B* and *C* are mutually exclusive events. P(A) = 0.2, P(B) = 0.5 and P(C) = 0.3.
   a Work out P(A or B).
   b Work out P(A and B).
   c Show that they are exhaustive events.
   d Work out P(not C).

2 The probability of a student staying for school dinners is 0.6. The probability of a student coming to school on the school bus is 0.3. These are independent events. Work out the probability of a student catching the school bus and stopping for school dinners.

3 A survey shows that the probability of a train arriving on time at station A is 0.7. The probability that a train arrives on time at station B is 0.4. For two trains selected at random, one going to each station, find:
   a the probability that they both arrive on time
   b the probability that only one of them arrives on time.

7.6: Tree diagrams

 Draw and use tree diagrams and probability tree diagrams for independent events

Tree diagrams

Need more help?
For more on this topic, see pages 275–280 of the main Edexcel textbook (ISBN 978-1-84690-454-7).

edexcel ⠿ key terms

tree diagram A diagram that shows all the possible combinations of outcomes and their probabilities.

A **tree diagram** can be used for combined events. Each branch of the tree represents a possible combination of outcomes. The probability of the outcome is written on the branch.

For example, the tree diagram on the left shows the outcomes of drawing a ball from a bag containing five red and four green balls, noting its colour, replacing it and then drawing another ball and noting its colour.

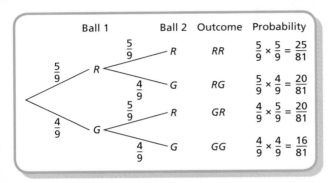

The probability is found by multiplying the probabilities along the branches used to get to the outcome.

Information can be taken from a tree diagram.

The probability of getting two balls the same colour would be:

$$P(R \text{ and } R) + P(G \text{ and } G) = \frac{25}{81} + \frac{16}{81} = \frac{41}{81}$$

The probability of getting a red and a green ball would be:

$$P(R \text{ and } G) + P(G \text{ and } R) = \frac{20}{81} + \frac{20}{81} = \frac{40}{81}$$

Test yourself

1 Bag A contains six red balls and four white balls. Bag B contains three red balls and seven white balls. One ball is drawn at random from each bag.
   a Draw a tree diagram for the possible outcomes.
   b Work out the probability that both balls are the same colour.
   c Work out the probability that there is one red and one white ball drawn.

2 Three fair plastic discs have an X on one side and an N on the other side.
   a Draw a tree diagram to show all the possible results and their probabilities when the three discs are flipped.
   b Work out the probability of getting exactly two Xs.
   c Work out the probability of getting at least two Ns.

The tree diagram can be extended to three (or more) branches.

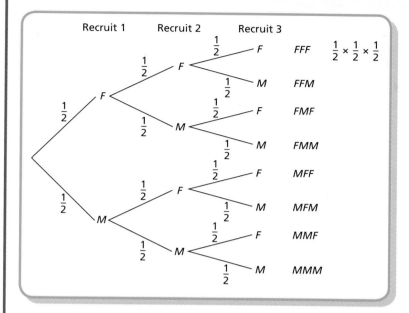

Sometimes one branch may end earlier than others.

This tree diagram shows the probability of winning a game that consists of drawing a red ball from a bag containing one red ball and three black balls. You have three goes and stop if you draw a red ball.

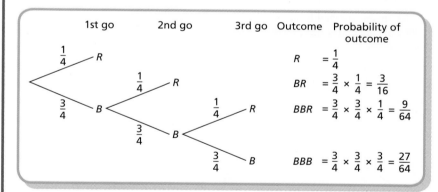

Test yourself

3 A bag contains three red balls and 17 green ones. A person is allowed to have up to three goes at picking out a red ball, the ball being replaced after each attempt.

   a Draw a tree diagram to show all possible outcomes.

   b Work out the probability of selecting a red ball.

   c Work out the probability of not getting a red ball.

ResultsPlus
Exam Question Report

Abbey Road MOT testing station carried out 30 MOT tests. Fifteen cars failed because of lighting faults and independently six cars failed because of steering faults. A car is chosen at random from the 30 tested.
a On the probability scale below:
   i   use L to mark the probability that the car fails because of lighting faults (1)
   ii use S to mark the probability that the car fails because of steering faults. (1)

b Complete the probability tree diagram below. (2)

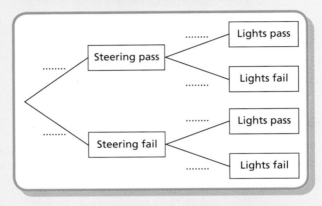

c i   Work out the probability that the car had both steering and lighting faults. (2)
   ii Work out the probability that the car had only one of these faults. You must show your working. (2)

How students answered

a ▲ L at 0.5, S at 0.2 (accept between 0.1 and 0.3).

b ▲

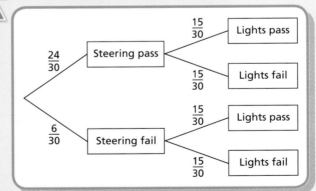

█ Many students could not complete the tree diagram. They wrote integers on the branches and then proceeded to do the rest of the question using whole numbers rather than probability.

c ▲ i $\frac{6}{30} \times \frac{15}{30} = \frac{90}{900}$ or equivalent.

█ Students who did cope with the tree diagram often added the probabilities rather than multiplying them.

▲ ii $\left(\frac{24}{30} \times \frac{15}{30}\right) + \left(\frac{6}{30} \times \frac{15}{30}\right) = \frac{450}{900}$ or equivalent.

⬤ The last part of the question required working to be shown since it was possible to get the answer correct through incorrect means. Many candidates did not show working and lost a mark.

7.7: Conditional probability

✓ Draw and use tree diagrams and probability tree diagrams for independent events and conditional cases

✓ Understand, use and apply the multiplication law for independent events and conditional events and outcomes

Need more help?
For more on this topic, see pages 281–283 of the main Edexcel textbook (ISBN 978-1-84690-454-7).

Conditional probability

When the probability of an event B happening depends on the outcome of a previous event A it is called **conditional probability**. We write the probability as $P(B\,|\,A)$.

For example, if you take a coloured ball from a bag of mixed colours then take another ball without replacing the first ball, the probability of getting a particular coloured ball depends on what colour the first ball was.

If there were three red balls and seven yellow balls in the bag then the probability of getting a red ball on the second occasion is $\frac{2}{9}$ if the first ball is red (because there are only two red balls out of the nine left in the bag). However, it is $\frac{3}{9} = \frac{1}{3}$ if the first ball is yellow (because there are three red balls out of the nine left in the bag).

edexcel key terms

conditional probability When the probability of an event happening depends on the outcome of a previous event.
multiplication law $P(A \text{ and } B) = P(B\,|\,A) \times P(A)$
tree diagram A diagram that shows all the possible combinations of outcomes and their probabilities when the probability of one event depends on the outcome of the other event.

Multiplication law for events that are not independent

Two events are not independent if the outcome of one event affects the outcome of the second.

If A and B are not independent events, $P(A \text{ and } B) = P(B\,|\,A) \times P(A) = P(A\,|\,B) \times P(B)$.

In the example above, if X is getting a red ball on the second draw and Y is getting a yellow ball on the first draw:

$P(X\,|\,Y) = \frac{1}{3}$ $P(Y) = \frac{7}{10}$ (there are seven yellow balls out of 10)
so $P(X \text{ and } Y) = \frac{1}{3} \times \frac{7}{10} = \frac{7}{30}$

This outcome is represented on the tree diagram below right.

ResultsPlus
Exam tip

Most problems in probability can be solved using two-way tables, Venn diagrams or tree diagrams.

Tree diagrams for conditional cases

The tree diagram for the example above is:

The probability of getting a red ball and a yellow ball is
$P(R \text{ and } Y) + P(Y \text{ and } R) = \frac{7}{15}$.

$P(R\ R) = \frac{3}{10} \times \frac{2}{9} = \frac{1}{15}$
$P(R\ Y) = \frac{3}{10} \times \frac{7}{9} = \frac{7}{30}$
$P(Y\ R) = \frac{7}{10} \times \frac{3}{9} = \frac{7}{30}$
$P(Y\ Y) = \frac{7}{10} \times \frac{6}{9} = \frac{7}{15}$

Test yourself

1 A bag of marbles contains 12 red marbles and eight white marbles. Marbles are taken from the bag one at a time without replacement. Work out the probability that:
  a the second marble is white if the first is not white
  b the first two marbles are red
  c the first two marbles are red and the third is white.

ResultsPlus
Exam Question Report

In a screening test a saliva sample is taken and tested for bacteria. The result of a screening test can be either positive (T+) or negative (T−). The probability of a person showing a positive (T+) result to the test is 0.1.

a Work out the probability that a person chosen at random will show a negative (T−) result to the screening test. (1)

The probability that a person who gave a positive (T+) result to the screening test goes on to get tooth decay (D+) within 18 months of the screening test was found to be 0.2. The probability that a person who gave a negative (T−) result to the screening test does not go on to get tooth decay (D−) was found to be 0.9.

b Complete the tree diagram below. (3)

c Given that a person has tooth decay (D+), what is the probability that the person gave a positive (T+) result in the screening test within the last 18 months? (2)

d What can you infer from this result about the usefulness of the screening test? (2)

(Data source: *Dental Journal*)

Screening test result	Tooth decay	Outcome	Probability of outcome
	0.2 → D+	T+D+	0.02
0.1 → T+			
	...... D−	T+D−	......
	...... D+	T−D+	......
...... T−			
	0.9 → D−	T−D−	......

How students answered

a ▲ 0.9, $\frac{9}{10}$ or 90%

b ▲

c ▲ $\frac{0.02}{0.02 + 0.09} = \frac{2}{11}$ or 0.18 (or anything which rounds to this).

■ Most students cannot cope with conditional probability using a tree diagram. An answer of 0.02 was common.

d ▲ The test does not appear to be a good predictor of tooth decay. Plus any justifying statement, e.g. Out of every 11 that got tooth decay, only two were predicted to get it OR Only two had a positive result.

■ Many students found it hard to draw any conclusions at all.

Screening test result	Tooth decay	Outcome	Probability of outcome
	0.2 → D+	T+D+	0.02
0.1 → T+			
	0.8 → D−	T+D−	0.08
	0.1 → D+	T−D+	0.09
0.9 → T−			
	0.9 → D−	T−D−	0.81

Test yourself

2 A certain disease occurs in 5% of the population. A test is available that tests to see if a patient has the disease. In 80% of cases where the patient has the disease, the test shows a positive result. If the patient does not have the disease the test shows a positive result in 5% of those tested.

a Draw a tree diagram to represent this information.

Use the tree diagram to find the probability that a randomly selected person:

b does not have the disease but gives a positive result

c gives a positive result

d has the disease.

8.1: Discrete uniform and binomial distributions

 Use simple cases of the binomial and discrete uniform distribution

Probability distribution

A **probability distribution** is a list of all possible outcomes of an event together with their probabilities. It should be remembered that all the probabilities added together must equal one.

A probability distribution is often shown in table form. For example, the probability distribution for throwing a biased die might be:

Outcomes (x)	1	2	3	4	5	6
Probability p(x)	$\frac{1}{6}$	$\frac{1}{6}$	$\frac{1}{12}$	$\frac{1}{12}$	k	k

Since all the probabilities added together must equal one, then k must be

$$\frac{1 - \left(\frac{1}{6} + \frac{1}{6} + \frac{1}{12} + \frac{1}{12}\right)}{2} = \frac{1}{4}$$

Probability of throwing a four or five $= \frac{1}{12} + \frac{1}{4} = \frac{4}{12} = \frac{1}{3}$

Discrete uniform distribution

A **discrete uniform distribution** is one where all the x values are discrete numbers and the probabilities are all the same.

The throwing of an unbiased die is a discrete uniform distribution since the outcomes one, two, three, four, five and six are discrete numbers and all these outcomes have the probability of occurring of $\frac{1}{6}$. This is shown in the following table:

Outcomes (x)	1	2	3	4	5	6
Probability p(x)	$\frac{1}{6}$	$\frac{1}{6}$	$\frac{1}{6}$	$\frac{1}{6}$	$\frac{1}{6}$	$\frac{1}{6}$

Binomial distribution

This occurs when there are a fixed number of independent trials (n), each trial having only two possible outcomes. The outcomes are defined as a success or a failure. The probability of success is p. The probability of failure is q, where $q = 1 - p$ (since $p + q = 1$).

The probabilities for the events of n binomial trials are the terms of the expansion of $(p + q)^n$. For example, the probability of an oboe reed being faulty is 0.1 and a packet holds four reeds. You want to find the probability that there are one or fewer faulty oboe reeds. You are given that:

$$(p + q)^4 = p^4 \quad + \quad 4p^3q \quad + \quad 6p^2q^2 \quad + \quad 4pq^3 \quad + \quad q^4$$

(4 good)   (3 good 1 faulty)   (2 good 2 faulty)   (1 good 3 faulty)   (4 faulty)

Need more help?
For more on this topic, see pages 296–301 of the main Edexcel textbook (ISBN 978-1-84690-454-7).

edexcel ⋮⋮⋮ **key terms**

binomial distribution This occurs when there are a fixed number of independent trials (n) with each event having only two possible outcomes. The probability of success is p and the probability of failure is q, where: $q = 1 - p$. The probabilities for the events of n binomial trials are the terms of the expansion of $(p + q)^n$. If $n = 2$ then $(p + q)^2 = p^2 + 2pq + q^2$.

discrete uniform distribution This has n distinct outcomes. Each outcome is equally likely and each has a probability of $\frac{1}{n}$ of happening.

probability distribution List of all possible outcomes and their probabilities.

ResultsPlus
Exam tip

Always add the probabilities together in a table of this type to make sure they add up to one.

ResultsPlus
Exam tip

In an exam you will be expected to deal with values of n up to and including five. You will be given expansions of $(p + q)^n$ for $n = 3$, 4 and 5 but you will need to know the expansion for $n = 2$.

In this case p = success = $1 - 0.1 = 0.9$, and q = failure = 0.1. So the terms we want are $p^4 + 4 p^3 q = 0.9^4 + (4 \times 0.9^3 \times 0.1) = 0.6561 + 0.2916 = 0.9477$. The probability of having one or fewer (0) faulty oboe reeds in a pack is 0.9477 (94.77%). (And the probability of having two or more faulty oboe reeds in a pack is $1 - 0.9477 = 0.0523$ (5.23%).)

Test yourself

1 The probability distribution for a biased eight-faced die is shown below.

Outcomes	1	2	3	4	5	6	7	8
Probability p	0.1	0.3	0.05	0.05	k	$2k$	k	k

  a Find the value of k.
  b Write down the probability of the die showing a four, five or six.

2 A fair spinner has five sections numbered 1, 2, 3, 4 and 5. X is the number showing on the side on which the spinner falls.
  a What is the name given to the distribution of X?
  b Draw up a probability distribution table for X.
  c Write down the probability of the spinner showing an even number on the side on which it falls.

3 The probability of a bulb being faulty is 0.15. There are three bulbs in a pack. Work out the probability of getting two or three faulty bulbs.

Use $(p + q)^3 = p^3 + 3 p^2 q + 3 pq^2 + q^3$

4 One person in every five will get flu this winter.
  a Write down the probability of a person getting flu this winter.
  b Write down the probability of a person not getting flu this winter.

For a group of four people work out the probability that:

  c i all of them will get flu this winter
    ii one or less will get flu this winter.

You may use:
$(p + q)^4 = p^4 + 4 p^3 q + 6 p^2 q^2 + 4 pq^3 + q^4$

ResultsPlus
Exam Question Report

Abena and Kofi want to have four children together. The probability that any child born to them will have sickle cell disease is $\frac{1}{4}$. Work out the probability that at most one of their four children will have sickle cell disease.
(You may use: $(p + q)^4 = p^4 + 4 p^3 q + 6 p^2 q^2 + 4 pq^3 + q^4$) (4)

Answer: 0.74

How students answered

Students found this question very difficult. A common error was to use the fractions from the previous unconnected part of the question, $\frac{1}{10}$ and $\frac{9}{10}$, and ignore the $\frac{1}{4}$. Many students circled one or both correct terms on the equation but did not evaluate them. Some students got one mark for using $\frac{1}{4}$ in their working.

56% 0–1 marks

Some students got three marks if $(\frac{3}{4})^4 + 4 (\frac{1}{4}) \times (\frac{3}{4})^3$ was seen in their working; others got two marks if $(\frac{3}{4})^4$ OR $4 (\frac{1}{4}) \times (\frac{3}{4})^3$ was seen OR 0.42 was seen. Note that 0.42 was a common incorrect answer – only one term was worked out here.

28% 2–3 marks

Only 16% of students managed to achieve all four of the available marks.

16% 4 marks

8.2: The normal distribution

 Understand the shape and simple properties of the normal distribution

 Know that many populations can be modelled by the normal distribution

Need more help?
For more on this topic, see pages 302–310 of the main Edexcel textbook (ISBN 978-1-84690-454-7).

The normal distribution

This is a **continuous distribution**. This means that it applies to continuous data only. It generally occurs as a result of natural processes, such as height and weight of people or circumferences of apples.

It is a **bell-shaped distribution** where the area under the bell represents the probability of the occurrence of the whole distribution. Thus the area is one.

Important properties:

* The distribution is symmetrical about the mean μ.
* The mean, mode and median are all equal.
* 95% of the observations lie within ± 2 standard deviations (σ) of the mean.
* Almost all (99.8%) of the observations lie within ± 3 standard deviations (σ) of the mean.

edexcel ⠿ key terms

normal distribution This is a continuous distribution that is bell-shaped. It is symmetrical about the mean.

properties of a normal distribution:
* mean = mode = median
* 95% of the observations within $\pm 2\ \sigma$ of the mean
* almost all (99.8%) of the observations within $\pm 3\ \sigma$ of the mean.

variance This is a measure of spread. It is equal to σ^2.

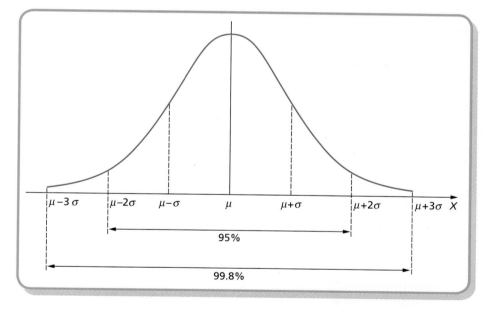

For example, if the mean time of a phone call to a call centre is eight minutes and the time is modelled by a normal distribution with $\sigma = 1$ minute, you can find the percentage of calls that are between six and ten minutes. Six minutes is 2σ below the mean and ten minutes is 2σ above the mean. This means that 95% of the calls lie between these times.

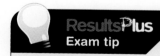
ResultsPlus
Exam tip

It often helps to draw a sketch.

Comparing normal distributions

The **variance** (standard deviation squared) is a measure of spread of the distribution. To compare two distributions you need to look at a measure of spread and a measure of central tendency. To compare normal distributions you must compare the mean μ and the standard deviation σ.

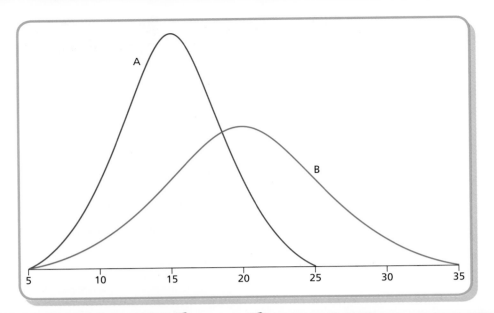

This diagram shows two normal distributions. Both have bell shapes.

The areas under the curves are both equal to one.

B has a greater mean μ (20) than A (15).

B has a greater standard deviation σ than A. You can see this because it is more spread out.

Because B has the greater standard deviation, in order to keep both areas the same, its maximum height is less than that of A.

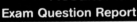

ResultsPlus
Exam Question Report

Peter calculates the mean weight for each sample of ten packets. These mean weights are normally distributed with a mean of 505 g and a standard deviation of 1.6 g. Write down the percentage of the samples that have a mean weight within ± 2 standard deviations of 505 g. (1)

How students answered

Few students tackled this question.

 The correct answer was 95%.

Common incorrect answers were 50%, 75% and 98%. Note that one property of the normal distribution is that 95% of items are within ± 2 standard deviations of the mean.

ResultsPlus
Exam Question Report

A steel manufacturer finds that the total quantity of raw materials used by his company each week is normally distributed with a mean of 1000 tonnes and a standard deviation of 200 tonnes.
a   Calculate an estimate of the maximum quantity of raw materials the company is likely to use per week. (1)

The manager of the steel manufacturing company decides to make a regular order for the same amount of raw materials to be delivered each week on a Monday.
b   Discuss what would be a suitable figure for the quantity to be ordered. (2)

Answers:

a   1400 or 1600 tonnes (1 mark).
b   One of the following would get the first mark: The mean would be best OR One standard deviation more than the mean OR Any figure between 1000 and 1200.
One of the following would get the second mark: The maximum quantity is likely to be wasteful OR The maximum quantity will build up too much stock OR The mean or a little more should cover the needs over time OR To avoid shortfall or build-up of stock.

How students answered

a   This question was generally done badly. Few students recognised the significance of the standard deviation. A common incorrect answer was 200 000 tonnes. Students did not seem to realise that this was obviously incorrect.

75% 0 marks

Only a quarter of students managed to earn this mark.

25% 1 mark

b   Many students had no concept of stock usage and more than half got no marks at all.

57% 0 marks

Some students managed to get 1 mark in **b** for a sensible discussion of the amount of stock that might be required, although they often gave no suggestion of a figure.

25% 1 mark

Only 18% of students achieved both marks here.

18% 2 marks

ResultsPlus
Build Better Answers

The life, in years, of an 'Excellent' car battery is normally distributed with a mean of 3.1 and standard deviation of 0.6. The life, in years, of a 'Super' car battery is normally distributed with mean 4.0 and standard deviation 0.3.

a   On the graph paper sketch the distributions of the two types of battery. (5)
b   What is the probability that an 'Excellent' battery lasts longer than 4.3 years? (1)
    A 'Super' battery costs more than an 'Excellent' battery.
c   Give one reason why you might still buy a 'Super' battery. (1)

How students answered

Students find this style of question very difficult.

a   ▲

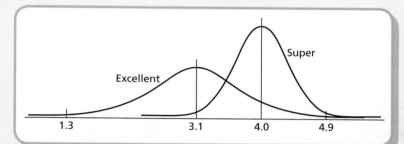

1 mark for the mean of 3.1; 1 mark for the mean of 4;
1 mark for differing heights (Excellent lower); 1 mark for
correct spreads (Excellent greater spread than Super);
1 mark for labels showing which is which and a scale on
the axis.

b   ▲   2.5% or 0.025 (1 mark).

Note that 4.3 is two standard deviations above the mean. Two standard deviations above and below the mean contain 95%. So the two tails must contain 5%. So one tail is 2.5%.

c   ▲   Super batteries last longer (1 mark).

Look at the curves. Half the curve for the Super is above four but only a small amount of the Excellent curve is above four. Remember, the area under each curve represents a probability of one.

Test yourself

1   Jam is packed in tins of weight 1 kg. The weight of the tins is normally distributed with standard deviation 10 g.
    a   Work out the percentage of tins that lie between 980 g and 1020 g.
    b   Between what weights will almost all the tins lie?

2   Students travelling to college take a mean time of 20 minutes. The times are normally distributed with standard deviation 3.5 minutes.
    a   Calculate the percentage of students that take more than 27 minutes to get to college.

    There are 800 students in the college.
    b   Work out how many take less than 13 minutes to get to college.

3   The table gives some information about the distributions of the weights (g) of two types of rodent. The weights are normally distributed.

ResultsPlus
Exam tip

Sketch a diagram of the area you want.

	Rodent A	Rodent B
Mean μ	800 g	500 g
Standard deviation σ	25	50

Sketch on the same axes the normal curves for these two distributions.

Need more help?
For more on this topic, see pages 310–315 of the main Edexcel textbook (ISBN 978-1-84690-454-7).

8.3: Quality assurance

✓ Plot sample means, medians and ranges over time on quality control charts that have target values, and action and warning limits

✓ Understand that in a process under control almost all of the means, medians or ranges fall inside the action limits, and only 1 in 20 falls outside the warning limits

✓ Know the action to be taken if a sample mean, median or range falls outside of each type of limit

edexcel ⠿ key terms

action limits These are the values beyond which action needs to be taken. Stop machine and reset.

control chart This is a time series chart used for process control.

control chart for means This is a chart that compares sample means with a target mean.

control chart for medians This is a chart that compares sample medians with a target median.

control chart for ranges This is a chart that compares sample ranges with action and warning limits.

quality assurance This is a process used to check the quality of a product.

warning limits These are the values at which you are being warned that the process might be going wrong. Take another sample.

Quality assurance

Quality assurance is used to check the quality of a product. Samples are taken at regular time intervals and compared with what they should be. Generally you compare the mean or median of the sample and the range.

Control charts

A **control chart** is a time series chart used for process control.

Control charts for the means

A line on the chart indicates the target value (the mean). Warning limits are set at $\mu \pm 2\sigma$. Action limits are set at $\mu \pm 3\sigma$ (where σ is the standard deviation of the sample means).

If the sample mean is between the warning and action limits, another sample is taken. If the sample mean is outside the action limits the machine is stopped and reset.

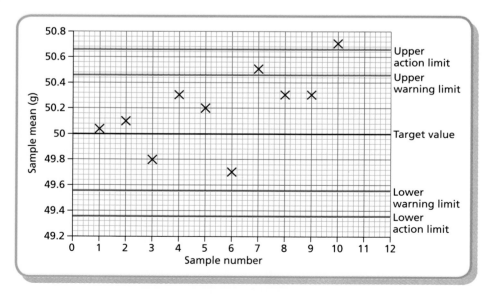

This control chart for means shows that another sample needed to be taken after sample 7 and the machine had to be stopped and reset after sample 10.

Control charts for medians

This looks exactly the same as the control chart for the means and works in exactly the same way.

Control chart for ranges

In an ideal situation the range would be zero. This would mean that each product produced would be exactly the same size. Range is controlled by the accuracy of the machine and so no target range is set. Control charts for ranges have warning and action limits in the same way as the control chart for the means. If a sample range falls between the warning and action limits another sample is taken. If a sample range falls outside the action limits then the machine needs checking.

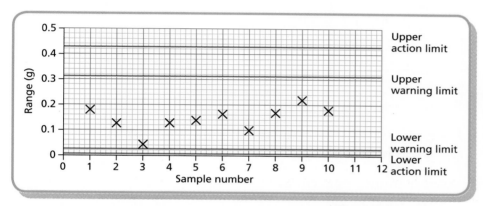

 ResultsPlus
Exam tip

Limits for ranges are more complex than those for means. You would only be asked to plot the points and state actions to be taken.

This control chart for the range shows that the ten samples are all within the warning limits.

 ResultsPlus
Exam Question Report

On a production line in a factory, baked beans in tomato sauce are put in tins.
The label on each tin says that the contents weigh 415 g.
a   Give two reasons why it is not practical to check the weight of the contents of each tin. (2)

Samples of tins are taken at intervals and the weights of the contents are found. It has been found that the mean weight of the samples is 417 g and the standard deviation of the mean weights of the samples is 0.6 g. The mean weights of the samples are normally distributed.
b   Between what limits would you expect 99.8% of the sample means to lie? (3)

The target weight of the contents is set at 417 g.
c   Using your answer to part b, give a reason why the target weight is 417 g rather than 415 g. (1)

A sample of tins is taken each half hour during a six-hour shift and the mean weight of the contents is found. The mean weights of the samples are plotted on the chart below. The allowable limits for the weights of the samples are ±3 standard deviations from the target weight.

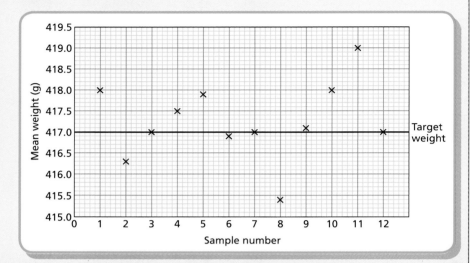

d   Comment on any action that would have been taken during the six-hour shift. (2)

How students answered

a   ▲ EITHER It would take too long OR There are too many tins (1 mark) PLUS Sampling would destroy the tin OR It is too costly (1 mark).

   ● Many candidates could give only one reason why it is not practical to check all the tins so only got 1 mark.

   ■ Common incorrect answers were 'Not necessary as they'll all be the same' or 'A few beans don't make much difference'.

b   ▲ An answer of 415.2 and 418.8 received all 3 marks.

   ● Only about half of the candidates were able to relate the 99.8% of the normal distribution to ±3 standard deviations from the mean. Many calculated these limits as ±1 or ±2 standard deviations from the mean. It was encouraging to see virtually all of these candidates gave the details of their calculation. Using '417 ± 3 × 0.6' got 1 method mark, or 2 marks if one of the correct answers was shown.

   ■ A common incorrect answer was gained from using 417 ± 2 × 0.6.

c   ▲ By making the target weight 417 g, 99.9% of the tins should weigh more than 415.2 g. This ensures that virtually all of the tins are over the marked weight. If 415 g was used as the target, half the tins would have a content that is below 415 g.

   ■ Part **c** was not done very well. There were many responses that discussed the legal aspects of selling underweight tins, but very few could use their answer from part **b** in an appropriate manner. A common close but wrong answer was 'So that none of the tins fall below 415 g'.

d   ▲ At sample 11 (1 mark) the process should be stopped and reset (1 mark).

   ● Mentioning sample 11 got one mark.

   ■ A common wrong answer was 'Stop and reset' with no reference to when/which sample. Many students, including some that got part **b** correct, used 1 cm on the grid to represent one standard deviation. Consequently sample 8 was also included in their action plan. Many candidates thought that the required action was merely to remove samples 8 and 11 from the production.

Test yourself

1 A machine packs chocolates into boxes. The mean weights of the boxes of chocolates are normally distributed with a mean weight of 500 g and a standard deviation of 10 g.

  a Work out the warning limits.

  b Work out the action limits.

Samples of ten boxes are taken every hour and the sample means worked out.

  c After the third hour the mean weight of the sample is found to be 525 g. What action should the machine operator take?

  d After the seventh hour the mean weight of the sample is found to be 535 g. What action should the machine operator take?

2 A machine packs sugar into bags. The mean weights of the bags of sugar are normally distributed with a mean weight of 1000 g and a standard deviation of 12 g.

  a Work out the action limits.

  b Work out the warning limits.

Samples of 20 are taken every half hour and the sample means worked out.

  c A sample mean is found to be 1015 g. What action should be taken?

3 A machine in a factory fills bags with pasta.

  a Give **one** reason why a quality assurance chart should be used.

The mean weight of pasta in the bags is 260 g. The standard deviation of the weight of pasta in the bags is 5 g.

  b Write down the target value for this process.

Samples were taken every hour for eight hours and the mean weights of the samples were calculated. The table shows the mean weights of the samples.

Sample number	1	2	3	4	5	6	7	8
Mean weight (g)	265	260	258	270	260	255	252	262

  c Draw a quality assurance chart for the means using these data.

  d Did the machine need to be reset during this period? Give a reason for your answer.

Answers

1: Collecting data

1.1: Types of data

1 The new toothpaste is better than the old toothpaste; or the converse.
2 C and D
3 B and C
4 B and C
5 162.5 cm minimum and 163.5 cm maximum

1.2: Populations and sampling

1 Two of: cheaper; quicker; less data to be considered.
2 simple random sampling
3 a 100, 053, 128, 104, 060
   b Number the population from either 0 to 129 or 1 to 130. Use the people with the numbers 100, 053, 128, 104, 060 as your sample.
4 6 boys and 4 girls
5 a the students
   b a list of all students in Years 11 and 12
   c stratified sampling

1.3: Non-random sampling

1 Advantage, one of: simple; cheap.
   Disadvantage, one of: you need a sampling frame; not good for large populations.
2 Number the students from 1 to 100. Find a random number between 1 and 10. Starting with the student with that random number, pick every 10th student.
3 quota sampling
4 cluster sampling
5 a systematic   b cluster   c stratified

1.4: Collecting data

1 a secondary   b secondary   c primary
2 a A survey conducted on a small sample.
   b It identifies problems/errors before the main survey takes place.
3 It leaves the respondent to decide their own answer.
4 A set of answers are given that the respondent must choose from.
5 A question that is biased. It tries to suggest what the answer should be.
6 agree, good
7 a There is no option for greater than 5 times.
   b Biased. It suggests that one should agree and also that it is a good idea.
   c It is an open question. It will get lots of different answers and be difficult to analyse.
   d The expression 'don't you' makes you feel you should give the answer yes. Also there are no answer boxes so it is an open question.

1.5: Other methods of collecting data

1 face to face or telephone
2 He could do a face to face interview with his patients or give them a questionnaire after treatment that included the anaesthetic.
3 They need to look at speeds before the speed bumps are put in and speeds after the speed bumps are put in.
4 Interviewers can explain questions; it is suitable for complex questions. Disadvantages are it is costly, and the interviewer may cause bias.
5 It is not a satisfactory sample so the member of the company is right. It does not give everyone in the country an equal chance of being selected; 50 is too small a sample; 10 towns in the south-east is very biased.
6 $\frac{5}{80} = \frac{50}{x}$ so there are 800 finches

2: Representing and processing qualitative and discrete data

2.1: Tallies, frequency tables and two-way tables

1 a

Number of games	Frequency
0	1
1	4
2	6
3	4
4	8
5	4
6	3

  b 4

2 a

Number of crisp packets	Frequency
0–4	4
5–9	10
10–14	12
15–19	8
20–24	6

  b 10–14

3 a

	School dinner	Packed	Other	Total
Males	12	2	2	16
Females	7	7	3	17
Total	19	9	5	33

  b 33
  c 5

4

Number of sweets	Frequency	Cumulative frequency
48	6	6
49	3	9
50	4	13
51	2	15
52	5	20

2.2: Pictograms, line graphs and bar charts

1 a 2 pictures
  b $5\frac{1}{2}$
  c 42

2

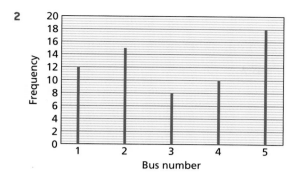

3 a 20
  b Faroes
  c 18

2.3: Stem and leaf diagrams and pie charts

1 a 22
  b 4 and 47
  c 7

2

Stem	Leaves				
5	5	9			
6	0	3	4	4	5	8
7	1	3	3	4	5	6
8	0	1	5	8		
9	0	4				

3 a gas-fired
  b 25
4 120°

5

2	5	6	7	8	8	9						
3	2	2	2	3	4	4	4	4	5	6	7	7	7	9
4	0	0	1	1	1	2	2	3	3	3	5	8	8
5	0	1	1	2	3	5						

2.4: Cumulative frequency step polygons

1 a 50
  b 5
  c 2 days
2 cumulative frequencies: 0, 1, 6, 12, 16
Cumulative frequency step polygon correctly drawn with straight lines. Number of words on *x*-axis and frequency on *y*-axis. Axes should be labelled. Polygon goes through the points (2, 0), (2, 1), (3, 1), (3, 6), (4, 6), (4, 12), (5, 12), (5, 16), (6, 16).

2.5: Using bar charts to make comparisons

1 a 1000
  b 360
  c More papers were sold overall on Saturday than on weekdays. There were the same number of paper C sold on weekdays as on Saturdays.
  d Bars correctly drawn: red bar from 0 to 360, blue bar from 360 to 600, yellow bar from 600 to 680.
2 a Bars drawn correctly: 0 to 8 for boys and 0 to 12 for girls. Two bars should be touching, boys on left, girls on right.
  b 32
  c 7

2.6: Using pie charts to make comparisons

1 a More girls went to school by car. The area of the sector for girls going by car is greater than the area of the sector for boys going by car.
  b The proportion of boys walking to school is greater than the proportion of girls walking to school. The angle/percentage for boys (37%) is greater than that for girls (19%).
  c more girls
2 4 cm

3: Representing and processing continuous data

3.1: Frequency tables for continuous data

1 a $2 \leq r < 3$
  b $2 \leq r < 3$
2 frequencies: 3, 7, 10, 10
3 a 147.5–148.5
  b They overlap.

  c

Height (cm)	Frequency
$130 < h \leq 140$	3
$140 < h \leq 150$	7
$150 < h \leq 160$	11
$160 < h \leq 170$	3

4 a She cannot tell whether to put it in the 0–5 or 6–10 group as it is mid-way between 5 and 6.
  b Mark's. It allows for all values to be included.

3.2: Cumulative frequency diagrams for continuous data

1 a cumulative frequencies: 2, 11, 34, 54, 60
  b Cumulative frequency diagram drawn with the following points connected by a smooth curve or straight lines: (1, 0), (1.5, 2), (2, 11), (2.5, 34), (3, 54), (3.5, 60). Diameter on *x*-axis and cumulative frequency on *y*-axis. Axes should be labelled.
  c Any figure between 5 and 6.5.
  d Any figure between 36 and 39.
2 a cumulative frequencies: 6, 20, 48, 68, 80
  Cumulative frequency diagram drawn with the following points connected by a smooth curve or straight lines: (1.4, 0), (1.5, 6), (1.6, 20), (1.7, 48), (1.8, 68), (1.9, 80). Height on *x*-axis and cumulative frequency on *y*-axis. Axes should be labelled.
  b Any figure between 33 and 35.
  c 52 to 53

3.3: Histograms and frequency polygons

1 a

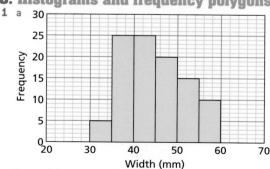

  b positive skew
2 Girls generally have a lower weight than boys.
The range of the girls' weights is greater than the range of the boys' weights.
Most girls weigh less than 60 kg. Most boys weigh more than 50 kg.
3 a negative skew
  b positive skew
  c symmetrical (no skew)

3.4: Histograms with unequal class intervals

1 a

Lifetime (hrs)	Frequency	Class width	Frequency density
$20 < l \le 24$	14	4	3.5
$24 < l \le 26$	36	2	18
$26 < l \le 28$	10	2	5
$28 < l \le 30$	10	2	5

b

2 a 28
b 18

3.5: Population pyramids and choropleth maps

1 a females
b 20–30
c over 80

2 a

b A1, as there are most cows around there.

3.6: Misleading diagrams

1 The line is thick and the vertical scale is wrong. It jumps from 0 to 4.
2 There is no key. The money bags are different sizes.

4: Summarising data: measures of central tendency and dispersion

4.1: Averages

1 a 8
b 6
c 6.5
d 6.875
2 a 6
b 6
c 6
3 a 8–10
b 9.5
c 9.6

4.2: Averages of grouped data

1 a

Speed (mph) x	Frequency f	Mid-point	$f \times$ mid-point
$30 < x \le 40$	9	35	315
$40 < x \le 50$	14	45	630
$50 < x \le 60$	15	55	825
$60 < x \le 70$	20	65	1300
$70 < x \le 80$	2	75	150
Total	60		3220

b $60 < x \le 70$
c 54.7
d 53.7
2 a $4 \le s < 8$
b 7.2
c 6.8

4.3: Deciding which average to use, transforming data and weighted means

1 a mode
b median
c mean
2 Using subtract 515 gives $(12 + 57 + 30 + 66 + 3)/5 = 33.6$
$33.6 + 515 = 548.6$
3 £497

4.4: Ranges and quartiles

1 a 9
b $Q1 = 10, Q2 = 13, Q3 = 15$
c 5
2 a cumulative frequencies: 4, 20, 28, 37, 49, 54, 58, 60
b Cumulative frequency step polygon correctly drawn with straight lines as follows. Polygon goes through the points $(0, 4)$, $(1, 4)$, $(1, 20)$, $(2, 20)$, $(2, 28)$, $(3, 28)$, $(3, 37)$, $(4, 37)$, $(4, 49)$, $(5, 49)$, $(5, 54)$, $(6, 54)$, $(6, 58)$, $(7, 58)$, $(7, 60)$, $(8, 60)$. Number of times late on x-axis and cumulative frequency on y-axis. Axes should be labelled.
c $Q_1 = 1, Q_2 = 3, Q_3 = 4$
d range = 7, IQR = 3
3 a cumulative frequencies: 2, 12, 30, 64, 88, 96, 100

Speed (mph)	$20 < x \le 30$	$30 < x \le 40$	$40 < x \le 50$	$50 < x \le 60$	$60 < x \le 70$	$70 < x \le 80$	$80 < x \le 90$
Frequency	2	10	18	34	24	8	4
Cum. freq.	2	12	30	64	88	96	100

b Cumulative frequency diagram drawn with the following points connected by a smooth curve or straight lines: $(20, 0)$, $(30, 2)$, $(40, 12)$, $(50, 30)$, $(60, 64)$, $(70, 88)$, $(80, 96)$, $(90, 100)$. Speeds on x-axis and cumulative frequency on y-axis. Axes should be labelled.
c $Q_1 = 46–48, Q_2 = 56, Q_3 = 64–66, IQR = Q_3 - Q_1 = 16–20$
d 53–55, 50
4 a 44.29
b 63.5
c 54.67

4.5: Box plots

1 a $Q_1 = 2, Q_2 = 5, Q_3 = 8$
  b
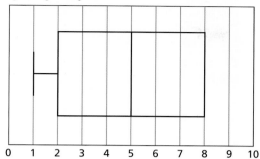

  c symmetrical
2 a
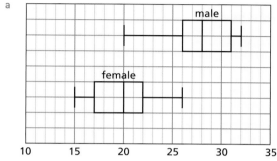

  b positive skew
  c negative skew
  d The males have a greater range. They both have the same IQR.
3 2 and 34
4 a $Q_1 = 24, Q_2 = 33, Q_3 = 35$
  b IQR = 11, 1.5 × 11 = 16.5, limits are 7.5 and 51.5. Therefore 5 is an outlier.
  c
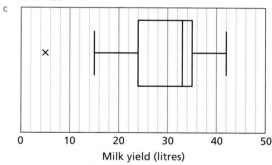

  d negative skew

4.6: Variance and standard deviation

1 The range (the difference between the fastest and slowest) and interquartile range (the speed of the middle 50%) are both good measures in this situation.
  The range is badly affected by extreme values (e.g. a car travelling at 130 mph). The interquartile range does not show the higher and lower speeds.
2 1.76
3 mean = 7, variance = 3.8, SD = 1.95
4 1.18
5 4.24
6 Advantages: all values used, used in maths calculations, used when data nearly symmetrical.
  Disadvantages: not good if data very skewed.

4.7: Comparing data sets and standardised scores

1 a
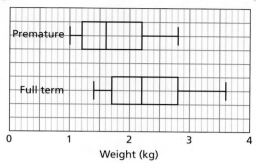

  b The median for the full term babies is greater than the median for the premature babies.
    Both the range and the IQR for the premature babies are less than for the full term babies.
    Both have positive skew.
2 Girls are generally slower than boys. The slowest runners are girls. The modal group for girls is 56 to 58 seconds but for boys it is 52 to 54 seconds.
3 a French −2, Spanish $+1\frac{1}{3}$
  b Charles did better in Spanish. His standardised score was higher.

4.8: Index numbers

1 85.7
2 14%
3 Price went up by 2% between 2006 and 2007.
  Price went down 5% between 2006 and 2008.
  Price went up 3% between 2006 and 2009.
  Cheapest in 2008 and most expensive in 2009.
4 2008 = 73.8; 2009 = 62.5; 2010 = 50
5 Price went up by 5% between 2007 and 2008. It then dropped by 2% between 2008 and 2009. Between 2009 and 2010 it rose by 10%.
6 a 90
  b went down by 10%

5: Scatter diagrams and correlation

5.1: Scatter diagrams

1 a Scatter diagram drawn correctly, with distance on x-axis and density on y-axis. Axes should be labelled.
  b Straight line drawn from (0.6, 49) to (4, 6).
  c negative
  d As distance increases so density decreases.
2 a Scatter diagram drawn correctly, with year after restocking on x-axis and number of fish caught on y-axis. Axes should be labelled.
  b Straight line drawn from (1, 200) through (4.5, 150) to (8, 100).
  c negative
  d As the number of years increases so the number of fish caught decreases.
3 a Scatter diagram drawn correctly, with Maths on x-axis and English on y-axis. Axes should be labelled.
  b (28, 26)
  c Straight line drawn from (5, 13) through (28, 26) to (50, 39).
  d positive
  e The higher the Maths mark the higher the English mark.

5.2: Using a line of best fit

1 Extrapolation is estimating outside the data range. It can be unreliable.
  Interpolation is estimating inside the data range. It is reliable.

2 a 25 cm
  b 80 cm
  c It is outside the data range. It is extrapolation. The trend might not continue.

3 a Scatter diagram drawn correctly, with French on x-axis and History on y-axis. Axes should be labelled.
  b Straight line drawn from $(25, 39)$ to $(80, 70)$.
  c i 65 to 67 ii interpolation
  d i 72 to 74 ii extrapolation

5.3: Equations of lines of best fit

1 $y = 1.5x + 3$
2 a 44
  b 92
3 For every 3 weeks it grows 1 cm.
4 a For every 300 metres rise the temperature drops 1°C.
  b The temperature at sea level.
5 a Scatter diagram plotted correctly.
  b $(15, 9)$
  c Line of best fit drawn from $(12, 6)$ through $(15, 9)$ to $(18, 12)$
  d $y = x - 6$
  e a is 1 which means there is a rise of 1 hour for every rise of 1 year in age.
    b is -6. This has no sensible meaning. It is -6 hours at age 0 years.
  f That would be extrapolation (going outside the data range) which is unreliable.

5.4: Fitting a line of best fit to a non-linear model

1 a $y = ax + b$
  b $y = a\sqrt{x} + b$
  c $y = \dfrac{a}{x} + b$
2 a and b

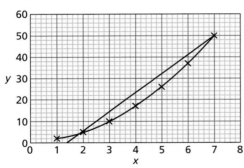

  c the curve
3 a Scatter diagram drawn with time on x-axis and number of aphids on y-axis. Axes should be labelled.
  b Curve of best fit drawn as a smooth curve going through all the points.
  c $y = ax^2 + b$

5.5: Spearman's rank correlation

1 -0.55. This means there is negative correlation between the ranks. There is some disagreement between the judges.

2 a

Goals	28	24	42	33	27	20
League position	1	2	3	4	5	6
Rank goals	3	5	1	2	4	6
d	2	3	-2	-2	-1	0
d^2	4	9	4	4	1	0

  b 0.37
  c There is very low positive correlation. There is only a little evidence that the higher the number of goals scored the higher the league position.

3 a 0.7
  b Positive correlation. There is evidence that the more years you smoke the greater the lung damage.

6: Time series

6.1: Time series

1 Time series graph correctly drawn with days on the x-axis and frequency on the y-axis. Axes should be labelled.
2 a red line B
  b a rising trend
  c level trend

6.2: Moving averages

1 a, b and c

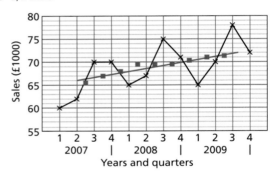

  b 65.5, 66.75, 68, 69.25, 69.5, 69.5, 70.25, 71, 71.25

6.3: Average seasonal variation

1 Q1: 1.1; Q2: -5; Q3: 7; Q4: 3
2 a, b and c

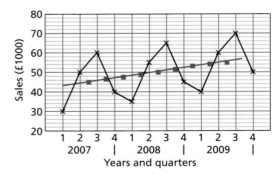

  b 45, 46.25, 47.5, 48.75, 50, 51.25, 52.5, 53.75, 55
  d $-£13\,000 - £13\,500$
  e $£45\,000 - £46\,000$

7: Probability

7.1: Events, outcomes and probability

1 a head, tail
  b win, lose, draw
2 a evens
  b very unlikely
  c certain
3 A marked on scale at 1/7 (near 0); B marked at 1 and C marked at zero or very close to zero.

7.2: Probability of an event and sample spaces

1 a 0.5 or $\frac{1}{2}$
  b $\frac{1}{6}$
  c $\frac{2}{3}$
2 a 0.5 or $\frac{1}{2}$
  b $\frac{3}{26}$
  c $\frac{10}{13}$
3 a

HHH		
HHT	HTH	THH
TTH	THT	HTT
TTT		

  b $\frac{3}{8}$
  c $\frac{1}{8}$

7.3: Venn diagrams

1 a

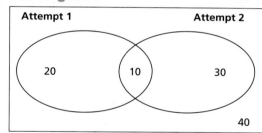

  b 100
  c $\frac{1}{10}$
2 a

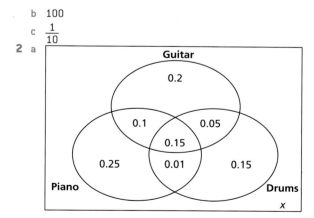

  b 0.09

7.4: Experimental probability

1 $\frac{35}{100}$ or $\frac{7}{20}$
2 a $\frac{1}{150}$
  b £2000
3 a Allocate numbers 0 to 19 inclusive to salad, 20 to 49 to roast, 50 to 89 to pasta and 89 to 99 to vegetarian. Generate 30 random numbers between 0 and 99. The meals with those numbers form the simulation results.
  b Repeated simulations put together would give results nearer and nearer an accurate estimate of the actual result.

7.5: Mutually exclusive and exhaustive events

1 a 0.7
  b 0.1
  c $P(A) + P(B) + P(C) = 1$
  d 0.7
2 0.18
3 a 0.28
  b 0.54

7.6: Tree diagrams

1 a

A tree diagram:

Columns labelled **A** and **B**

0.6 → R, then 0.3 → R and 0.7 → W
0.4 → W, then 0.3 → R and 0.7 → W

  b $\frac{46}{100}$ or $\frac{23}{50}$
  c $\frac{54}{100}$ or $\frac{27}{50}$
2 a

0.5 → X, 0.5 → X, 0.5 → X   XXX 0.125
                    0.5 → N   XXN 0.125
         0.5 → N, 0.5 → X   XNX 0.125
                    0.5 → N   XNN 0.125
0.5 → N, 0.5 → X, 0.5 → X   NXX 0.125
                    0.5 → N   NXN 0.125
         0.5 → N, 0.5 → X   NNX 0.125
                    0.5 → N   NNN 0.125

  b $\frac{3}{8}$
  c $\frac{1}{2}$
3 a

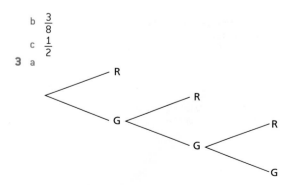

  b $\frac{3087}{8000}$
  c $\frac{4913}{8000}$

7.7: Conditional probability

1 a $\dfrac{96}{380} = \dfrac{24}{95}$

  b $\dfrac{132}{380}$ or $\dfrac{66}{190}$ or $\dfrac{33}{95}$

  c $\dfrac{1056}{6840}$ or $\dfrac{264}{1710}$ or $\dfrac{132}{855}$ or $\dfrac{44}{285}$

2 a

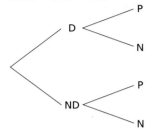

  b $\dfrac{19}{400}$

  c $\dfrac{7}{80}$

  d $\dfrac{1}{20}$

8: Probability distributions and quality assurance

8.1: Discrete uniform and binomial distributions

1 a 0.1

  b 0.35

2 a discrete uniform distribution

  b

Outcomes	1	2	3	4	5
Probability	0.2	0.2	0.2	0.2	0.2

  c 0.4

3 0.06

4 a 0.2

  b 0.8

  c i 0.0016 ii 0.8192

8.2: The normal distribution

1 a 95%

  b 970 g and 1030 g

2 a 2.5%

  b 20

3

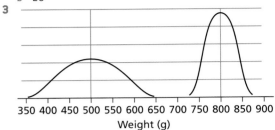

Weight (g)

8.3: Quality assurance

1 a 480 g and 520 g

  b 470 g and 530 g

  c Take another sample.

  d Stop the machine and reset it.

2 a 964 and 1036

  b 976 and 1024

  c none

3 a To check that the correct amount of pasta goes into each bag.

  b 260 g

  c

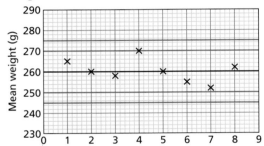

  d No since the action limits are 245 g and 275 g.

Index

Published by Pearson Education Limited, a company incorporated in England and Wales, having its registered office at Edinburgh Gate, Harlow, Essex, CM20 2JE. Registered company number: 872828

www.pearsonschoolsandfecolleges.co.uk

Edexcel is a registered trademark of Edexcel Limited

Text © Pearson Education Limited 2010

The rights of Gill Dyer have been asserted by her in accordance with the Copyright, Designs and Patents Act of 1988.

First published 2010

18 17 16 15 14

10 9 8 7 6 5 4 3

British Library Cataloguing in Publication Data

A catalogue record for this book is available from the British Library.

ISBN 978 1 846905 91 9

Project management by Jim Newall
Edited by Kate Redmond
Typeset by HL Studios
Original illustrations © Pearson Education 2009
Illustrated by HL Studios
Cover photo © Masterfile: I Dream Stock
Printed in Malaysia (CTP-VVP)

Acknowledgements

The author and publisher would like to thank the following individuals and organisations for permission to reproduce photographs:
Cover images: Front: Masterfile: I Dream Stock

All other images © Pearson Education

Every effort has been made to contact copyright holders and we apologise in advance for any unintentional omissions. We would be pleased to insert the appropriate acknowledgement in any subsequent edition of this publication.

Disclaimer

This material has been published on behalf of Edexcel and offers high-quality support for the delivery of Edexcel qualifications.

This does not mean that the material is essential to achieve any Edexcel qualification, nor does it mean that it is the only suitable material available to support any Edexcel qualification. Edexcel material will not be used verbatim in setting any Edexcel examination or assessment. Any resource lists produced by Edexcel shall include this and other appropriate resources.

Copies of official specifications for all Edexcel qualifications may be found on the Edexcel website: www.edexcel.com

Mainstreaming Biodiversity in Production Landscapes

Caroline Petersen
Brian Huntley

IEEM
43 Southgate Street
Winchester
Hampshire
SO23 9EH

Contents

Foreword

Len Good

The international conservation community has reason to celebrate the setting aside of over 12 percent of the Earth's land surface for long-term protection. From minute reserves on oceanic islands to extensive mega reserves in tropical savannas and boreal forests, the protected area systems of the world have become the cornerstone of biodiversity conservation. During the past decade, the Global Environment Facility (GEF) has contributed over $1.2 billion, and leveraged $3.1 billion in cofinancing, to supporting this agenda.

What we at the GEF have learned, however, is that protected areas alone cannot ensure that our goal of achieving global biodiversity benefits for the planet and its six billion people will be met. Unless we address the root causes of biodiversity loss and incorporate biodiversity conservation into all development actions—and simultaneously incorporate development goals into our conservation programs—we will not reduce, much less reverse, the current rates of biodiversity loss.

This realization has convinced the GEF Council to approve new strategies within the GEF biodiversity work program. Strategic Priority 2 seeks to "mainstream biodiversity in production landscapes and sectors." In attempting to position mainstreaming approaches into our work program, however, we found that the concept and its application were poorly understood by many stakeholders. It was, therefore, considered appropriate to refer this topic to the GEF's Scientific and Technical Advisory Panel (STAP), which was established in 1992 to provide the GEF Council with strategic advice where appropriate.

STAP's response is presented in this volume, based on a workshop held in Cape Town, South Africa, in September 2004. The workshop brought together experts from around the globe to review the mainstreaming concept, and to develop principles and conditions for its effective application. The workshop also identified areas for GEF interventions to promote the mainstreaming of biodiversity and to propose tools to assess the effectiveness of such interventions.

It is a great pleasure to endorse the products of the Cape Town workshop and encourage the GEF family to apply, where possible and appropriate, the 10 principles for mainstreaming biodiversity described in the following pages and listed in Box 14.1. I am confident that the excellent synergies developed between the GEF, its Implementing Agencies, and the STAP team will help us continue to increase the benefits of global biodiversity.

Len Good
Chief Executive Officer and Chairman
Global Environment Facility

Introduction

Brian Huntley[1] and Caroline Petersen[2]

"The most important lesson of the last ten years is that the objectives of the Convention will be impossible to meet until consideration of biodiversity is fully integrated into other sectors. The need to mainstream the conservation and sustainable use of biological resources across all sectors of the national economy, society, and the policy-making framework is a complex challenge at the heart of the Convention."[3] COP VI

At the World Summit on Sustainable Development in Johannesburg, South Africa, in 2002, world leaders agreed that reducing the rate of biodiversity loss and improving the welfare of humankind were still elusive goals, despite the ambitious initiatives taken at the United Nations Conference on the Environment and Development in Rio de Janeiro, Brazil in 1992. Massive programs of integrated rural development, community-based resource management, and similar innovations had failed to deliver the results expected. A new paradigm was needed to integrate biodiversity conservation into thinking and action at all levels of intervention and across all sectors. The concept of "mainstreaming" biodiversity conservation was entering the language of the new debate, but its meaning and relevance were poorly understood, despite being a key concept in the new GEF program of work.

This volume contributes to broadening the understanding and application of the concept of mainstreaming biodiversity. It captures the inputs to and findings of an international workshop held in Cape Town, South Africa, in September 2004 on *Mainstreaming Biodiversity in Production Landscapes and Sectors*. The workshop, co-hosted by the South African National Biodiversity Institute (SANBI) and

the Scientific and Technical Advisory Panel (STAP) of the Global Environment Facility (GEF), was attended by individuals from those organizations, as well as the implementing agencies of the GEF—the United Nations Development Programme (UNDP), the United Nations Environment Programme (UNEP), and the World Bank—and by a diverse group of professionals from around the globe.[4, 5]

The aims of the workshop were:
- to determine an operational *definition* of the concept of mainstreaming biodiversity in production landscapes and sectors, building on the work of previous workshops[6]
- to demonstrate the *role* of mainstreaming in advancing Convention on Biological Diversity (CBD) goals and Strategic Priority 2 of the GEF-3 program of work
- to explore the *scale* at which mainstreaming can most effectively be carried out
- to critique *successes and failures* in achieving mainstreaming outcomes to date—consolidating and evaluating experience in different sectors
- to brainstorm on modified or new *approaches and tools* to assist in designing more effective interventions and achieving more effective main-

streaming outcomes in the future, such as models of best practice, principles, and indicators.

The first three of the workshop aims are addressed in the first paper in this volume, which explores what we mean by "mainstreaming biodiversity," while the new approaches and tools—the products of the workshop—are outlined in the final paper, on guidelines for effective intervention. The remaining papers, which were presented at the open symposium preceding the workshop, represent a broad range of mainstreaming initiatives—in Africa, Asia, Australia, Europe, and Latin America, and in a large number of production sectors. They are organized under themes as follows:

In *Biodiversity in the GEF Portfolio*, the GEF's Gonzalo Castro provides the context in which the issue of mainstreaming biodiversity in production landscapes and sectors is understood by the GEF and explains its growing importance to the GEF's biodiversity focal area. Richard M. Cowling then discusses some of the lessons learned from past work in mainstreaming biodiversity conservation, by exploring the key factors for success of mainstreaming initiatives and the constraints on and prospects for future mainstreaming efforts.

In *Mainstreaming Biodiversity Conservation Initiatives in New Zealand*, Robert McCallum assesses New Zealand's progress in mainstreaming biodiversity into agriculture, forestry, and tourism, building on a growing recognition of the value of biodiversity to economic development. A paper by Jeffery A. McNeely on agrobiodiversity argues for a systems approach to converting the potential benefits of mainstreaming agrobiodiversity into real and perceived goods and services for society at large. Paul Elkan and Sarah Elkan report on mainstreaming approaches in the Republic of Congo, where significant gains have been made in protecting species and habitats through working with logging companies to control the bushmeat trade.

In *Achieving Sustainable Landscapes*, Kent H. Redford presents a paper that explores a calculus of the biodiversity trade-offs involved in mainstreaming. Trevor Sandwith and his colleagues write about the opportunities provided by a bioregional approach to conservation programs in southern Africa. Carlos Toledo discusses the challenges of integrating biodiversity considerations into rural development programs in marginal but biodiversity-rich areas of Mexico. Finally, Tehmina Akhtar and Jeffrey F. Griffin analyze a set of mainstreaming projects in Eastern Europe, the Commonwealth of Independent States, and Asia, exploring the special challenges and opportunities posed by transitional economies.

In *Mainstreaming Biodiversity into the Tea Industry*, Pramod Krishnan proposes a model for mainstreaming the objectives of biodiversity conservation into the tea production sector of the High Ranges in Western Ghats, India, in the context of the pressures of globalization. The response of the oil and gas industry to the challenges of biodiversity loss is discussed by Sachin Kapila. Carl Grant and John Gardner present a case study of the successful mainstreaming of biodiversity conservation in the aluminium mining industry in Australia.

A final paper, drafted by the Cape Town workshop participants, provides guidelines on effective interventions in achieving mainstreaming outcomes.

As we advance into the 21st century, it is clear that the significant success of the protected area systems developed through the previous century will have to be extended well beyond the boundaries of national parks. Achieving the Conference of Parties' 2010 goal of a significant reduction in the rate of biodiversity loss will require innovations in policy and practice such as offered by mainstreaming biodiversity into the full spectrum of economic sectors and across landscapes and seascapes.

Endnotes

1   Scientific and Technical Advisory Panel of the Global Environment Facility (GEF); South African National Biodiversity Institute

2   South African National Biodiversity Institute

3   Hague Ministerial Declaration from the Convention on Biological Diversity (CBD) Conference of Parties (COP) VI to the World Summit on Sustainable Development, Johannesburg, 2002.

4   On September 1, 2004, the National Botanical Institute became the South African National Biodiversity Institute (SANBI), under the terms of the National Environmental Management: Biodiversity Act 10 of 2004.

5   STAP is the scientific body of the GEF. It provides independent, strategic advice to the GEF family on science and technology issues; see www.unep.org/stapgef.

6   Although significant mainstreaming work is being carried out in production water bodies—rivers, lakes, coastal and marine systems—it was decided to limit the Cape Town workshop to the terrestrial environment for purposes of focus.

Part 1.

Mainstreaming Biodiversity: Setting the Scene

1. What is Mainstreaming Biodiversity?

Caroline Petersen[1] and Brian Huntley[2]

The term "mainstreaming" is used in a variety of ways, but within broad environment-development circles "mainstreaming biodiversity" has come to have a particular meaning. Consensus on a precise definition of the concept has proven elusive, but participants at the September 2004 Global Environment Facility (GEF) workshop on biodiversity held in Cape Town, South Africa, agreed that the objective of mainstreaming biodiversity is:

to internalize the goals of biodiversity conservation and the sustainable use of biological resources into economic sectors and development models, policies and programmes, and therefore into all human behaviour.

This paper examines the ways in which the concept has been used, the common elements revealed, its relevance and use in relation to the goals of the Convention on Biological Diversity (CBD), the differing scales at which it can be applied, and experience in recent attempts to achieve mainstreaming outcomes.

Common Elements

A review of the literature on mainstreaming biodiversity reveals common elements in the way the concept has been used:

- Mainstreaming biodiversity involves the integration of biodiversity conservation and sustainable use principles into policies, plans, programs, and production systems where the primary focus has previously been on production, economic activity, and development, rather than on biodiversity conservation losses or gains.

- Mainstreaming of biodiversity may occur on the ground in production landscapes and seascapes or within economic sectors, particularly those directly related to natural resource use and management—agriculture, forestry, fisheries, invasive alien species control, wildlife utilization, mining, and tourism.[3] Biodiversity may also be mainstreamed in areas of economic activity such as energy, infrastructure, manufacturing, transport, construction, international trade, and even in military activities.

- Mainstreaming also involves the integration of biodiversity values into the enabling environment, ranging from national policy making to global financial markets. This may include development policy, legislation, land-use planning, finance, taxation, economic incentives, international trade, capacity building, research, and technology.

- Mainstreaming can be a process that occurs through a conscious intervention. At other times, however, a mainstreaming outcome may be achieved without such a deliberate intervention, for example, through the action of market forces. The achievement of mainstreaming outcomes needs to be measurable so that progress can be assessed.

- Mainstreaming biodiversity into broad landscapes may involve using a range of tools, including protected areas, buffer zones, and biological corridors, as well as interventions affecting privately owned land such as incentives, subsidies, and direct payments. The emphasis in mainstreaming biodiversity, however, is on the roughly 90 percent of land not under formal protection.

- Although mainstreaming initiatives may be generated by conservation agencies, increasingly often they originate within economic sectors, and typically involve a broad range of actors, with partnerships between nongovernmental organizations (NGOs); government; industry; small, medium, and micro enterprises; and communities.

Mainstreaming in Relation to the Goals of the CBD and GEF

The main objectives of the CBD are the conservation and sustainable use of biological diversity, and the fair and equitable sharing of benefits arising from the utilization of genetic resources (CBD 2003, p. xvii). Biological diversity, or biodiversity, is defined as "the variability among living organisms from all sources including inter alia, terrestrial, marine and other aquatic ecosystems and the ecological complexes of which they are part; this includes diversity within species, between species and of ecosystems" (CBD 2003, p. 5).

Mainstreaming biodiversity in production landscapes and sectors contributes to the fulfilment of article 6(b) of the CBD, which calls on the contracting parties to "integrate, as far as possible and as appropriate, the conservation and sustainable use of biological diversity into relevant sectoral or cross-sectoral plans, programmes and policies" (CBD 2003, p. 6). It also contributes toward fulfilling article 10(a), which calls on parties to "integrate consideration of the conservation and sustainable use of biological resources into national decision-making" (CBD 2003, p. 11).

The GEF assists the many countries who are signatories to the CBD, by providing finance to implement its provisions effectively. In the GEF-3 work program, four strategic priorities are set out. The Cape Town workshop aims to contribute toward the second and fourth strategic priorities. The strategic priorities (SPs) are as follows:

- SP 1: Catalyzing sustainability of protected areas—to conserve biodiversity through the expansion, consolidation, and rationalization of existing protected area systems
- SP 2: Mainstreaming biodiversity in production landscapes and sectors—to integrate biodiversity conservation into agriculture, forestry, fisheries, tourism, and other production sectors in order to secure national and global environmental benefits
- SP 3: Building capacity to implement the Cartagena Protocol on Biosafety—to recognize that modified living organisms pose potential risks and, therefore, biosafety constitutes a high priority for recipient countries
- SP 4: Generating and disseminating best practices—to maximize the sustainability and effectiveness of GEF impacts in the biodiversity focal area.

Strategic priority 2 reflects a shift in emphasis in GEF funding. Although protected areas remain dominant in its biodiversity portfolio, the GEF believes that attention needs urgently to be given to integrating biodiversity conservation into landscapes where the primary emphasis is on economic uses, in order to achieve the GEF's global biodiversity conservation goals.

Mainstreaming is seen as a way to increase the effectiveness of protected areas work, by integrating biodiversity conservation into broader production landscapes and into the national and international policy frameworks that affect them. This also involves a shift to a bigger scale and a longer time frame: "Mainstreaming means moving beyond a project-by-project emphasis to approaches that systematically target country-enabling environments and long-term institution building" (GEF 2004a, p. 32).

Because the SPs were only developed in 2003, the existing projects of the GEF's Implementing Agencies—United Nations Development Programme (UNDP), United Nations Environment

Programme (UNEP), and the World Bank—may or may not have explicit mainstreaming objectives. In the future, it is expected that focusing around SP 2 will assist projects to have the following impacts:

- Producing biodiversity gains in production systems in recipient countries
- Improving livelihoods based on more sustainable harvesting
- Replicating approaches applying incentive measures
- Having biodiversity mainstreamed into sector programs of the Implementing Agencies (GEF 2004b, p. 1).

Mainstreaming and Integration

The concept of mainstreaming biodiversity is closely related to the idea of "integration." Article 6(b) of the Convention on Biological Diversity calls on the contracting parties to "integrate, as far as possible and as appropriate, the conservation and sustainable use of biological diversity into relevant sectoral or cross-sectoral plans, programmes, and policies" (CBD 2003, p. 6).

Article 10(a) calls on Parties to "integrate consideration of the conservation and sustainable use of biological resources into national decision-making" (CBD 2003, p. 11). Although these articles have integration as their key concept, integration can be seen as another way of describing mainstreaming.

Integration was also the theme of the Biodiversity Planning Support Programme (BPSP) of UNEP/UNDP/GEF, which was given the mandate to provide assistance to national biodiversity conservation planners. As part of this program, UNEP commissioned a series of thematic studies, focusing on global best practice in the integration of biodiversity in eight specific areas, including national sectors in agriculture (UNEP 2002a), fisheries, forestry (UNEP 2002b), and tourism (UNEP 2002c), as well as integration with environmental assessment procedures and economic measures in biodiversity planning (IUCN 2001).

The "integrated responses" described in the Millennium Ecosystem Assessment (MA) are also of relevance to mainstreaming biodiversity. The MA defines integrated responses as initiatives that explicitly address more than one ecosystem service and which include objectives to enhance human well-being. Most mainstreaming interventions fulfill these criteria, and could thus also be described as integrated responses (see www.millenniumassessment.org).

Both concepts make provision for a simultaneous benefit to biodiversity and human well-being, with trade-offs and choices needing to be made in each situation. The MA takes a slightly broader perspective than simply focusing on biodiversity conservation and sustainable use, but nonetheless provides important insights for mainstreaming.

The MA provides a rich source of information on a range of processes that contribute to mainstreaming. At an international level these include Agenda 21, international environmental governance, multilateral environmental agreements, and integration between international trade and environmental governance regimes. National level processes considered are national policy integration, national environmental action plans, and national strategies for sustainable development and related initiatives.

Processes that are considered at multiple scales (including the subnational level) are Sustainable Forest Management, Integrated Conservation and Development Projects, Integrated Coastal Zone Management, and Watershed and River Basin Management. These processes all involve mainstreaming biodiversity into production landscapes.

Mainstreaming and the Ecosystem Approach

The "ecosystem approach" of the CBD is also related to the concept of mainstreaming biodiversity. The ecosystem approach was developed internationally in the 1980s, and is "based on the application of appropriate scientific methodologies focused on levels of biological organisation that encompasses the essential processes and interactions among organisms and their environment" (CBD 1998).

An ecosystem is defined as "a dynamic complex of plant, animal, and microorganism communities and their nonliving environment interacting as a functional unit" (CBD 2003, p. 5). The recognition that humans are an integral part of ecosystems is also a key feature of the ecosystem approach. A systems approach makes it possible to consider different levels of the biodiversity hierarchy—genes, species, populations, ecosystems, and landscapes in a holistic way. The ecosystem approach can be used at varying scales.

The 12 principles of the ecosystem approach (see box 1.1) endorsed by the Conference of Parties in 2000 are well known within the CBD but poorly understood beyond the convention's immediate stakeholders. The ecosystem approach is described as "the fundamental paradigm for the Convention's activities; a prism through which its activities are developed" (CBD 2003, p. xxiv). A large percentage of the project portfolios of GEF and its Implementing Agencies are targeted at one or more critical life-supporting ecosystems, and often at the interactions between ecosystems.

The ecosystem approach is highly compatible with mainstreaming biodiversity because of its emphasis on social and economic concerns, and on integrated and holistic decision making. A tension may sometimes exist, however, between the principle of the ecosystem approach that conservation of ecosystem structure and functioning should be a priority target, and the need for real-world compromises and trade-offs in some mainstreaming interventions.

Of direct relevance for mainstreaming biodiversity is the recognition in principle 4 of the ecosystem approach that ecosystems need to be understood and managed in an economic context. Economic tools important for mainstreaming interventions seek to influence the enabling environment, reducing market distortions that adversely affect biological diversity, aligning incentives to promote

---

Box 1.1
The 12 Principles of the Ecosystem Approach

1. Management objectives are a matter of societal choice.

2. Management should be decentralized to the lowest appropriate level.

3. Ecosystem managers should consider the effects (actual or potential) of their activities on adjacent and other ecosystems.

4. Recognizing potential gains from management, there is a need to understand the ecosystem in an economic context. Any ecosystem management program should
   a) reduce those market distortions that adversely affect biological diversity;
   b) align incentives to promote sustainable use;
   c) internalize costs and benefits in the given ecosystem to the extent feasible.

5. A key feature of the ecosystem approach includes conservation of ecosystem structure and functioning.

6. Ecosystems must be managed within the limits of their functioning.

7. The ecosystem approach should be undertaken at the appropriate scale.

8. Recognizing the varying temporal scales and lag effects that characterize ecosystem processes, objectives for ecosystem management should be set for the long term.

9. Management must recognize that change is inevitable.

10. The ecosystem approach should seek the appropriate balance between conservation and use of biological diversity.

11. The ecosystem approach should consider all forms of relevant information, including scientific and indigenous and local knowledge, innovations, and practices.

12. The ecosystem approach should involve all relevant sectors of society and scientific disciplines.

---

biodiversity conservation and sustainable use, and internalizing costs and benefits in a given ecosystem. Where possible in mainstreaming interventions, full accounting for biodiversity goods and services should be undertaken.

The ecosystem approach provides a good platform for work in the "real world" and contributes a sound scientific underpinning for an emphasis on mainstreaming biodiversity. It does not, however,

Box 1.2
Different Aspects of Scale

The question of scale can be considered in the following ways:

■ *Temporal scale.* A mainstreaming intervention could take place over a range of time periods, from a single day used to raise an issue, to a decade-long campaign. The benefits of a mainstreaming outcome could also be experienced over varying time scales.

■ *Geographical scale.* A mainstreaming intervention can be carried out in a range of physical spaces—ranging from a very small geographical area, such as a portion of one farm, to a bioregion or entire ocean. This will also affect the scale of biodiversity being addressed.

■ *Institutional scale.* A mainstreaming initiative may involve actors at differing levels, including, for example, a community of resource users at the local level, a national government department or business sector, a global financial market, or the parties to a multilateral environmental agreement.

■ *Financial scale.* Mainstreaming work may be carried out through projects with dedicated budgets of varying sizes, or through the regular operations of role-players such as landowners or private sector companies.

provide specific guidelines for mainstreaming interventions. Because of these limitations, the Cape Town workshop decided to develop a set of principles specifically designed to guide work in mainstreaming biodiversity.

Achieving Mainstreaming Outcomes at Different Scales

Mainstreaming outcomes can be achieved and mainstreaming interventions made at a range of scales in relation to time, geographic impact, and actors involved. The question of scale can be considered in a number of ways, as outlined in box 1.2.

Some commentators argue that mainstreaming is most effective at the highest possible level of national and international politics or economics. The opposite point has also been made: "for main-

streaming to achieve lasting impact, it must occur at a very local level, and become part of ordinary people's lives" (Sandwith in Pierce and others 2002). Both approaches may be valid, depending on the context of a specific project, the biodiversity properties being addressed, and the existing policy and institutional framework.

An example of planning for multilevel engagement is provided by a full-sized project concept being developed by the UNDP for the China Biodiversity Programme, which will engage various levels: the high policy level through the Five Year Development Plan, the sector level through sectoral plans and programs, and the provincial/prefecture level through focusing on piloting biodiversity-friendly management practices within local level projects and investments.

Addressing the Enabling Environment

The GEF Council has highlighted the importance of creating the right enabling environment for mainstreaming biodiversity, pointing to the need for "an effective institutional and enabling environment where biodiversity has been mainstreamed across the sectors. This is not an option; in fact, it is critical for ensuring sustained biodiversity benefits. Unless the institutional structures of a country are reinforced to mainstream biodiversity, they remain vulnerable (to alternative development options) and may become islands (in which case the biodiversity value may get eroded over time)" (GEF 2002).

The *GEF Biodiversity Program Study 2004* (Dublin and Volonte 2004) reviews components of the majority of GEF-financed projects that seek to improve the enabling environment for meeting objectives relating to biodiversity conservation, sustainable use of biodiversity, and mainstreaming. Components of the enabling environment where significant progress has been made include:

■ creating and implementing national policies or legislative action

- public awareness and environmental education
- partnerships
- targeted research, information generation, and knowledge sharing
- tool and technology development.

As noted previously, mainstreaming initiatives may operate simultaneously at different levels and strive for vertical integration between these levels. Projects that operate primarily at a local level nonetheless need to address the enabling environment by influencing decision making at regional, national, and even international levels. There is a need in particular to engage national governments that may have made commitments on paper to agreements promoting biodiversity conservation, but which may be simultaneously forging ahead with new developments that run contrary to those agreements or maintaining perverse incentives that drive economic sectors to destroy biodiversity rather than conserve it.

A number of global policy initiatives are relevant to the enabling environment for mainstreaming created in each country. One of the United Nations' Millennium Development Goals commits governments to "ensure environmental sustainability" by 2015, including targets around integrating the principles of sustainable development into country policies and programs (mainstreaming) and reversing the loss of environmental resources biodiversity (conservation). Similarly, many of the targets in the Plan of Implementation that came out of the 2002 World Summit on Sustainable Development in Johannesburg are relevant for mainstreaming. Further, it will be important for the findings of the Millennium Ecosystem Assessment on biodiversity conservation and sustainable use to be fed into the Poverty Reduction Strategy Papers being developed by the World Bank.

The development plans and policies of national governments are a crucial aspect of the enabling environment for mainstreaming work in production sectors and landscapes. National processes for developing National Sustainable Development Strategies and National Biodiversity Strategy and Action Plans

(NBSAPs) have the potential to make an enormous contribution to mainstreaming biodiversity considerations into government departments and sectors of the economy.

In a review of country experience in implementing NBSAPs, however, Swiderska (2002) finds that, despite having had some useful outcomes, "NBSAPs are not affecting the main forces degrading biodiversity, essentially because they have not influenced planning in economic sectors and are therefore not connected with the use of resources. NBSAPs have not paid enough attention to linkages with economic policies and plans, and have suffered from a lack of integration with other national institutions and planning mechanisms.... Many biodiversity plans have failed to arouse much political interest and remain on the shelf" (Swiderska 2002, p. 9). She points to the need for NBSAPs to establish systems and processes that engage sectors of society and government in action and the importance of integrating biodiversity and economic development objectives.

This is confirmed by the BPSP thematic study on the use of economic measures in NBSAPs, which states that "in many countries few people outside the conservation sector have any knowledge of the content or goals of the NBSAP. Yet it is macroeconomic and sectoral planners who decide the wider economic policies, activities, and conditions under which people conserve or degrade biodiversity" (Emerton 2001, p. 27). Influencing development policy at this level remains a major challenge facing the GEF and its Implementing Agencies.

The global arena of financial markets is another key aspect of the enabling environment that requires more attention. There is a need to engage the business and investment communities around achieving best practice on biodiversity conservation and sustainable use. Socially responsible investment strategies include avoidance/ethical screening, best in class/positive screening, environmental technology investment, engagement/advocacy, and integrated investment (Ten Kate 2004).

Ideally, the initiative in mainstreaming interventions should come increasingly from within the private sector, in partnership with other key actors, such as conservation agencies, government, NGOs, and communities. In engaging the private sector, Ten Kate suggests, conservationists need to focus on core business operations rather than corporate philanthropy, and develop useful tools for companies and investors, such as best practice standards and manuals, indicators for corporate performance, and literature for fund managers and pension fund trustees.

Success and Failure in Achieving Mainstreaming Outcomes

The *GEF Biodiversity Program Study 2004* assesses the achievement of mainstreaming outcomes by UNEP, UNDP, and World Bank projects in the agriculture, forestry, fisheries, and tourism sectors (Dublin and Volonte 2004). Most of the projects considered in the study were conceptualized and initiated long before the development of SP 2 in 2003, and the achievement of mainstreaming outcomes was thus not one of their original goals. The program study reviews all 141 projects in the BPS2004 cohort, in relation to their stated objectives around biodiversity conservation, sustainable

use of biodiversity resources, access to and benefit sharing of genetic resources between countries and the enabling environment, and mainstreaming biodiversity. It points out that projects with these objectives may operate in landscapes that include a continuum from fully protected areas to intensively modified areas. Projects working primarily in a production environment are classified as mainstreaming projects contributing to SP 2.

In relation to mainstreaming, the study reached the following broad conclusions (authors' emphasis added):

- Mainstreaming should form an *increasingly strong basis* for future GEF programming, because "over the long term, successful mainstreaming of biodiversity considerations in all aspects of society and governance will be the surest way to guarantee conservation gains" (Dublin and Volonte 2004, p. 101). Mainstreaming should occur at appropriate levels of priority across all sectors of society.
- The current focus on working in individual sectors such as agriculture, forestry, fisheries, and tourism should be expanded to address *cross-sectoral needs* (such as finance, energy, transport, mining, and health).
- GEF projects included in the program study can be categorized as shown in table 1.1. These *two*

Table 1.1
Typology of GEF-Supported Mainstreaming Projects

	Local / Subnational	National
Enabling Environment	Many projects to build the capacity of local institutions (for example, community-based forest management); establishing good conditions for governance (for example, stakeholder participation, and transparent and devolved decision making)	Some interventions to improve institutional capacity of national-level institutions and systemic capacity related to biodiversity conservation
Demonstrations	Many interventions aiming to influence local livelihoods in such a way that the economic goals of local stakeholders are more compatible with biodiversity conservation; and to increase the biodiversity value of the production activities themselves	A limited number of projects to influence resource management systems at a national level, often through sector-based approaches

Source: Adapted from Dublin and Volonte (2004), p. 73.

mutually supportive approaches should be continued—working at the policy level to establish a more favorable enabling environment, and working at the level of demonstration projects that operate in the existing policy environment to improve resource management.

- In many countries *governments lack commitment* to the incorporation of biodiversity considerations and approve development projects that run contrary to GEF mainstreaming efforts. Stronger evidence of commitment should be required, for example, through endorsement letters, cofinancing agreements, and monitoring and evaluation plans that include commitment milestones.

- A small number of projects have been carried out with a wide range of *private sector actors*. This trend should be encouraged, as the GEF shifts from working mainly in the public sector to developing partnerships with the private sector, based on a clear understanding of their role and motivation.

- Current *successful trends* within mainstreaming projects should be continued, particularly providing technical assistance to national governments, and linking government agencies with each other and with local-level actors.

- Some projects have been successful in *empowering communities* and involving them in resource management, and these should serve as models for future projects.

- The *length of time* required for meaningful mainstreaming to occur is often underestimated, and successful projects have often relied on prior capacity-building interventions. New projects should ideally have an initial capacity-building phase before mainstreaming interventions begin.

- *Reviews of project proposals* should consider whether the necessary prerequisites and stimuli for a successful intervention are in place. In sectors which lack experience of mainstreaming, projects should be carefully designed.

- *Quantitative impact indicators* need to be developed. The GEF's *Tracking Tool for Reporting Project Progress on Mainstreaming Biodiversity in Production Environments* (GEF 2004b)—which includes coverage indicators and impact indicators, with questions to be answered for each project on the

---

Box 1.3
Characteristics of Successful Mainstreaming Outcomes

Situations where mainstreaming of biodiversity has occurred might be characterized by:
- the incorporation of biodiversity considerations into policies governing sectoral activities
- the simultaneous achievement of gains in biodiversity and gains in an economic sector (the "win-win" scenario)
- sectoral activity being recognized as based on, or dependent on, the sustainable use of biodiversity
- situations where sectoral activities result in overall gains for biodiversity exceeding biodiversity losses.

Source: Sandwith (2002), p. 1

---

enabling environment, management practices, financial sustainability, replication, monitoring, and evaluation—should be further developed, as well as other indicators for use in future projects.

- Given that there has been some confusion within Implementing Agencies about what exactly mainstreaming encompasses, *guidelines and clear definitions* should be developed "to clarify exactly what types of activities, processes, and interventions are covered under the mainstreaming concept in the GEF context" (Dublin and Volonte 2004, p. 102).

Defining Successful Outcomes

Critical to the evaluation of mainstreaming work are the questions "how do we define a successful outcome" and "how do we measure it"? A report on a World Bank funded mainstreaming workshop (Pierce and others 2002), which examined a number of South African case studies, argues that situations where mainstreaming can be said to have occurred successfully include those listed in box 1.3.

Pierce and others point out that mainstreaming may arise gradually, with improved understanding of biodiversity issues in a sector, or suddenly, when an opportunity for mutual benefit presents itself. In ideal cases, they argue, biodiversity gains exceed losses without compromising sectoral activities, occasionally involving the change of land use away from production to conservation, but most often involving mitigation of impacts. Essentially, they argue, "integration of biodiversity is achieved when the sectoral activity becomes dependent on the sustainable use, or preservation of biodiversity" (Pierce and others 2002, p. 144).

A debate exists on the extent to which "win–win solutions" that benefit both conservation and development are actually possible to attain. According to Wells and others (2004), over the period since the 1992 Earth Summit, in which "Integrated Conservation and Development Projects" became fashionable, "the myth of 'win-win' solutions created a culture in which overly ambitious projects proliferated based on weak assumptions and little evidence." They argue that, while "poverty alleviation and conservation of biodiversity must work hand-in-hand in today's world," trade-offs must be made, mistakes avoided, and future projects based on "explicit testable assumptions, clearly stated objectives, and measurable conservation targets" (Christensen 2004, p. 7).

A win-win situation in which significant and equal gains are made in both biodiversity and an economic sector may occasionally be possible. But often this is not the case. In some cases, alternative livelihood options provided as a "sweetener" may fail to compensate for income losses by communities that are being asked to stop activities which have a negative impact on biodiversity but are important to their immediate needs. In other cases there are powerful vested interests involved in the destruction of biodiversity, who have no incentive to cooperate with a conservation agenda. Policymakers have to consider the long-term costs of conserving biodiversity in certain contexts, and develop scenarios and plans in which the additional costs can be internalized. Successful outcomes will take many forms and will always necessitate compromises and trade-offs.

It is important for the GEF and its Implementing Agencies to build tools to monitor and evaluate the effectiveness of mainstreaming interventions and their eventual impact on biodiversity. Indicators can be designed at differing levels—to track the outputs, outcomes, and impacts of projects and the interrelationships between these. The Cape Town workshop suggests a wide range of potential indicators for consideration by the GEF and its stakeholders.

The authors thank Richard Cowling, Kristal Maze, Trevor Sandwith, Nik Sekhran, Holly Dublin, Peter Schei, David Duthie, and John Hough for valuable comments on early drafts of this paper.

Endnotes

1   South African National Biodiversity Institute

2   South African National Biodiversity Institute; Scientific and Technical Advisory Panel of the GEF

3   For purposes of focus, however, the papers in this volume are limited to the terrestrial environment.

4   According to the Sustainable Use Specialist Group of IUCN (The World Conservation Union), the likelihood that no more than 15 percent of the Earth's surface will ever be effectively conserved in protected areas means that "the survival of Biodiversity largely depends on land use practices outside formal protected areas" (IUCN 2004, p. 1).

References

Christensen, J. 2004. "Win-Win Illusion." *Conservation in Practice 5* (1): 12-19.

CBD (Convention on Biological Diversity). 1998. *Report of the Workshop on the Ecosystem Approach.* Lilongwe, Malawi: CBD.

——. 2003. *Handbook of the Convention on Biological Diversity.* 2nd ed. (Updated to include the outcome of the 6th meeting of the Conference of Parties). Montreal: CBD.

Dublin, H., and C. Volonte, 2004. *GEF Biodiversity Program Study 2004.* Washington, DC: GEF Monitoring and Evaluation Unit.

Emerton, L. 2001. UNDP/UNEP/GEF Biodiversity Planning Support Programme/IUCN. *National Biodiversity Strategies and Action Plans: A Review of Experiences, Lessons Learned and Ways Forward.* IUCN—The World Conservation Union, Regional Environmental Economics Programme for Asia, Karachi. www.undp.org/bpsp/.

GEF (Global Environment Facility). 2002. *Summary of Negotiations on the Third Replenishment of the GEF Trust Fund.* GEF Council Document GEF/C.20/4. Washington, DC: GEF.

——. 2004a. *GEF and the Convention on Biological Diversity: A Strong Partnership with Solid Results.* Washington, DC: GEF.

——. 2004b. *Tracking Tool for "Reporting Project Progress on Mainstreaming Biodiversity in Production Environments" (GEF Strategic Priority 2).* Washington, DC: GEF.

IUCN (World Conservation Union). 2001. *The Use of Economic Measures in National Biodiversity Strategies and Action Plans: A Review of Experiences, Lessons Learned, and Ways Forward.* UNEP-GEF Biodiversity Planning Support Programme. www.undp.org/bpsp/.

——. 2004. "Mainstreaming Biodiversity in the Agricultural Landscapes of Southern South America and Southern Africa." Unpublished concept note for a project by the Sustainable Use Specialist Group of the IUCN/SSC (Species Survival Commission).

Pierce, S.M., R.M. Cowling, T. Sandwith, and K. MacKinnon. 2002. *Mainstreaming Biodiversity in Development: Case Studies from South Africa.* Washington, DC: World Bank.

Sandwith, T. 2002. Introduction. In S.M. Pierce, R.M. Cowling, T. Sandwith and K. MacKinnon. *Mainstreaming Biodiversity in Development: Case Studies from South Africa.* Washington, DC: World Bank.

Swiderska, K. 2002. *Mainstreaming Biodiversity in Development Policy and Planning: A Review of Country Experience.* Biodiversity and Livelihoods Group: International Institute for Environment and Development. September 2002.

Ten Kate, K. 2004. "Business, Investment, and the CBD." Presented at the 7th Conference of the Parties to the Convention on Biological Diversity, Kuala Lumpur, Malaysia, February 9-20.

UNEP (United Nations Environment Programme). 2002a. UNDP/UNEP/ GEF Biodiversity Planning Support Programme. *Integrating Biodiversity into the Agriculture Sector: A Guide to Best Practice.* www.undp.org/bpsp/.

——. 2002b. UNDP/UNEP/GEF Biodiversity Planning Support Programme. *Integrating Biodiversity into the Forestry Sector: A Guide to Best Practice.* www.undp.org/bpsp/.

——. 2002c. UNDP/UNEP/GEF Biodiversity Planning Support Programme. *Integrating Biodiversity into the Tourism Sector: A Guide to Best Practice.* www.undp.org/bpsp/.

Wells, M., T. McShane, H. Dublin, S. O'Connor, and K. Redford. 2004. "The Future of Integrated Conservation and Development Projects: Building on What Works." In T. McShane and M. Wells, eds. *Making Biodiversity Projects Work: Towards More Effective Conservation and Development.* New York: Columbia University Press.

Web site
www.millenniumassessment.org.

2. Biodiversity in the GEF Portfolio: The Role of Mainstreaming

Gonzalo Castro[1]

The purpose of this paper is to provide the context in which the issue of mainstreaming biodiversity in production landscapes and sectors is understood by the Global Environment Facility (GEF). As the paper shows, this issue is of central importance to the GEF's biodiversity focal area and is currently experiencing strong growth in funding. The findings and recommendations in this volume are, therefore, directly relevant to the way in which GEF resources are allocated.

The GEF in Its First Decade

Since 1990, the GEF has been addressing global environmental issues by providing grant financing to developing countries and countries with economies in transition. Financing is provided in the areas of climate change, biodiversity, international waters, land degradation, persistent organic pollutants, and ozone depletion. Today, the GEF is the largest international environmental donor, with a portfolio exceeding US$5 billion.

In the biodiversity focal area, the GEF has focused its support through operational programs (OPs) classified according to ecosystem types: Arid and Semi-Arid Zone Ecosystems (OP1); Coastal, Marine, and Freshwater Ecosystems (OP2); Forest Ecosystems (OP3); and Mountain Ecosystems (OP4). As a response to guidance from the Conference of Parties (COP) to the Convention on Biological Diversity (CBD), two additional OPs were added later: Integrated Ecosystem Management (OP12) and Conservation and Sustainable Use of Biological Diversity Important to Agriculture (OP13).

Thematically, the GEF biodiversity portfolio has emphasized support for protected areas (PAs). The independent *GEF Biodiversity Program Study 2004* (Dublin and Volonte 2004) and the *Second Overall Performance Study (OPS2)* (GEF 2002) state that the majority of the biodiversity portfolio is focused on in situ conservation, based on supporting existing or new PAs. To a lesser extent the portfolio supports systemic capacity building, setting up sustainable financial instruments, education and awareness, and participatory management involving local stakeholders. Less funding has been allocated to support sustainable use, mainstreaming, and private sector initiatives.

According to the same studies, some of the key positive impacts of biodiversity projects financed by the GEF have been as follows:[2]

Innovative financing: GEF has supported innovative mechanisms, including conservation trust funds, to finance long-term biodiversity conservation by creating a basic level of resource security. In many instances, these institutions have become important building blocks within a diversified financing strategy for PA systems.

Representation and coverage: GEF projects have covered many globally important and threatened sites and ecosystems, thus reflecting the CBD's early emphasis on in situ conservation.

Capacity building: Biodiversity projects have been most successful in building capacity at the individual level, and to a lesser degree at the institutional level. Much of the capacity building has been devoted to conservation and sustainable use, both within PAs and in production landscapes.

Stakeholder participation: Stakeholder participation has been consistently strong in most GEF biodiversity projects.

Cross-cutting issues: GEF biodiversity projects substantially address related cross-cutting issues such as land degradation. Close synergies have been developed between biodiversity conservation activities and those aimed at preventing deforestation and desertification.

Science and technology issues: Many projects have substantially addressed science and technology issues.

The lessons learned in these studies also point to weaknesses in the portfolio, as outlined below:

Addressing root causes of biodiversity loss: Narrowly focused, individual site-specific projects have largely failed to address root causes of biodiversity loss, including economic and social policies. Project links to social and political aspects of sustainable development have been poorly developed and not mainstreamed.

Sectoral linkages: The portfolio exhibits weak links to other sectors of the economy that influence project success. The portfolio is overly structured toward individual projects, with a tendency for biodiversity to be stand-alone, resulting in poor mainstreaming within other sectors.

Funding patterns: In some cases, funding patterns have been incompatible with the absorptive capacity of project areas, of implementing or partner institutions, or with long-term needs.

Project sustainability: Only a few projects have substantially addressed sustainability. There is no system of post-completion assessments; therefore, it is difficult to establish whether or not results and institutional gains were continued after project completion.

Project design and objectives: There is a tendency for rigid project management design structures that do not allow for flexibility and innovation in project implementation. Unrealistic project objectives, including lack of time and funds to achieve objectives fully, have reduced benefits.

Private sector: There has been a failure to realize fully and disseminate innovative financing mechanisms and to strengthen private sector involvements in biodiversity.

Measuring results: Accurately and quantitatively measuring the impact of funding for biodiversity has proved to be difficult, because the majority of projects have not established a baseline against which results can be measured.

The GEF in Its Second Decade: Emerging Strategic Directions

Within the overarching guidance of the CBD, and building on the lessons learned (as summarized above from OPS2, project and program-level monitoring and evaluation [M&E], and issue-specific M&E studies), the key recommendations set out in box 2.1 form the basis for the emerging directions for the GEF in its second decade.

The emerging directions directly respond to the guidance received from the Conference of the Parties to the CBD. They complement, but do not replace existing GEF policies, procedures, and operational programs, emphasizing areas where desirable outcomes will be actively sought and building upon existing eligibility requirements.

Box 2.1
Emerging Directions for the GEF

- Place greater emphasis on the sustainability of results and the potential for replication.

- Move beyond the current project-based emphasis, where appropriate, to more strategic approaches that systematically target country-enabling environments to address biodiversity conservation over the long term.

- Insert biodiversity within other sectors through mainstreaming it in the wider sustainable development context.

- Engage with the private sector more effectively where appropriate.

- Increase support for CBD objectives on sustainable use and benefit sharing.

- Address stakeholder participation more systematically.

- Continue to strengthen the role of Implementing Agencies as brokers in the development agenda within the context of country-driven Poverty Reduction Strategy Papers, Country Assistance Strategies, and other such tools.

- Improve dissemination of tools, lessons learned, and best practices among broader audiences.

Strategic Priorities during the Third Replenishment of the GEF

The following four strategic priorities were adopted to guide the investment of the US$800 million allocated to biodiversity during the years 2003–6. These were designed to allow for operational flexibility, and depend on demand and relevant absorptive capacities as well as country contexts. They were established in relation to agreed phasing of long-term programmatic support.

Strategic Priority 1:
Catalyzing Sustainability of Protected Areas

Protected areas remain the critical foundation of biodiversity conservation worldwide, and as such, they continue to be supported as a major thrust of GEF-3. A total of US$400 million has been allocated to this priority in GEF-3. The priority encompasses the achievement of ecological, institu-

tional, social, political, and financial sustainability in the context of national-level PA systems.

Until now, individual projects have focused on building capacity and management effectiveness within the context of individual PAs, with limited attention to the long-term capacity and policy maturity that underpins the sustainability of PA systems. A shift has now been implemented toward a more comprehensive approach based on support for achieving sustainability of PA systems. This shift does not preclude support for individual PAs, provided that:

- individual support is justified within country contexts and demonstrates replication effects that contribute towards the maturation of a national-level system of PAs;[3]
- such a PA contains globally important biodiversity that is critically at risk and in need of immediate attention; or
- such a project demonstrates specific interventions such as public-private sector and/or community-indigenous group partnerships that are context driven and cannot be immediately replicated outside of the project.

The key objective of this priority is to conserve biodiversity through the expansion, consolidation, and rationalization of national PA systems. Its operational focus is flexible and is based on a thorough understanding of key strengths and weaknesses at the systemic and national institutional levels, and on how any given individual intervention contributes toward long-term sustainability within a PA systems context. The following list illustrates but does not constitute an exhaustive list of the types of operational activities that the GEF is supporting:

- *Demonstration and implementation of innovative financial mechanisms:* Promote the development and capitalization of conservation trust funds, systems of payments for environmental services, easements, debt-for-nature swaps, and certification processes and other mechanisms; internalize PA economic values within other government agencies (for example, ministries of agriculture, fisheries, industry, tourism, and finance).

■ *Capacity building for long-term sustainability:* Support activities that further develop institutional, managerial, and financial sustainability from both private and public sources; build systemic capacity through legislation, policy, and enabling activities to allow PAs to function effectively at the system and/or individual level; build institutional capacity to improve all aspects of management; and build individual capacity through targeted training to maximize skills for sustainability.

■ *Catalyzing community-indigenous initiatives:* Promote the participation of local community and indigenous groups in the design, implementation, management, and monitoring of projects to promote biodiversity conservation and sustainable use, through established frameworks such as biosphere reserves, land-use zoning (including corridors) and conservation areas for community/indigenous peoples; and promote broad stakeholder participation and comanagement between government and local communities for PAs where such management models are appropriate.

■ *Removing barriers to facilitate public-private partnerships:* Support policy reform and/or incentives to catalyze engagement of the private sector to attain improved financial sustainability of PAs; and assist the private sector in the development of innovative ventures that demonstrate commercial profit and biodiversity benefit within the context of PAs, recognizing that achieving financial sustainability across PA systems is a long-term proposition and that private sector involvement and innovative financial arrangements are therefore likely to be location- and context-specific.

Strategic Priority 2: Mainstreaming Biodiversity in Production Landscapes and Sectors

This is the second major GEF priority and was the focus of the Cape Town workshop on biodiversity. A total of US$260 million has been allocated within GEF-3, and this volume will have a strong influence on the way these resources are invested.

There is an ever more pressing need to mainstream biodiversity conservation within production systems where biodiversity faces the most critical threats. Evaluations have shown that GEF leverage in the mainstreaming of biodiversity has been limited, and that the emphasis should be on fostering broad-based integration of biodiversity conservation within the broader development agenda, through capacity building and demonstration projects.

The objective of this priority is to integrate biodiversity conservation in agriculture, forestry, fisheries, tourism, and other production systems and sectors to secure national and global environmental benefits. Given the broad character of mainstreaming, the operational emphasis is flexible, to allow for the development of tailored activities based on an understanding of country context, biodiversity conservation problems, opportunities, and demand. Consistent with the GEF's operational strategy, on-the-ground activities focus on areas of high global biodiversity, unless clear and measurable replication can be shown to result in global biodiversity gains elsewhere through the transformation of markets and demand. The following are examples of the types of activities that the GEF is considering. Since this is an emerging area of knowledge, it is expected that the focus of this priority will become sharper as new information emerges:

■ *Facilitating the mainstreaming of biodiversity within production systems:* Support will be provided for the development of the systemic and institutional capacities of government agencies and other stakeholders to secure biodiversity conservation by, for example, enabling legislation to remove barriers; policy reform or creation of new institutional structures and management procedures and relevant knowledge; and partnership building between agencies, local communities, and the private sector.

■ *Developing market incentive measures:* Support will be provided for innovative market incentive structures (for example, demand- and supply-side interventions such as certification of suppliers, purchasing agreements, and codes of conduct) to catalyze market forces. In doing so, the GEF will seek to develop partnerships with private sector stakeholders, small and medium-scale enterprises, and others to catalyze the development of innovative processes and activities that improve market efficiency and the ability to provide biodiversity and productive system gains.

■ *Demonstration:* Support will be provided for demonstration projects with high replication value.

The GEF recognizes that there are no uniform or quick solutions for mainstreaming within production systems. Projects will therefore target country interventions based on absorptive capacities and broad-based country demand, extending into line ministries and other sectors. In doing so, the GEF, through its implementing and executing agencies and other multilateral and bilateral stakeholders, will seek strong and sustained complementarities with their ongoing and planned programs and processes (for example, Poverty Reduction Strategy Papers and Country Assistance Strategies) in order strategically to maximize leverage of limited GEF funds. Although this direction presents higher challenges and risks, it also promises to generate sustainable impacts over the long term.

Strategic Priority 3: Capacity Building for the Implementation of the United Nations Convention on Biological Diversity, Cartagena Protocol on Biosafety

There is a recognition of the potential risks posed by modified living organisms, and biosafety therefore constitutes a high priority for recipient countries. This priority is also a response to guidance from the CBD and the Intergovernmental Committee for the Cartagena Protocol.

The objective of this priority is to build capacity for the implementation of the Cartagena Protocol on Biosafety.[4] Some of the types of operational activities that the GEF will consider are those related to:

■ *Developing systemic and institutional capacity building for biosafety:* Support will be provided

to countries for the development and implementation of national biosafety frameworks and enabling activities, including development and training in risk assessment and management of modified living organisms, with the participation of relevant government sectors such as agriculture, fisheries, forestry, industry, environment, education, manufacturing, trade, and health, as well as community and private sector stakeholders.

A total of US$75 million has been allocated to this priority.

Strategic Priority 4: Generation and Dissemination of Best Practices for Addressing Current and Emerging Biodiversity Issues

GEF evaluations have shown that lessons and best practices need to be better understood and more widely disseminated both internally and externally to produce further improvements in project design, implementation, and results. Furthermore, emerging biodiversity issues very often need to be addressed in the form of pilots before clear operational guidance and good practice are fully understood.

The key objective will be to improve the effectiveness of analysis, synthesis, and dissemination of best practices, innovative approaches, and new tools from projects and programs to improve the sustainability of GEF impacts in the biodiversity focal area. This objective will be cross-cutting and will address best practice in priorities 1 to 3, with a distinct emphasis on directions 1 and 2, in accordance with importance and financial allocations, and within the context of guidance from the COP of the CBD.[5]

The emphasis will be on best practices and making information available in a timely manner to enable a constant cycle of development and cross-fertilization of ideas, in order to improve the sustainability of project and programmatic interventions. Regional synthesis will be encouraged when comparative lessons provide added value or when economies of scale can be achieved. The following illustrate, but do not constitute an exhaustive list of, the types of operational activities the GEF will consider:

■ *Improving analysis, compilation, and dissemination of best practice:* Provide support for gathering and dissemination of information on best practice among Implementing and Executing Agencies, country government agencies, and other stakeholders such as nongovernmental organizations (NGOs) and communities, scientific institutions, and the private sector.

■ *Supporting the building of scientific and technical cooperation:* Provide support for knowledge generation and north-south and south-south exchange of information through knowledge networks such as the Clearing House Mechanism (CHM).

■ *Supporting demonstration projects that generate synergies:* Promote synergies between biodiversity, climate change, land degradation, and international waters to produce national and global environmental benefits. Two issues will be of particular interest: vulnerability and adaptation to global change, and demonstration of ecosystem approaches.

A total of $US60 million has been allocated to this priority.

This paper is based on the Biodiversity Strategic Priorities paper approved by the GEF Council in May 2003. The author wishes to recognize the GEF Biodiversity Task Force for producing the information contained herein.

Endnotes

1 Biodiversity Team, Global Environment Facility (GEF), Washington D.C., USA

2 Based on OPS2 findings (GEF 2002) and monitoring and evaluation results.

3 For example, where the PA system is so underdeveloped (as in postconflict situations) that individual PA projects represent the initial step to catalyze sustainability and conserve nationally and globally significant biodiversity.

4 The Cartagena Protocol on Biosafety entered into force in September 2003. The GEF gained some preliminary experience in this new field through the implementation of pilot projects in 18 countries for the development of biosafety frameworks. Once the Protocol was finalized, this activity was extended to cover another 100 countries and is now being implemented through United Nations Environment Programme (UNEP).

5 For example, see UNEP (http://www.unep.org/ bpsp/ts.html) thematic studies on integrating biodiversity into mainstream economic sectors. These documents were part of the GEF-funded United Nations Development Programme-United Nations Environment Programme Biodiversity Planning Support Program (UNEP 2002).

References

CBD (Convention on Biological Diversity). Cartagena Protocol on Biosafety. www.biodiv.org/biosafety/.

Dublin, H.T., and C. Volonte. 2004. *GEF Biodiversity Program Study 2004.* Washington, DC: Global Environment Facility.

GEF (Global Environment Facility). 2002. *Focusing on the Global Environment – The First Decade of the GEF: Second Overall Performance Study (OPS2).* Washington, DC: Global Environment Facility.

UNEP (United Nations Environment Programme). 2002. UNDP-UNEP Biodiversity Planning Support Programme Thematic Studies. www.unep.org/bpsp/ts.html.

3. The Process of Mainstreaming: Conditions, Constraints, and Prospects

Richard M. Cowling[1]

While protected areas (PAs) form the cornerstone of conserving wild nature (Redford and Richter 1999; Rodrigues and others 2004), it is now widely accepted that strict protection alone has no chance of achieving all of the goals and targets required to ensure the persistence of the world's biodiversity (Miller and Hobbs 2002; Rosenzweig 2003). The burden of conserving biodiversity will increasingly fall on sectors traditionally not associated with it, namely, agriculture, forestry, mining, urban development, and others (Burbidge and Wallace 1995; Hutton and Leader-Williams 2003).

The biodiversity community has responded to the challenge of "off-reserve" conservation by devising a number of interrelated concepts, strategies, and mechanisms (for example, incentives, easements, community-based conservation, and mainstreaming). Mainstreaming, the subject of this paper, has become a major strategic direction of the Global Environment Facility (GEF) and is embedded in the Convention on Biological Diversity (CBD) with its "ecosystem approach."

The topic of this paper is the process of mainstreaming: how it is done, when it can and cannot work, and how the process can be improved. It first provides some background on defining and doing mainstreaming, as well as outcomes. This is followed by a tentative framework for the mainstreaming process and evaluation of the elements of that framework, as derived from South African case studies; a list of the elements that constrain mainstream-ing; and finally, suggestions as to how the mainstreaming process can be more effective for biodiversity conservation.

Defining and Achieving Mainstreaming

Mainstreaming is a relative newcomer to the biodiversity lexicon and there is not a large literature to provide perspectives on the definition and use of this term. The September 2004 Cape Town workshop defined the objective of mainstreaming biodiversity thus:

to internalize the goals of biodiversity conservation and the sustainable use of biological resources into economic sectors and development models, policies, and programmes, and therefore into all human behaviour.

This implies, of course, that the norms and practices of the economic sectors are the prevailing view, and that those relating to biodiversity persistence are atypical. This correct—but disturbing—observation is revisited later in this paper.

The basic goal of mainstreaming is to spread the burden of conserving biodiversity across a diverse range of sectors, by identifying "win-win" scenarios, and implementing actions to realize these scenarios. This requires the biodiversity community to form alliances and partnerships with the whole suite of economic sectors and, indeed, all of global corporate capitalism (Daily and Ellison 2002; Johns 2003). Mainstreaming is done by changing the behavior of individuals and organizations through the creation of institutions (including incentives) that bind actors to supporting norms, values, and practices that promote biodiversity persistence. This is not an easy task. Always lurking is the danger that the norms and values of the biodiversity sector become corrupted by those of the economic sectors it seeks to infiltrate (Oates 1998; Orr 2002a; Collar 2003).

Mainstreaming interventions may happen at all scales of organization and geography (for example, from encouraging backyard biodiversity in a neighborhood to the impact of a multilateral environmental agreement on the global ocean transport system). Similarly, a wide range of actors will bear the costs and enjoy the benefits, material and spiritual, associated with mainstreaming; and these will accrue over short and long time scales. With regard to scale, it is probably wise to encourage the "nutcracker approach" (Lochner and others 2003). In this approach, local level (bottom-up) perspectives provide insights as to what is constraining behavioral change, and higher level (top-down) perspectives provide mechanisms for securing behavior change via legislation, policy, and other institutional arrangements. Interaction between levels is crucial for success. However, democratic and accountable governance is required in order to achieve effective integration between organizational levels.

It is likely that mainstreaming can be more easily achieved in some situations than others. Relevant lessons have been learned in community-based conservation, which has struggled for many years to mainstream biodiversity into the development requirements of the rural poor. These lessons (see for example, Wells and Brandon 1993; Infield and Adams 1999; Adams and Hulme 2001; Mahanty 2002; and Sayer and Campbell 2004) suggest that it will be easier to get biodiversity mainstreamed into sectors where the following factors are in place: demand for resources does not exceed the sustainable supply, the material benefits of sustainable use or conservation are direct and immediate, there are

few actors, governance is democratic and accountable, and there are supportive institutions. This combination of conditions is quite rare, and efforts should be made to get the prerequisites in place before intervening.

What are the desired outcomes of mainstreaming? Borrowing from the gray literature—published mainly by the World Bank—Pierce and others (2002) identified the following list:

- the incorporation of biodiversity considerations into policies governing sectoral activities
- the simultaneous achievement of gains in biodiversity and gains in an economic sector (the "win-win" scenario)
- the recognition of sectoral activity as being based on, or dependent on, the sustainable use of biodiversity
- sectoral activities in certain situations result in overall gains for biodiversity, exceeding biodiversity losses.

Examples of nascent and successful mainstreaming interventions are provided by Daily and Ellison (2002), Pierce and others (2002), and Rosenzweig (2003). But further debate is required on defining the desired outcomes of mainstreaming. The identification of measurable outcomes is essential for monitoring and evaluation programs designed to assess the effectiveness of mainstreaming interventions.

Toward a Framework for Mainstreaming

A first attempt to develop a framework for the mainstreaming process was made at the World Bank-funded Giant's Castle workshop, held in South Africa, in June 2001 (Pierce and others 2002). Three points are worth noting regarding this workshop: (1) social scientists were very poorly represented among the contributors; (2) contributors were encouraged to present their case studies as narratives, stressing the experiential rather than the analytical aspects; and (3) of the 11 case studies considered, 5 were in the urban and landscape planning sector, 4 in the natural resource (including agriculture) sector, and 3 in the conservation sector; the manufacturing, mining, and transport sectors were not represented, nor were (with one exception) interventions on communal lands.

Figure 3.1
A Framework for the Process of Mainstreaming

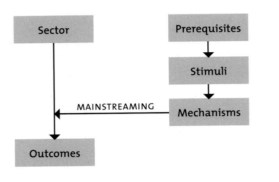

Source: Adapted from Cowling, Pierce, and Sandwith (2002).

Cowling, Pierce, and Sandwith (2002) devised a framework for the mainstreaming process, based on the experiences documented in the case studies. The framework therefore has an empirical or inductive rather than a theoretical foundation. It comprises four major components: prerequisites, stimuli, mechanisms, and outcomes (figure 3.1). These are defined thus:

■ *prerequisites:* elements without which mainstreaming cannot happen
■ *stimuli:* elements external and internal to the sector that catalyse awareness of the need for mainstreaming
■ *mechanisms:* the actual activities that seek to effect mainstreaming
■ *outcomes:* the measurable indicators of mainstreaming effectiveness.

Cowling, Pierce, and Sandwith (2002) describe the mainstreaming process as follows (p. 144): "Given that certain prerequisites are in place, a set of specific stimuli can catalyse activities which then lead to the identification of appropriate mechanisms, with the net result that effective mainstreaming, as measured by outcomes, will happen." The inductive framework is thus formulated as a predictive one—a theory of mainstreaming in the making.

In order to distill the key elements of the mainstreaming process, Cowling, Pierce, and Sandwith (2002) identified categories within each of the framework components (prerequisites and so forth) and summed the score across all case studies for each category. Examples of categories in the prerequisite component are: "adequate institutional capacity," "scientific knowledge and understanding," and "effective NGO involvement." I simplified the results further by collapsing categories. For example, I collapsed "adequate institutional capacity," "effective NGO involvement," and "commitment of stakeholders/champions" into "organizational and institutional capacity."

The results of this analysis are shown in table 3.1. The most frequently cited prerequisites were awareness and knowledge of biodiversity issues, and adequate capacity. To this list has been added good governance, an element essential for effective conservation interventions (Smith and others 2003).[2] There is nothing new here; an examination of the lessons learned literature in any aspect of conservation would confirm the importance of these elements for enabling interventions (see, for example, Wells and Brandon 1993; Infield and Adams 1999; and Mahanty 2002).

Among developing countries, South Africa is unusual in its high level of skills in biodiversity science, and its capacity to undertake research and implement actions in the conservation sector (Huntley 1997). Until the emergence of a democratic state in 1994, however, governance structures and institutions were not democratic; and they lacked transparency and accountability. The establishment of democracy

Table 3.1:
The Most Frequently Cited Elements Associated with Three Components of a Mainstreaming Framework

Prerequisites	Stimuli	Mechanisms
Democratic and accountable governance	Improved governance	Effective communication
Awareness and knowledge	Resource decline	Strengthening institutional capacity
Organizational and institutional capacity	Socioeconomic incentives	Enabling legislation and policy

Source: Developed from the analysis of South African case studies from Cowling and others (2002).

introduced new and significant opportunities for mainstreaming biodiversity, and all the case studies cited improved governance as a stimulus for mainstreaming. For the first time, South Africa's global biodiversity contributions and responsibilities were formally acknowledged, and access to support from international agencies was possible.

More important, however, the new politicians and civil servants were committed to democratic practices, and open to biodiversity as a source of socioeconomic development. They provided the environment for participation by civil society in developing legislation and policy that was biodiversity friendly. The general point here is that democratic and accountable governance is essential for a process as complex as mainstreaming (Stephens, Brown, and Thornley 2002).

The other stimuli frequently cited in the South African case studies (see table 3.1) were resource decline (and the concern this engendered) and the identification of socioeconomic incentives for biodiversity conservation (for example, in the burgeoning tourism sector post-1994). Indeed, the linkage to socioeconomic delivery is, and will remain, a key stimulus for mainstreaming biodiversity in the developing world.

Interestingly, the most frequently cited mechanism for mainstreaming (table 3.1) was effective communication of the issues to key stakeholders, including politicians. While communication was invariably part of a package of mechanisms (the others most

often being capacity strengthening and the development of enabling legislation and policy), the case studies showed convincingly that communicating the issues in language that was comprehensible to stakeholders was absolutely essential for initiating the implementation of mainstreaming actions (Jepson and Canney 2003; Johns 2003).

As mentioned earlier, much more thought needs to be given to identifying measurable mainstreaming outcomes. Clearly, in the spirit of the "win-win" aspirations of the mainstreaming process, attention must be given to both biodiversity and socioeconomic indicators (Margoulis and Salafsky 1998; Stephens, Brown, and Thornley 2002).

Constraints on Mainstreaming

Mainstreaming biodiversity into sectors that have previously ignored or marginalized environmental concerns is a difficult process. The prerequisites or enabling factors for effective mainstreaming have already been discussed. Thus, poor governance (Smith and others 2003), weak capacity of organizations and institutions in all spheres of government and civil society (Wells and Brandon 1993; Infield and Adams 1999; Steiner, Kimball, and Scanton 2003), and a lack of scientific knowledge about biodiversity issues (Raven and Wilson 1992) are all major constraints to mainstreaming. Some additional constraining factors are discussed further on in this section.

Another major constraint for mainstreaming biodiversity is that the rhythm and run of unrestrained market economies are inherently in conflict with those of ecosystems (Orr 2002a). According to Orr (2002a, p. 107), "Markets, driven by the logic of self interest, are intended to maximize profits and minimize costs for the owners of capital in the short term. Ecosystems, in contrast, operate by the laws of thermodynamics and processes of evolution and ecology that are played out over the long term." In short, the national and international goals of economic growth and biodiversity conservation are frequently in conflict (Czech 2003). Can biodiversity concerns really be taken seriously by sectors that operate along such completely different lines?

There are, of course, cases where the sustainable management of a resource is compatible with market forces (Adams and Hulme 2001), or where the introduction of incentives can effectively secure sustainability (Hutton and Leader-Williams 2003). However, deeper examination indicates that even in some of the best publicized cases of mainstreaming, such as ecotourism (for example, Gossling 1999) and certification of forest products (for example, Gullison 2003), success is tenuous.

Another constraint to mainstreaming is the dwindling awareness of biodiversity among the citizenry of most countries of the world, including many developed ones (Orr 2002a; Balmford and others 2002). In today's highly urbanized world of short attention spans and vicarious thrills, people have become disconnected from nature (Pyle 2003). The human-biodiversity connection may be stronger in developing countries where many people still have regular contact with wild nature. However, with increasing urbanization and the global roll-out of consumer culture, circumstances are changing rapidly in even the most remote of developing nations. How can we hope to mainstream biodiversity when most people do not know what biodiversity is or how it affects their lives?

Overcoming the constraints on mainstreaming represents a major challenge. The key message is: Invest in overcoming these barriers before initiating any mainstreaming interventions. This will be a long and difficult process (involving the transformation of the world economic order!), which will not be suited to the short time frames and logical frameworks so important to donors.

Mainstreaming for a Sustainable Future

Given these rather formidable constraints, what are the prospects for mainstreaming? In this, the final section of the paper, the focus is on a few issues that could have some bearing on how mainstreaming is taken into the future. Most of the points made here are discussed in more detail by Orr (2002a, b) and Pyle (2003).

The first issue is the flawed conceptualization of sustainable development used by most governments, nongovernmental organizations (NGOs), and other actors. There are three main models of sustainable development, based on economic, social, and environmental concerns (figure 3.2). The so-called three-legged-stool model envisages the environmental, social, and economic "legs" as equal foundations for sustainability. This model prevails today, being entrenched in the CBD and underpinning the ecosystem approach and the Millennium Ecosystem Assessment. To the left of this in figure 3.2 is the economic rationalist model of sustainable development, which is based on the notion that a healthy environment is dependent on a buoyant economy (Brunckhorst 1998). To the right is the strong sustainability model, which acknowledges that human well-being depends fundamentally on the maintenance of critical natural capital, the features of our natural environment that cannot be replaced by manufactured capital (Ekins and others 2003). Thus, the foundation for social and economic sustainability should be a healthy environment (Orr 2002b; Dawe and Ryan 2003).

Mainstreaming will only be comprehensively effective when all actors accept the concept of strong sustainability. Ultimately, biodiversity concerns should become the mainstream; and it should be incumbent on economic sectors to ensure that their activities are not in conflict with these, rather than the other way around. Although this makes good sense for the survival of human and other species, it is going to take some time and considerable effort (and perhaps a few disasters) before we can expect any real commitment to the "biodiversity as the mainstream" concept.

A feature of human endeavor that is definitely not compatible with strong sustainability is the "perpetual growth model" of neoclassical economics (Orr 2002a; Nadeau 2003). For some time now, ecological economists have been arguing that economic health does not require growth in material consumption (Daly 1992). What is clear is that the establishment of a consumer-crazed culture across the entire world is simply not feasible, let alone sustainable. One only has to look at the devastating impacts of rapid economic growth in China on the forests of Southeast Asia (Sun, Katsigris, and White 2004). We, the human inhabitants of the world, need collectively to plan our descent from the consumer culture that is gaining ascendancy everywhere (Orr 2002a, b). At present, the prospects for this look bleak.

Many of the difficulties facing mainstreaming have to do with the ignorance of ordinary people about the importance of biodiversity to their livelihoods. The biodiversity community has failed dismally to communicate its messages effectively. This is largely because of the use of inappropriate media, norms, values, and messages in most communications. Communication needs to strike the right emotional chords by telling stories that touch people's values (Freyfogle and Newton 2002; Jepson and Canney 2003; Johns 2003). Why, one might ask, have we failed so badly when the advertising industry has been so successful in convincing people to buy all

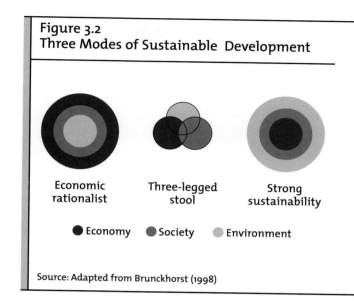

Figure 3.2
Three Modes of Sustainable Development

Economic rationalist · Three-legged stool · Strong sustainability

● Economy ● Society ● Environment

Source: Adapted from Brunckhorst (1998)

manner of goods and services that either they do not need or are downright harmful to their health and well-being? Perhaps the biodiversity sector needs to take a leaf out of the advertising industry's book and start investing in using the media more effectively to change human behavior.

Conclusions

Mainstreaming biodiversity into other sectors as a means of seeking solutions to biodiversity loss is a challenging activity. We should not underestimate the difficulties of achieving the triple bottom line of social, economic, and environmental sustainability, especially in the context of a market-driven, perpetual growth economy. At present, biodiversity is a sidestream, still viewed by most as a luxury (Martens, Rotmans, and de Groot 2003). Ultimately, we would like to see biodiversity as the mainstream, but this will take time. In the meantime, we must work toward solutions by being innovative, reflective, adaptable, and patient.

Endnotes

1   Botany Department and Terrestrial Ecology Research Unit, Nelson Mandela Metropolitan University, Port Elizabeth, South Africa

2   It is interesting that the contributors to the Giant's Castle workshop document (Pierce and others 2002) overlooked good governance as a prerequisite for mainstreaming. Despite the racist policies of the apartheid regime, and the negative impacts these had on South Africa's biodiversity (Hoffman and Ashwell 2001), there has been a long history of efficient (though not transparent and accountable) governance in the conservation sector in areas designated for white control (see, for example, Hughes 2002). This may have contributed to the oversight. All contributors identified as a major stimulus for mainstreaming, the improvement in governance following the 1994 democratic elections.

References

Adams, W. M., and D. Hulme. 2001. "If Community Conservation is the Answer in Africa, What is the Question?" *Oryx* 35: 193-200.

Balmford A., L. Clegg, T. Coulson, and J. Taylor. 2002. "Why conservationists should heed Pokémon." *Science* 295, 2367.

Brunckhorst, D.J. 1998. "Guest Editorial: Creating Institutions to Ensure Sustainable Use of Resources." *Habitat International* 22: 347-54.

Burbidge, A. A., and K. J. Wallace. 1995. "Practical Methods of Conserving Biodiversity." In R.A. Bradstock, T.D. Auld, D.A. Keith, R.T. Kingsford, D. Lunney, and D.P. Sivertsen, eds. *Conserving Biodiversity: Threats and Solutions*. Sydney, Australia: Surrey Beatty & Sons, pp. 11-26.

Collar, N.J. 2003. "Beyond Value: Biodiversity and the Freedom of the Mind." *Global Ecology & Biogeography* 12: 265-69.

Cowling, R.M., S.M. Pierce, and T. Sandwith. 2002. "Conclusions: The Fundamentals of Mainstreaming Biodiversity." In S.M. Pierce, R.M. Cowling, T. Sandwith, and K. MacKinnon, eds. *Mainstreaming Biodiversity in Development: Case Studies from South Africa*. Washington, DC: World Bank, pp. 143-53.

Czech, B. 2003. "Technological Progress and Biodiversity Conservation: A Dollar Spent, A Dollar Burned." *Conservation Biology* 17(5): 1455-57.

Daily, G.C., and K. Ellison. 2002. *The New Economy of Nature: The Quest to Make Conservation Profitable*. Washington, DC: Island Press.

Daly, H.E. 1992. "Allocation, Distribution, and Scale: Towards an Economics That Is Efficient, Just, and Sustainable." *Ecological Economics* 6: 185-93.

Dawe, N.K., and K.I. Ryan. 2003. "The Faulty Three-Legged-Stool Model of Sustainable Development." *Conservation Biology* 17 (5): 1458-60.

Ekins, P., S. Simon, L. Deutsch, C. Folke, and R. de Groot. 2003. "A Framework for the Practical Application of the Concepts of Critical Natural Capital and Strong Sustainability." *Ecological Economics* 44: 165-85.

Freyfogle, E.T., and J.L. Newton. 2002. "Putting Science into Place." *Conservation Biology* 16 (4): 863-73.

Gossling, S. 1999. "Ecotourism: A Means to Safeguard Biodiversity and Ecosystem Functions?" *Ecological Economics* 29: 303-20.

Gullison, R.E. 2003. "Does Forest Certification Conserve Biodiversity?" *Oryx* 37: 153-65.

Hoffman, T., and A. Ashwell. 2001. *Nature Divided: Land Degradation in South Africa*. Cape Town, South Africa: University of Cape Town Press.

Hughes, G. R. 2002. "Democratization: Biodiversity for All People: A Case Study from KwaZulu-Natal." In S.M. Pierce, R.M. Cowling, T. Sandwith, and K. MacKinnon, eds. *Mainstreaming Biodiversity in Development: Case Studies from South Africa*. Washington, DC: World Bank, pp. 67-78.

Huntley, B.J. 1997. "Foreword." In R.M. Cowling, D.M. Richardson, and S.M. Pierce, eds. *Vegetation of Southern Africa*. Cambridge, UK: Cambridge University Press, pp. xxvii-xxviii.

Hutton, J.M., and N. Leader-Williams. 2003. "Sustainable Use and Incentive-Driven Conservation: Realigning Human and Conservation Interests." *Oryx* 37: 215-26.

Infield, M., and W.A. Adams. 1999. "Institutional Sustainability and Community Conservation: A Case Study from Uganda." *Journal of International Development* 11: 305-15.

Jepson, P., and S. Canney. 2003. "Values-Led Conservation." *Global Ecology & Biogeography* 12: 271-74.

Johns, D.M. 2003. "Growth, Conservation, and the Necessity of New Alliances." *Conservation Biology* 17 (5): 1229-37.

Lochner, P., A. Weaver, C. Gelderblom, R. Peart, T. Sandwith, and S. Fowkes. 2003. "Aligning the Diverse: The Development of a Biodiversity Conservation Strategy for the Cape Floristic Region." *Biological Conservation* 112: 29-43.

Mahanty, S. 2002. "Conservation and Development Interventions as Networks: The Case of the India Ecodevelopment Project, Karnataka." *World Development* 30: 1369-86.

Margoulis, R., and N. Salafsky. 1998. *Measures of Success: Designing, Managing, and Monitoring Conservation and Development Projects.* Washington, DC: Island Press.

Martens, P., J. Rotmans, and D. de Groot. 2003. "Biodiversity: Luxury or Necessity?" *Global Environ. Change* 13: 75-81.

Miller, J.R., and R.J. Hobbs. 2002. "Conservation Where People Live and Work." *Conservation Biology* 16: 330-37.

Nadeau, R.L. 2003. *The Wealth of Nature: How Mainstream Economics Has Failed the Environment.* New York: Columbia University Press.

Oates, J.F. 1998. *Myth and Reality in the Rain Forest.* Berkeley, CA: University of California Press.

Orr, D.W. 2002a. *The Nature of Design: Ecology, Culture, and Human Intention.* New York: Oxford University Press.

———. 2002b. "Four Challenges to Sustainability." *Conservation Biology* 16: 1457-60.

Pierce, S.M., R.M. Cowling, T. Sandwith, and K. MacKinnon, eds. 2002. *Mainstreaming Biodiversity in Development: Case Studies from South Africa.* Washington, DC: World Bank.

Pyle, R.M. 2003. "Nature Matrix: Reconnecting People and Nature." *Oryx* 37: 206-14.

Raven, P.H., and E.O. Wilson. 1992. "A Fifty-Year Plan for Biodiversity Surveys." *Science* 258: 1099-100.

Redford K.H., and B.D. Richter. 1999. "Conservation of Biodiversity in a World of Use." *Conservation Biology* 13: 1246-56.

Rodrigues, A.S.L., S.J. Andelman, M.I. Bakarr, L. Boitani, T.M. Brooks, R.M. Cowling, L.D.C. Fishpool, G.A.B. da Fonseca, K.J. Gaston, M. Hoffmann, J.S. Long, P.A. Marquet, J.D. Pilgrim, R.L. Pressey, J. Schipper, W. Sechrest, S.N. Stuart, L.G. Underhill, R.W. Waller, M.E.J. Watts, and X. Yan. 2004. "Effectiveness of the Global Protected Area Network in Representing Species." *Nature* 428: 640-43.

Rosenzweig, M.L. 2003. *Win-Win Ecology: How the Earth's Species Can Survive in the Midst of Human Enterprise.* New York: Oxford University Press.

Sayer, J., and B.M. Campbell. 2004. *The Science of Sustainable Development: Local Livelihoods and the Global Environment.* Cambridge, UK: Cambridge University Press.

Smith, R.J., R.D.J. Muir, M.J. Walpole, A. Balmford, and N. Leader-Williams. 2003. "Governance and the Loss of Biodiversity." *Nature* 426: 67-70.

Steiner, A., L.A. Kimball, and J. Scanton. 2003. "Global Governance for the Environment and the Role of Multilateral Environmental Agreements in Conservation." *Oryx* 37: 227-37.

Stephens T., D. Brown, and N. Thornley. 2002. "Measuring Conservation Achievement: Concepts and Their Application over the Twizel Area." In *Science for Conservation 2002.* Wellington, New Zealand: Department of Conservation.

Sun X., E. Katsigris, and A. White. 2004. "Meeting China's Demand for Forest Products: An Overview of Import Trends, Ports of Entry, and Supplying Countries, with Emphasis on the Asia-Pacific Region." In *Forest Trends.* Washington, DC: Chinese Center for Agricultural Policy and Centre for International Forestry Research.

Wells, M.P., and K.E. Brandon. 1993. "The Principles and Practice of Buffer Zones and Local Participation in Biodiversity Conservation." *Ambio* 22: 157-62.

Part 2.

Case Studies in Production Landscapes

4. Mainstreaming Biodiversity Conservation Initiatives in New Zealand

Robert McCallum[1]

New Zealand has some 33 percent of its terrestrial landmass set aside as protected natural area. Despite this, the country's biodiversity, characterized by high levels of endemicity, is under siege from the wealth of plant and animal pests that have been introduced, primarily during the 170 years of European colonization.

To prevent extinctions, New Zealand's many islands are steadily being returned to pest-free status for use as "biodiversity banks," as the mainland indigenous biodiversity continues to decline. Biodiversity conservation on public land is undertaken by a single integrated conservation management government agency, the Department of Conservation (DOC). The New Zealand Biodiversity Strategy (NZBS) aims to broaden this approach to ensure that biodiversity conservation is undertaken as much as possible on private land and through funding other than that provided through core government expenditure.

New Zealand's economic backbone is the foreign exchange generated by a vibrant tourism industry. This industry has capitalized on a "clean green" image that utilizes the country's conservation areas and panoramic landscapes as its primary draw. Ecotourism and adventure tourism have always been reliant on public conservation land as their industrial base, but are now also utilizing private land with high conservation value for specific tourism initiatives. As the relationship between conservation values and the primary production sector becomes more widely recognized, tourism operators are taking an increasingly strong role in supporting biodiversity conservation on public land, and, more importantly, are mainstreaming biodiversity conservation by extending it onto private land.

This paper examines how, in mainstreaming biodiversity conservation in a New Zealand setting, public land cannot be divorced from private land when defining "production landscapes," with particular reference to the tourism industry. It will also present several examples of case studies that show how the implementation of the key actions listed in the NZBS provides the best way forward to mainstreaming biodiversity conservation into the agricultural, forestry, and tourism industries.

The Biodiversity Context

New Zealand is a primordial biodiversity refugium. As an early breakaway landmass from the continent of Gondwana approximately 80 million years ago, New Zealand developed without any terrestrial mammals, and as a modern storehouse of ancient forest types. Free of predators and browsing animals, New Zealand's birds and plants developed in splendid isolation. This highly specialized environment, with a high level of endemicity, has meant that indigenous species are highly susceptible to browsing and predation by the wealth of introduced plant and animal species. These species were introduced by early Polynesian settlers, and more particularly, by recent European colonizers (about 170 years ago).

As the last significant landmass on earth to be colonized by humans, New Zealand has been ravaged by immigrant killer species.

Although similar in size to Great Britain, New Zealand's population has only recently (in 2004) reached four million. It is a stable democracy with a high standard of living and excellent quality of life. New Zealand was early to engage in setting aside large areas for legal protection, and today has some 33 percent of the terrestrial landmass set aside as protected natural area. This land, nearly nine million hectares, is held under a variety of statutes that provide a broad range of legal protective classifications. Significantly, some 18 percent of the country enjoys a high standard of protection under the classification of national park.

Despite this high degree of protection, biodiversity continues to decline, as conservation managers struggle to find widespread and long-term solutions to dealing with introduced pests such as possums, mustelids, cats, and rats.[2,3] Interim, but perhaps ultimately unsustainable, methods such as the establishment of "mainland islands," the widespread application of vertebrate toxins and the close order management of endangered species have yielded some success.[4] Longer-term conservation management effort is being directed to the eradication of introduced species from many of New Zealand's 281 offshore islands of greater than 5 hectares, in an effort to prepare them as "biodiversity banks" for species at risk of extinction on the mainland.

The Policy Setting

The 1997 report on *The State of New Zealand's Environment* considered that the "threatened" status of over 1,000 known animal, plant, and fungi species was the country's "most pervasive environmental problem" (MfE 1997). This is reflected in the New Zealand government's adoption of "halting the decline of indigenous biodiversity" as one of its 10 strategic priorities (DOC and MfE 2000).

> ### Box 4.1
> ### New Zealand Biodiversity Strategy Initiatives
>
> - The establishment of biodiversity condition and advice funds
> - Increased government funding for national programs to assist landowners and increase the extent of formally protected areas
> - Enhancing the capacity of local government to manage biodiversity at a local level
> - Amending the Resource Management Act (1991) to clarify the role that regional councils and other territorial authorities have in biodiversity conservation management
> - The preparation of a draft national policy statement on indigenous biodiversity.

The government's practical response was to launch the 2000 *New Zealand Biodiversity Strategy: "Our Chance to Turn the Tide,"* a multiagency broad-spectrum approach designed to halt biodiversity decline.[5] This document sets a high-level framework that has nurtured the majority of mainstreaming policy initiatives to date. These initiatives cover a wide spectrum, including a substantive strengthening of resource management legislation, greater focus and effort on conservation management, and a rapid improvement in biosecurity management. Specifically, the strategy contains initiatives such as those highlighted in box 4.1.

The NZBS makes it clear that further gains in biodiversity conservation are likely to be made on private land, and will only be possible with the assistance of landowners, local communities, and corporate sponsors. "Biodiversity is everyone's business…as mutual beneficiaries of New Zealand's biodiversity, we can all play a part in implementing this Strategy; by working in partnerships with and alongside management agencies, businesses, community groups and landowners" (DOC and MfE 2000).[6] While the strategy sets out bold national goals (and a series of key actions) to conserve biodiversity, it does not prescribe the detail of how the actions will be undertaken.

Since involving resource users and owners is critical to the long-term success of the strategy, further, more-detailed work is recommended, particularly in the final development and implementation of a national policy statement on indigenous biodiversity. This statement, to be produced under the 1991 Resource Management Act (RMA 1991) has been in development for a number of years, but has been delayed by the considerable debate between various government agencies and with representatives of the agricultural sector and territorial authorities. The central debate has been around how finely "at risk" is defined, and around the balance between private property rights and public good. Once completed, it is envisaged that the statement will provide a detailed list of "at risk" environments at a national level. Since the statement is being produced under the RMA, it will require local government (territorial authorities) to implement regulatory protection mechanisms for those areas, specifically those in private ownership.

Future mainstreaming initiatives in New Zealand then, are likely to result from the implementation of one of the key actions contained in the NZBS. This is a reflection of both the overarching nature of the strategy and the close interrelationship between primary production and conservation that characterizes the New Zealand biodiversity context. "Increasingly, New Zealand's international reputation and trade opportunities will depend on our performance in maintaining a quality natural environment, of which biodiversity is a key element" (DOC and MfE 2000).

Mainstreaming Biodiversity Conservation

New Zealand poses a unique environment for conservation proponents seeking to improve biodiversity. Paradoxically, despite so much of the landmass being formally protected, mainland biodiversity looks set to decline under the pressure of predation and browsing by introduced mammals. Clearly, future successes in the conservation of biodiversity

are going to have to include initiatives on both public and private land, and are going to rely on the support of a broader range of proponents than just Government agencies, conservation nongovernmental organizations (NGOs) and other "traditional" conservation proponents. Mainstreaming in a New Zealand context is as much about how industries reliant on the conservation estate can contribute to its management and the well-being of its indigenous species as it is about extending DOC-led conservation programs out into privately owned and/or managed landscapes. There are a number of existing examples of both, and the case studies presented in the following sections may provide insight into the potential for future successful mainstreaming of biodiversity conservation into the wider New Zealand production landscape.

Forestry

As a result of the NZBS, the government brought about the effective cessation of indigenous logging in New Zealand by phasing out indigenous forest logging on Crown-owned land.[7] In practical terms, this involved transferring the remaining 130,000 hectares of state-owned forestry enterprise on the West Coast of the South Island to protective management by the Department of Conservation (DOC) in 2001. With 73 percent of the West Coast province under the legal protection of DOC, local communities were concerned about the economic viability of the region. Recent figures, however, suggest that the value of tourism from these areas now exceeds any previous revenue for forest harvest, with broad-scale indigenous forest landscapes providing a powerful draw for tourists.[8]

Exotic logging continues to provide a significant contribution to the New Zealand economy, but forest managers are experiencing a tightening of regulatory controls that attempt to protect biodiversity conservation values, particularly those associated with icon species such as kiwi. Unfortunately, however, the costs associated with these controls are in some instances driving up overall costs to the point where commercial forestry becomes uneconomic and the land is converted into pasture. In this case, regulatory controls designed to protect biodiversity instead act as a disincentive to conservation, with grazed lands supporting minimal conservation values. In areas where forestry has a sound foothold, foresters are working to develop environmental agreements that ensure the protection of riparian margins, the exclusion of indigenous remnants from operational forestry areas, and the utilization of wise management practices in regrowth areas. The driver for these initiatives is an attempt to forge agreements with conservation proponents that would allow the pursuit of "eco-labelling." This in turn attracts a premium at sale for wood products, or potentially lifts nontariff barriers to trade.

Agriculture

There has been a groundswell of government-funded schemes to assist farmers and other private landowners in implementing biodiversity conservation initiatives such as the restoration of natural areas.[9,10] Two of the most successful of these have been the Biodiversity Advice Fund, which supports the provision of advice and information to land managers wanting to improve the condition of biodiversity on private land, and the Biodiversity Condition Fund, which aims to improve and maintain indigenous vegetation, wildlife, and habitats. In 2003, these funds amounted to $NZ2.1 million that was allocated to 105 projects nationally. With applications for 3.8 dollars for each dollar funded, however, the fund was increased to $NZ3.1 million in 2004 and is being reviewed, pending a potential increase in 2006.

Increasingly, private landowners are choosing to protect their land formally through mechanisms such as covenants coordinated by the Queen Elizabeth (QE) II National Trust. The trust offers covenants as a highly effective and adaptable mechanism for protecting significant features and biodiversity values on private land. Since its humble beginnings, the trust has established some 2,000 covenants throughout the country, over a wide range of habitat types, and reports that 95.4 percent of associated vegetative canopy under-storey in

these areas is either stable or improving (QE II National Trust 2004).

Another success is the increasing number of "landcare" groups around the country. These groups typically combine landowners, local Maori, the local territorial authority, and relevant government agencies to carry out initiatives such as localized pest control, the fencing of forest remnants, and the implementation of water and soil conservation activities. On a larger scale, pest control of the country's main introduced browser, the brush-tailed possum, is undertaken both by the DOC for conservation reasons, and by animal health boards to control the spread of bovine tuberculosis (TB). As carriers of TB, possums have catalyzed a relationship between agriculturalists, foresters, horticulturalists, and conservationists. This forced collaboration against a common foe has served as a unifying agent, as groups from different sectors work together to achieve other mutually beneficial conservation and environmental outcomes.

These opportunities for private landowners to improve biodiversity on land under their management will become an important feature for the future management of the valleys and river flats in the South Island. Currently the government is reviewing the tenure of high-country grazing licenses along the spine of the South Island, with many of the low-value grazing areas likely to return to government ownership and control. This has important implications for biodiversity, with up to a further one million hectares of subalpine landscapes likely to be placed in conservation management. The biodiversity conservation values of the valley floors, wetlands, and river terraces, however, are likely to be placed into permanent farming tenure through freehold private ownership, and, as such, are prime candidates for funding through the various conservation initiatives available to private landowners.

Tourism

New Zealand's conservation image is a powerful drawing card. There are few internal tourist destinations that do not feature areas of high conservation value either as a core part of their attraction or as a main backdrop to their activity. Indeed, with such a high proportion of the nation set aside for legal protection, it is inevitable that most New Zealand landscapes contain protected areas. In 2003, some two million tourists spent $US4 billion in New Zealand, which was voted by the Lonely Planet travel organization as the world's top travel destination for the year. Yet despite the fact that tourism generates 16 percent of New Zealand's export earnings and directly employs 1 in 10 New Zealanders, it occupies only some 0.45 percent of the global market (TSG 2001). The opportunities for controlled growth are immense. It is increasingly acknowledged that tourism plays a vitally important part in the nation's economic well-being; and is likely to be an even greater factor in its future economic success—with current predictions by the New Zealand industry of a 30-percent increase in tourism revenue by 2010, and no hint of an easing beyond that.

The New Zealand Tourism Strategy 2010 sets out to prepare the way for the industry's expansion by setting out a general framework under the umbrella philosophy of "Welcome Visitors: Protect our Environment—Celebrate our Culture." The strategy underlines the importance of the sector taking on a larger role in conservation management, which "traditionally has been the responsibility of DOC. However, acting responsibly...offers the tourism sector the opportunity to be, and to be seen as a responsible sector and responsible in the long term" (TSG 2001). The importance of this thinking has been recently demonstrated in the New Zealand Tourism global tourism advertising campaign, "100% Pure New Zealand," which features a range of New Zealand natural settings as tourism destinations. Similarly, the recent production of several large-scale movie productions in New Zealand, including "Lord of the Rings," which was filmed on and around high-value conservation sites, has underlined the fundamental importance of the natural environment to the country brand and most tourism products.

Mainstreaming initiatives by the tourism industry occur on both public and private lands. On public lands, there are currently 1,056 tourism concessions that allow commercial tourism operators to conduct business on land managed for conservation purposes. These businesses pay a concession fee that last year generated total revenues of $NZ5.44 million to the DOC (author's communication with H. Maher, DOC). This yield could potentially be seen as low, given the high use of conservation land for tourism activities. Of the 33.2 million visits to DOC land each year, tourists reported using conservation land for glacier walks (12 percent), glow worm caves (13 percent), jet boating (11 percent), and trekking/tramping/ walking (23 percent) (author's communication with R. Hutchings, DOC). Some of the larger tour operators make contributions to biodiversity conservation over and above those accrued indirectly through their concession fee. For example, Fiordland National Park's primary concessionaire, Real Journeys, sponsors the DOC's endangered Blue Duck research program and notifies potential clients that it will contribute $NZ10 from each booking on certain activities.

Mainstreaming initiatives by the tourism industry on private land are more diversified, and are usually the result of an operator or other beneficiary seeking to protect the biodiversity values that underline their commercial interest. As local communities take "ownership" of biodiversity conservation initiatives, and local economies experience the increase in economic values underpinned by a flourishing tourism industry, biodiversity conservation is viewed as a core part of New Zealand's identity, rather than as a separate government-funded program undertaken only on public conservation land.

As an example, many tourists (5 percent) take the opportunity to view one of the 14 species of penguins found in New Zealand waters. In the township of Oamaru on the South Island's east coast, over 40,000 visitors a year visit the nearby Little Blue Penguin colony located on land managed by the territorial authority. The colony is managed by a community trust and contributes some $NZ4 million per year to the local economy, since the penguins, being nocturnal, require visitors to stay overnight in the town. The trust has been careful to establish a monitoring program to ensure that the tourism operation is not having significant adverse effects on the colony and has supported government research (via DOC) to assist the conservation management of this species. Importantly, as the community recognizes the economic spin-offs of the colony, they are more inclined to act swiftly to minimize threats to the penguins; and more recently, they have begun promoting the town as a tourism destination using the penguins as the primary draw.

A more ambitious example of the types of biodiversity conservation initiative that will be necessary to extend biodiversity conservation management beyond public land is provided by the Maungatautari Ecological Island Restoration Project, outlined in box 4.2. Such projects have the potential to implement the concept of mainstreaming in a New Zealand context.

Given the decline of indigenous species despite the vast array of legally protected areas, the place of species-led conservation mainstreaming initiatives is also important. The high endemicity of New Zealand wildlife assures a keen interest by tourists, particularly in national icon species such as kiwis. Nationally, some 14 tourism operators provide opportunities to view kiwis which, being rare, endangered, and nocturnal, are difficult to see in a natural setting. These "kiwi houses" play an important role as advocates for the conservation of kiwis and other endangered species, by highlighting the decline in biodiversity through introduced pests. Indeed, both government agencies and NGOs use the iconic status of kiwis to strengthen the case for greater resources to be allocated to endangered species conservation initiatives.

A further nonterritorial example is provided by New Zealand's flourishing whale watching industry. With over 50 species of marine mammals frequenting New Zealand waters, whale watching is a popular tourist pastime, with 4 percent of international tourists engaging in a whale watching activity provided by one of the over 100 specialized tourism operators. Legislation provides marine mammals with a high standard of protection, and the industry is subject to strong regulatory control. Tourism operators, however, provide important contributions to marine mammal conservation, both directly, through sponsoring or conducting research on behalf of DOC, and, indirectly, through conservation advocacy and wildlife education initiatives.

The importance of biodiversity conservation to the tourism industry has not yet been fully recognized and has only recently become a feature of the strategic management policy and plans of the tourism sector. It is likely that this will grow rapidly as operators move to protect the cornerstone natural and conservation values that support their industry. Early initiatives have included promoting the Qualmark standards, and encouraging operators to participate in international schemes such as Green Globe, which are voluntary accreditation initiatives

---

Box 4.2
The Maungatautari Ecological Island Restoration Project

A community trust has embarked on an ambitious project to establish a mainland "island" around Maungatautari mountain, an area of approximately 3,500 hectares in the North Island's Waikato district. [11, 12] The island will be created by erecting a 45 kilometer "excluder fence" to create a barrier against introduced predators and browsers. All introduced mammals within the island will then be eradicated, allowing indigenous species to flourish. The $NZ15-16 million cost of establishing the mainland island was prohibitive to this small community, which has elected to use tourism revenue and a staged approach to achieve the overall outcome. Two smaller "cells" of forest (30 hectares and 70 hectares in size) will be established as smaller mainland islands in the first instance. Following the removal of pests, the trust will use reintroduced endangered indigenous species living in a high-quality protected forest as a draw to tourism operators. Supporting infrastructure such as tracks, viewing areas, cafés, and a visitor center will serve as a source of tourism revenue, as well as demonstrating that the mainland island concept is valid for the wider mountain.

that establish quality tourism standards. Qualmark is a New Zealand standard that rates tourism operators on six assessments, including environmental and cultural impacts. It is a first generation attempt to put sustainability into practice. Green Globe 21 is an international certification program in which New Zealand tourism operators lead the world. These standards have been developed by the industry for the industry, but are customer driven, as tourists seek to ensure that their activities are supportive, or at least nondetrimental to environmental and conservation values.

Conclusions

New Zealand provides a unique case study of biodiversity conservation mainstreaming initiatives. The high proportion of the landmass under formal conservation protection has not automatically led to a halt in the decline of indigenous biodiversity. Indeed, in the long term, the future of indigenous biodiversity on the mainland looks bleak, in the absence of a widespread, cost-effective, and timely pest control tool for the large number of vertebrate pests. Short- to medium-term protection of indigenous species on the mainland will entail close-order intensive pest management, or the exclusion of pests through the establishment of artificial mainland islands.

The NZBS provides an excellent overarching strategy for government agencies, NGOs, indigenous tribes, and communities to work together toward halting the decline of biodiversity. The strategy has already led to a number of significant improvements, including the strengthening of legislation,

greater conservation management effort, and biosecurity management. Importantly, it has led to the development and implementation of initiatives on private land that will provide a key component in the halt of biodiversity decline. To date, however, these initiatives have been voluntary and have been sweetened by the provision of central government funds contributing to initiatives on private land. The completion of a national policy statement on indigenous biodiversity is likely to pose regulatory, and unpopular, controls on many landowners, particularly those on land with conservation values considered at risk nationally. The challenge for conservation proponents will be to ease the transition of these restrictions by highlighting both the values of biodiversity conservation to all sectors, and the combined benefits of all contributions to the protection of indigenous biodiversity.

The practical implementation of many mainstreaming efforts will be fuelled by the potential downstream economic benefits flowing from the agricultural, forestry, and, most importantly, tourism sectors. All three sectors will play a key part in extending traditional conservation efforts beyond public land onto private land. The tourism industry plays a key role in the mainstreaming of conservation initiatives in both public and private landscapes. Since the New Zealand tourism industry uses natural landscapes and indigenous species as its primary draw, tourism is likely to retain an important role in advocating for the maintenance of biodiversity management on public conservation land, and to remain an important vehicle for taking biodiversity conservation outside of statutory protected areas.

Endnotes

1   Department of Conservation, Auckland, New Zealand

2   The brush-tailed possum was originally introduced from Australia in an effort to start a lucrative fur trade. Possums have now become New Zealand's single most harmful introduced browser, with some 80 million of them consuming an estimated 22,000 tons of vegetation each night. Possums have detrimental effects on native vegetation, the horticultural industry, exotic forestry, and the agricultural sector.

3   Family *Mustelidae*—in New Zealand, this family includes stoats, ferrets, and weasels.

4   Mainland islands are areas of mainland that have been fenced off with predator-proof fences and then had all introduced species eradicated. Early examples have allowed indigenous biodiversity to thrive, albeit in relatively small areas of land, and at a substantial cost. Mainland islands will pose long-term maintenance challenges for conservation managers.

5   The New Zealand Biodiversity Strategy (NZBS) involves contributions from these New Zealand agencies: Department of Conservation; Ministry for the Environment; Ministry of Agriculture and Forestry; Ministry of Fisheries; Ministry of Maori Development; Ministry of Foreign Affairs and Trade; Ministry of Science, Research, and Technology; State Services Commission; The Treasury; Office of Treaty Settlements; Department of the Prime Minister and Cabinet; Department of Women's Affairs; and Department of Internal Affairs.

6   Helen Clark, Prime Minister of New Zealand, NZ Biodiversity Strategy

7   Indigenous logging has been halted on Crown-owned land. Some residual logging is yet to be completed on Maori-owned land. Landowners can apply for a permit to harvest a maximum of 50 cubic meters every 10 years, but this is uncommon.

8   Environmental tourism initiatives on the West Coast now employ 814 people and generate $NZ212 million per year.

9   These mechanisms include the Queen Elizabeth II National Trust, the New Zealand Nature Heritage Fund, and Nga Whenua Rahui.

10 Between 1990 and 2000, some 236,740 hectares of private land of high conservation value has been formally protected through acquisition, covenants, kawenata, and Maori reservations; most have been fenced (DOC and MfE 2000).

11 The Maungatautari Ecological Island Restoration Project is made up of surrounding landowners, community groups, local iwi (indigenous Maori tribes), territorial authorities, and the Department of Conservation (DOC).

12 The tenure of Maungatautari Mountain is made up of approximately 1,000 hectares of private land, and 2,500 hectares of Crown-owned land held as "Scenic Reserve" and administered by the Waipa District Council.

References

DOC and MfE (Department of Conservation and the Ministry for the Environment). 2000. *The New Zealand Biodiversity Strategy: "Our Chance to Turn the Tide."* Wellington, New Zealand: DOC and MfE.

MfE (Ministry for the Environment). 1997. *The State of New Zealand's Environment.* Wellington, New Zealand: MfE.

QE II (Queen Elizabeth) National Trust. 2004. *Protecting Our Coast and Lakesides on Private Land.* Wellington, New Zealand: QE II National Trust.

TSG (Tourism Strategy Group). 2001. *New Zealand Tourism Strategy 2010.* Wellington, New Zealand: Tourism New Zealand.

Web sites

www.doc.govt.nz (New Zealand Department of Conservation and associated information)

www.biodiversity.govt.nz (New Zealand Biodiversity Strategy and associated information)

5. Mainstreaming Agrobiodiversity

Jeffrey A. McNeely[1]

Global demand for food and fiber is expected to grow by at least 50 percent by 2030, so the challenges to conserving biodiversity in agricultural ecosystems are certain to increase in the coming decades. With increasing human populations and changing consumption patterns as people become wealthier, demand will increase for food, forest, and fisheries production. At the same time, society will demand the protection of wild plant and animal species, as well as the conservation of the ecosystem services upon which all life depends.

The ecological footprint of agriculture on planet Earth is already substantial:

- Nearly half of all temperate broad-leaf forest and tropical and subtropical dry forest, and a third of temperate grass- and shrubland have been lost as wildlife habitat, through conversion to agricultural use (Williams 2003).
- Over half of the world's wetlands—among the planet's most valuable wildlife habitats—have been converted to agriculture.
- Farming has led to significant soil degradation on 16 percent of all crop, pasture, and forestland worldwide, and half of all land within the agricultural extent, thereby affecting the diversity of soil microorganisms (Scherr 1999).
- Excessive use and poor management of crop nutrients, pesticides, and the waste products of penned livestock are a major cause of habitat pollution that can kill wildlife directly or impair reproduction.

Continuing loss of biodiversity is of considerable concern to farmers, who draw on both wild and domestic genetic resources to maintain productivity in their crops. Farmers also depend on pollinators (often from the wild) to enable their crops to ripen and reproduce, use water from watersheds whose productivity is maintained at least partly through biodiversity, and so forth. But how can farmers be encouraged to conserve biodiversity actively as part of their daily work? In fact, such conservation is already being widely practiced (McNeely and Scherr 2003; Imhoff 2003; Swaminathan 2001; Jackson and Jackson 2002); and one can find considerable support for the idea that much of today's biodiversity remains as a result of the actions of farmers over the past 10,000 years (Williams 2003).

On the other hand, agriculture is facing new challenges in meeting expanding production needs within growing environmental constraints. Declining environmental conditions in many parts of the world will make it more difficult to provide more food. Loss of biodiversity, deforestation, water shortages, desertification, soil erosion, global climate change, and various other dynamic factors make it increasingly difficult to improve productivity. Irrigation has historically been an important means of increasing productivity, and the area of irrigated crop lands increased by an average of 2.8 percent per year between 1950 and 1980, but the rate of increase has now declined to only 1.2 percent per year. On a per capita basis, irrigated lands declined by 6 percent between 1978 and 1990 and are expected to contract by a further 12 percent per capita by the year 2010; and irrigation already consumes over 70 percent of the freshwater used by people (89 percent in low-income countries) (Postel 1999). Agricultural land is becoming an increasingly limited resource, and per capita arable land has declined by an average of 1.9 percent per year since 1984. Some agricultural lands are being so abused that they lose much of their agricultural value, while other areas are falling victim to urban sprawl and the spread of industries into farming areas.

In recent decades, the development of new agricultural technologies, such as biotechnology and the expanding use of chemicals, has been driven by the private sector and by economic integration of agricultural processes and products. These technologies have helped to support the quadrupling of the human population over the past 100 years, primarily through enhancing yields on the land most suited to agriculture. When famines occurred, they were not the result of food shortage but of lack of economic access to food supplies. Despite the sincere efforts of some governments and "public goods research" carried out by the Consultative Group on International Agricultural Research (CGIAR), feeding people continues to receive lower priority in the current global food system than does the substantial profit to be made by international trade in "luxury foods," which ironically may have negative impacts on both human and ecosystem health. While governments may claim concern about alleviating poverty, the reality is that they behave as if accumulating wealth were more important.

The Global Biodiversity Assessment (Heywood and Watson 1995), in an extensive review of the literature, concluded that "overwhelming evidence leads to the conclusion that modern commercial agriculture has had a direct negative impact on biodiversity at all levels: ecosystem, species and genetic; and on natural and domestic diversity. On the other hand, the same modern intensive agriculture has made it possible for the ever-increasing human population to be fed without extensive destruction of habitat." Thus agriculture has both positive and negative impacts on biodiversity, and depends on biodiversity for its continued existence. This diversity is currently being threatened by the very activities that depend on it, with habitat conversion being the most serious threat to biodiversity (IUCN 2003).

Based on these findings, it is argued that there is an urgent need for a means of reshaping the food system to emphasize sustainable agriculture, based on nurturing biodiversity rather than unsustainably increasing production at the expense of biodiversity.

Strategies for Mainstreaming Agrobiodiversity

The challenge is to find ways to promote the conservation of biological diversity and the sustainable use of biological resources by farmers, in other words, "mainstreaming agrobiodiversity" (Pagiola and Kellenberg 1997). This section suggests 10 major strategies or tactics for doing so, drawing on examples from various parts of the world.

1. Maintain nondomestic habitats within production landscapes.

Many farmers value the goods and services that are provided by nondomestic habitats found within the farmstead, or in adjacent lands. Designing production landscapes explicitly to enhance production or profitability, while also conserving this wild biodiversity, has been called "ecoagriculture" (McNeely and Scherr 2003). Maintaining hedgerows, natural vegetation along watercourses, patches of forest, and other nondomestic habitats can make a significant contribution to conserving biodiversity across the landscape, even when conserving biodiversity is not a specific objective (Buskirk and Willi 2004).

For example, in Sonoma County, California, a premium wine grape-growing region, Hilty and Merenlender (2004) examined mammalian predator use of 21 riparian corridors classified as denuded, narrow, or wide, according to the width of the remaining natural vegetation. Mammalian predators were 11 times more common in riparian areas than in vineyards, with more native mammalian predator species found in wide corridors than in narrow or denuded creek corridors. They concluded that maintaining wide and well-vegetated riparian corridors may be important in maintaining the connectivity of native predator populations to ensure their long-term survival, as well as enabling these predators to control species that feed on grapes.

In South Africa, research has shown that both the population of helmeted guinea fowl (*Numida meleagris*) and overall avian diversity declined with increasingly intensive agriculture and disappearance of edge habitat and the associated optimally fragmented habitat mosaic. On the other hand, traditional agriculture in the form of contouring in a pesticide-free environment resulted in extensive edge habitat that provided food and cover for birds, leading to an increase in overall bird diversity. While not all species benefit from such edge habitats, the overall diversity of birds seems to increase with appropriate agricultural practices that maintain such patches (Ratcliffe and Crow 2001).

In many parts of Asia and Central America, poor farmers have been using fences made from living plants or trees, to which barbed wire is attached. Living fences provide numerous benefits for the farmer; they are often cheaper than other fences, and they provide biomass, firewood, and source materials to make more fences. At the same time, living fences fertilize the soil (the plants used are often good nitrogen fixers), control erosion, and provide shelter or habitat for wildlife (Swaminathan 1994).

In the humid tropics, research has demonstrated the benefits for both sustainability of production and biodiversity conservation of farming systems that "mimic" the structure of the natural forest ecosystems. Millions of hectares of multistrata "agroforests" in Indonesia produce commercial rubber, fruits, spices, and timber, often in a mosaic with rice fields and rice fallows. The number of wild plant and animal species in these agroforests is often nearly as high as in natural forests. Maintaining

these systems involves policy reforms to strengthen the tenure claims of farmers and "level the playing field" with subsidized rice production (Tomich and others 2001).

Daily and others (2003) investigated the distribution of nonflying mammals in five habitats of southern Costa Rica, including relatively intact forests, coffee plantations, pastures, coffee with adjacent forest remnants, and pasture with adjacent forest remnants. Of the 26 species recorded in the study plots, nine were restricted to forest habitats, 14 occurred in both forest and agricultural habitats, and three were found only in agricultural habitats. Small forest remnants contiguous with coffee plantations did not differ from more extensive forests in species richness, and were richer than other agricultural habitat types. Small remnants contiguous with pasture were poor in species. When clearing started, the study region may have supported around 60 species, but at least six species have been extirpated; these were the largest in their families and included carnivores such as the jaguar (*Panthera onca*), herbivores such as the bearded tapir (*Tapirus bairdii*), and arboreal species such as the mantled howler monkey (*Alouatta palliata*).

Although native forest habitat is essential to conserving the full range of biodiversity, the majority of native nonflying mammal species use countryside habitats. The populations of many such species persist even more than 5 kilometers from relatively extensive forests, at least over the 40 years since forest clearance. If hunting were to cease, it is quite possible that some of the extirpated species could be reestablished in the existing landscape, so opportunities still remain for maintaining and restoring the diversity, abundance, and ecosystem roles in at least some of the human-dominated parts of the Neotropics.

Ecoagriculture might not work in all agricultural settings, especially those where economics strongly favors mass production of only a few crops. But diverse, attractive farmscapes are often found where farming is interspersed with hills, forests, and land from failed farms. Some evidence suggests that farmers are more likely to participate in conservation efforts in marginal farming areas rather than the most productive ones, primarily because land-use choices usually favor the most rewarding financial opportunities (Jackson and Jackson 2002). That said, conservation easements or even government purchase of corridors providing networks of trails, wildlife refuges, hunting and fishing areas, bicycle paths, and other types of natural habitats that wind through farms and adjacent forested lands could help to build better connections between people and the land.

2. Use economic incentives to encourage farmers to conserve wild biodiversity.

Given that farmers—like other people—seek rewarding financial opportunities, some governments are using economic incentives to encourage them to conserve wild or domestic biodiversity, or otherwise maintain healthy environmental conditions on their farms. In Europe, the controversial subsidies of agricultural production are increasingly being converted to subsidies for environmental conditions. Such subsidies increased from US$60 million per year in 1993 to about US$350 million in 2003. Farmers can earn an additional US$40 per hectare by joining a basic environmental scheme, such as leaving the edges of fields unploughed in order to support insects and birds that feed in such areas. It also appears that some farmers will simply allow at least part of their land to lie fallow, collecting the subsidy that requires them to keep the land in "good agricultural and environmental condition," but forgoing the income from crops.

Roughly 20 percent of the farmland in the European Union (EU) is now under some form of agrienvironment scheme to counteract the negative environmental impacts of modern agriculture, at a cost of about US$1.5 billion (about 4 percent of the EU expenditure on the Common Agricultural Policy). The Netherlands has been implementing management agreements designed to conserve biodiversity on farms since 1981, often obliging farmers to postpone agricultural activities on individual fields

until a set date that will allow certain species of birds to safely hatch their chicks. Other management agreements are designed to conserve species-rich vegetation in grasslands, restricting the use of fertilizer or postponing the first mowing or grazing date.

Some of the management activities may have had perverse effects. For example, in some cases, postponing the first mowing or grazing date forced farmers to reduce the input of fertilizer, which may have adversely affected the abundance of soil animals that certain bird species use for food. However, management agreements appear to have a positive effect on the reproductive success of birds, leading to an "ecological trap" where the cues that individual birds use to select their nesting habitat (for example, food availability) are decoupled from the main factor that determines their reproductive success (delayed mowing/grazing) (Kleijn and others 2001). Since the primary concern of farmers is necessarily to secure their income, nature conservation will be of secondary importance to them, especially in the context of a farming system that is driven by economic pressures to increase its intensity. These results are not surprising, but highlight the need for such agrienvironment schemes to be accompanied by a scientifically sound evaluation plan, and to be carefully designed as ecologically appropriate.

Payments to farmers for carbon, water, salinity control, or other environmental services could potentially be combined to generate payments high enough to justify farmer investment in ecoagriculture (Swingland 2003; Pagiola and others 2004). Various countries are experimenting with payments to land managers in upper watersheds, to provide water quality and flow control to downstream water users for urban consumption or irrigation use. The World Bank is experimenting with direct contracts for biodiversity conservation that involve improved silvopastoral practices in degraded pasture areas (Pagiola and others 2004). Experience from various parts of the world demonstrates that the good natural vegetative cover needed to maintain healthy watersheds that produce a steady and reliable source of water may also provide good biodiversity protection.

The Kyoto Protocol of the Convention on Climate Change may allow companies to pay farmers and forest owners for carbon sequestration to offset industrial emissions. Pilot projects and private sector offset initiatives are already underway in many parts of the world. To date, at least US$12 million has gone to protected areas as part of carbon offset initiatives, involving Belize, Bolivia, Costa Rica, Ecuador, Guatemala, Paraguay, Peru, and Uganda. Such projects typically involve an energy firm, such as Wisconsin Electric Power Company or American Electric Power, and non-governmental organizations (NGOs), such as The Nature Conservancy, CARE, or OXFAM. Financial instruments are being developed that would allow credits for these payments to be traded in secondary and futures markets, and thus be included in investment portfolios (Wilson, Moura Costa, and Stuart 1999).

The redirection of so-called perverse incentives (Myers and Kent 2001) can also be an effective means of conserving biodiversity, and indeed is being included in new agricultural support programs in many industrialized countries. Many agrarian countries continue to provide economic subsidies to farmers, thus tending to undermine efforts to conserve biodiversity. Reversing such incentive programs can be a significant contributor to conserving agrobiodiversity.

3. Compensate farmers for economic damage from wild species.

While many of those interested in conserving biodiversity will emphasize the benefits for the landscape of maintaining many species, farmers have historically sought to simplify ecosystems, particularly to control species that are harmful to their crops or livestock and thereby their profitability. If farms are expected to refrain from retaliating against species that cause economic damage, they will need to be compensated for their costs. Hence, many governments have established systems of compensation for such damage.

The loss of crops to wildlife is significant in many countries. In Africa, the red-billed quelea (*Quelea quelea*) and several species of weaver birds (*Ploceus* spp) can lead to losses of cereals amounting to tens of millions of dollars (Ntiamoa-Baidu 1997). Various species of rodents also feed on cereals, ground nuts, rice, maize, sugar cane, and cassava; elephants, baboons, bush pigs, and various antelope can be highly destructive of field crops, while rodents can also cause considerable damage to stored products. In Asia, rats alone eat enough rice each year to feed 200 million people (Stenseth and others 2003).

Virtually all wild herbivores will eat crops; fruit bats can significantly damage plantations, seed-eating birds can harvest a farmer's whole crop, and rats and mice cause serious damage to stored grain. In one study in Nepal, a village with 80 households lost nearly 40,000 kilograms of agricultural produce to monkeys, deer, porcupines, and birds (Chalise 2001). Farmers use various management techniques to repel the wildlife, including dogs; noisemakers; planting a buffer zone with chili, garlic, or tobacco; and other management techniques. But far more effective measures will be needed. Numerous efforts are being made to deal with problem animals in various parts of the world (see, for example, Clark and others 1998; Seidensticker 1984; Messmer 2000).

4. Recognize the value of traditional farming systems in conserving domestic and wild biodiversity.

So far, this paper has focused on wild biodiversity, but domesticated biodiversity is also threatened. Farmers have long been custodians of the genetic wealth present in the land races they use. Indian farmers, for example, have planted over 30,000 varieties of rice over the past 50 years, but now some 75 percent of the land is planted in just 10 varieties. Conservation is especially important in the case of disappearing, specially adapted or resistant varieties, calling for renewed efforts to support farmers as gene custodians.

While modern agriculture tends to reduce the genetic diversity of the crops being planted, most traditional farmers have long recognized the value of maintaining genetic diversity in the varieties they plant. In many parts of Asia, it is not uncommon to find 30 or more varieties of rice being planted by a single farmer; and in the highlands of the Andes, many farmers plant multiple varieties of potatoes, selecting them for taste, disease resistance, frost tolerance, and other characteristics. Maintaining this genetic diversity on the farm is an effective food security measure in places where self-reliance is a matter of life or death. The contribution of such farmers to conserving domestic biodiversity deserves greater attention.

Maize, potatoes, barley, sorghum, apples, and tomatoes originated in mountain areas, while wheat, rice, beans, oats, grapes, oranges, and rye found new homes in the mountains and diversified into many different varieties. The mountainous regions of developing countries continue to produce a multitude of traditional varieties of these important crops, providing an essential biological resource. Such agricultural biodiversity accompanies cultural diversity, as each of the many ethnic groups in mountain areas tends to grow its own particular assortment of varieties of plants. For many human uses, the genetic resources that are most vital to the improvement of modern varieties tend to be found in human-altered ecosystems rather than the more pristine systems. In Nepal alone, more than 2,000 indigenous varieties of rice are being grown, along with indigenous species or varieties of mustards, gourds, pumpkins, cucumbers, tomatoes, peppers, garlic, and cowpeas. Women tend to be the guardians of the seeds (Fleury 1999).

India provides some useful models that might be adapted more widely. In three biodiversity-rich districts of Orissa, a Community Gene Management System has been developed to enable the (often rural, poor) people conserving genetic varieties also to benefit from the in situ conservation work they do. The system has several components: a field gene bank at the village level, an area seed bank at the

Box 5.1
Modern Approaches to Conserving Traditional Agrobiodiversity

In order to conserve the diversity of crop varieties in Yunnan Province, China, Leung and others (2003) promoted crop diversity by mixed planting (intercropping) of traditional and hybrid rice varieties. Since the adoption of this form of crop diversity management in 1997, the number of traditional rice varieties in cultivation has increased dramatically and now includes some varieties that formerly were locally extinct. The cultivated area of traditional varieties has also been greatly expanded. They point out that this form of management is easy to implement and links the economic concerns of the farmers with conservation. Management for crop diversity can promote on-farm conservation of rice, and potentially other crops as well, in a feasible and sustainable way.

Other modern approaches are also seeking greater crop diversity. Crop breeders in the United States are developing native perennial grains (such as bundleflower, leymus, eastern gamagrass, and Maximilian sunflower) that can be grown more sustainably with much less environmental damage in dryland farming regions (Pimm and Raven 2000). The systems are not yet economically competitive, but yields have reached 70 percent of those of annual wheat varieties, while production costs are lower, and habitat value for wildlife is many times higher than in conventional wheat fields. Promoting these species will require changes in agricultural subsidy policies.

level of a cluster of villages, and a community gene bank and herbarium for cryogenic preservation. Farmers at the Field Gene Bank level provide a very important on-farm conservation service (Swaminathan 2001).

Several biovillages have been set up and tested in Pondicherry, using simple techniques that allow farmers to increase productivity and income (even the landless, for example, through mushroom production). Many of the techniques used reduce damage to the environment or even have a beneficial effect. A good example is "green manuring" of rice fields, a traditional practice. Leaves from a common tree species are plucked, spread on the paddy fields, and plowed into the rice fields. The nitrogen fixing properties of some of the varieties used reduce the need for chemical fertilizers, with benefits for biodiversity (Swaminathan 1994). Other conservation examples are presented in box 5.1.

5. Remove trade barriers to farmers in developing countries.

According to Organisation for Economic Co-operation and Development (OECD), agricultural support in relation to production value was 23 percent in the United States and 36 percent in the EU. These subsidies undermine agricultural development in many parts of the developing world. U.S. cotton that was exported at 37 cents a pound in 2002 cost agricultural companies 86 cents a pound to produce, even before shipping, according to U.S. Department of Agriculture statistics. The difference was made up by agricultural subsidies, which for cotton amounted to $3 billion in 2001 and $1.7 billion in 2002. Cotton is an important export for at least 20 of the 50 least developed countries, such as Benin, Burkina Faso, Chad, and Mali, but their competitive position is undermined by U.S. cotton subsidies.

While grain dealers in Zambia can buy grain from the EU or the United States at a lower price than from local farmers, Zambia is unlikely to become self-sufficient in food. Small farmers simply will not grow maize when they can buy it for less than it costs to produce. Sugar is perhaps worse, with the remarkable surpluses of North America and Europe being dumped below world market price in developing countries. And even worse than that, EU trade barriers prevent many African farmers from earning profits through exports to Europe, making it impossible for southern farmers to sell the products they can produce cheaply. This of course has implications for biodiversity, because as long as it is easier to sell ivory than food, the logical consequence is illegal hunting of elephants.

Even *The Economist* has characterized the EU agricultural subsidies as among the "most idiotic" ever created by the western world, especially because they eliminate market forces, increase poverty and hunger in developing countries, and lead to more expensive food and higher taxes in the EU. One estimate is that agricultural policies in OECD countries lead to an annual loss in developing countries of US$20 billion, roughly 40 percent of total development aid. Another telling statistic is that EU support to milk production per cow is 90 times higher than the average budget for education per inhabitant in the least developed countries.

6. Apply modern technology to mainstreaming biodiversity in agroecosystems.

An easy step forward in mainstreaming agrobiodiversity is to enhance information and communications technology. Well-informed farmers will be better able to respond to market conditions, or to prepare for extreme weather events. Once farmers are provided with the means easily and quickly to exchange information, they will themselves find multiple ways of using such technology to their benefit.

Biotechnology is more controversial. In Europe at least, the general public often equates biotechnology with genetic modification, and is very concerned about ethical and environmental risk issues. Much of the public opposition to biotechnology has been fuelled by issues that have little to do with biodiversity, such as the suspicion raised by resistance to product labelling by the food industry, potential impacts on organic agriculture, general concerns about the industrialization of agriculture, and concerns about the increasing control of international economies by large multinational corporations. The very real risks to biodiversity remain poorly quantified. It has also been pointed out that those who can afford to oppose this new technology continue to do so, while the rural poor in the developing world (who comprise 80 percent of the world's population but earn only a little over 10 percent of the wealth) are being denied even the opportunity to explore the possibility of using genetically modified crops as another tool for agricultural improvement. Trying to balance the power of the new technology with the appropriate degree of humility, precaution, and social responsibility will require considerable attention by farms and scientists.

At the same time, biotechnology is beginning to be more widely applied in many developing countries, often drawing on new discoveries made by scientists in these countries. Argentina, Brazil, China, Egypt, India, Kenya, Mexico, South Africa, Uganda, and Zimbabwe are already taking practical steps to apply biotechnology to sustainable development, for example, by using tissue-culture technologies for banana, sugar cane, pyrethrum, cassava, and other crops—and developing their own capacity for genetic manipulation. The major challenge is to find a balanced formula for how local institutions can participate in transgenic product development and share the benefits, risks, and profits of the technology that is based on local germplasm. This will require developing countries to strengthen their capacity to deal with various aspects of biotechnology, including issues of biosafety, creating and sustaining gene banks, and encouraging the emergence of both public support for research and a biotechnology private sector (Wambugu 1999).

7. Recognize property rights of farmers for genetic resources.

The rising dominance of private companies rather than public-sector research institutions in the genetic improvement of agricultural species, and the promising commercial prospects for genetically modified organisms in agriculture and other sectors, have ushered in a period of intense debate and conflict about "property rights" for genetic resources. Who "owns" a gene? Who should benefit from the commercial application of that gene? Will the patenting of genetic improvements restrict farmers and local people from using and distributing the native plants or indigenously developed varieties that were the original source of the gene? Should farmers be compensated financially for past or current in situ conservation of genetic material from valuable domesticated or wild plants and their wild

relatives? The ultimate legal frameworks that are established nationally and internationally to govern these rights will have a profound effect on farmers, agribusiness, environmentalists, and research initiatives to maintain, control, and access biodiversity.

With the entry into force of the Convention on Biological Diversity (CBD) in 1993, bioprospecting and the transfer of benefits arising from the use of genetic resources have become much more complicated. Today's bioprospectors must meet the CBD's Article 15 requirements for prior informed consent, access on mutually agreed terms, and the fair and equitable sharing of benefits. They must also address issues of intellectual property rights and technology transfer; obtain appropriate permits to collect, enter land, and export and import materials; and satisfy phytosanitary requirements. Thus bioprospecting depends for its success on the shared and realistic expectations of the partners and their ability to meet each other's needs.

The Philippines has already introduced restrictive legislation governing access to genetic resources, while access and benefit-sharing measures have been concluded or are under development in Australia, Fiji, India, Indonesia, Malaysia, the Philippines, Thailand, and elsewhere (Ten Kate and Laird 1999). In 1994, the CGIAR formalized their status as trustees, rather than owners, of the ex situ germplasm collections they hold, by signing legally binding agreements with the Food and Agriculture Organization of the United Nations (FAO). The collection must remain in the public domain and genetic resources should remain available without restriction to all users. A new standard Material Transfer Agreement binds recipients of germplasm held or developed by the centers to the terms of the FAO agreements (IPGRI 1999). The International Treaty on Plant Genetic Resources for Food and Agriculture (ITPGR), entered into force in June 2004, intended to encourage the conservation of plant genetic resources—specifically the leading crop and forage plants—through national and international collections of seeds and plants.

8. Recognize indigenous land rights for biodiversity conservation.

A high proportion of remaining wild biodiversity is found in areas of traditional indigenous settlement where indigenous resource management systems are still functioning. For example, 30 percent of the remaining natural forest in Mexico—and that with the greatest biodiversity—is on lands controlled by indigenous people (Scherr, White, and Kaimowitz 2001). However, in many developing countries, as a result of colonial rule, the nationalization of natural resources at independence, or the establishment of protected areas, indigenous claims to natural resources have been denied or weakened. In the process, traditional rules regulating resource access have lost their legitimacy, invariably leading to overexploitation of resources. Even where land tenure for agriculture is secure (through titling or usufruct rights to individuals or communities), indigenous people have often lost their rights to manage natural resources.

Many recent initiatives have reestablished the rights of indigenous people to manage their own lands, including protected areas, to conserve both biodiversity and compatible agricultural systems. Some 80 percent of Latin America's natural forest is now under indigenous control (White and Martin 2002). In Nicaragua, the Miskito people have formed their own NGO to manage the Miskito Coast Protected Area, overseen by a commission including government, regional, NGO, and community representatives (Barzetti 1993). In the Philippines, a local NGO established by the Ikalahan Tribe is managing the 14,730 hectare Kalahan reserve in Luesan. They are implementing an integrated program of community forest management and the extraction of nontimber forest products, leading to production of jams and jellies from forest fruits, extraction of essential oils, collection and cultivation of flowers and mushrooms, and manufacture of furniture.

9. Use market instruments to support agrobiodiversity.

Another way to use markets to support biodiversity is to charge a premium for agricultural commodities that are grown in ways that support biodiversity. The most important instrument to achieve this has been producer certification, with the global trade in certified organic agriculture currently worth over US$21 billion worldwide. In Austria, the European country where organics have become most important, 10 percent of the food consumed is now organic. The World Organic Commodity Exchange (see www.wocx.net) represents over 2,500 organic products, including textiles, furniture, cosmetics, wine, vegetables, fruits, dog food, baby food, ice cream, and water. One might wonder about "organic water," but public interest in such products is high and growing, often mainly in response to human health concerns, but increasingly because of environmental concerns as well.

The Rainforest Alliance has established a certification program for coffee plantations that maintain forest cover, limit agrochemical applications, and control soil erosion. Consumers in many industrialized countries are interested in supporting better habitats for migratory birds in agricultural lands. Rainforest Alliance-certified coffee from Guatemala is now widely available in the United States, and vendors who sell it emphasize its environmental advantages over standard coffee (Perfecto and others 1997; Giovannucci 2001).

Certifying bodies in various parts of the world have also begun to guarantee that forests are being managed and harvested in a sustainable manner. Major consumers, such as the Swedish multinational furniture retailer IKEA, are agreeing to use only certified timber. Both manufacturers and consumers in many developed countries have indicated a preference for certified timber products, and even willingness to pay a small price premium (Pearce, Putz, and Vanclay 1999). The Forest Stewardship Council (FSC), formed by several conservation organizations and retailers in 1993, has certified nearly 20 million hectares globally. Over 600 member companies have joined forest and trade networks around the world, including Home Depot in North America, B&Q in the United Kingdom, and many others.

Several certification programs have been recently established in developing countries. Certified forests now account for about 10 percent of the total land under timber concession in Latin America, 5.2 percent in Africa, and a mere 1.3 percent in the Asia-Pacific region. The FSC is beginning to certify nontimber forest products such as Brazil nuts, the resin base for chewing gum, and cork (WWF 2000). In addition to environmental certification criteria, FSC and other schemes require protection for local forest communities and users, and should promote production efficiency.

Certification of biodiversity impacts may become a consideration in financial markets, as "green" mutual funds seek agroindustries that contribute actively to "sustainable development" (Daily and Walker 2000). Large companies traded on stock exchanges around the world are judged by potential investors according to a variety of criteria. Increasingly, some of those criteria relate to environmental sustainability; many mutual funds exclusively invest in environment friendly companies (Ten Kate 2003). These companies can achieve a competitive advantage by marketing their products as sustainably produced and packaged, and by advertising their environmental responsibility in managing corporate land, water, and forest resources. With further efforts to educate and animate both investors and the public, their performance as stewards of biodiversity might also be rewarded.

10. Adopt a landscape scale when mainstreaming biodiversity.

Finally, when seeking to promote the mainstreaming of agrobiodiversity in production systems, it is often helpful to work at a landscape scale that includes numerous farms and the surrounding landscapes that support the farming communities. Such landscapes may often contain protected areas. While each individual farm has contributions to make, the entire farming system is the level at which biodiversity can most effectively be conserved. Species will move between farms, and between farms and the surrounding matrix. Maintaining habitat corridors may

be a useful contributing factor to conserving biodiversity within such landscapes.

Research on how ecosystems work is being applied to conservation of biodiversity. This research is finding that ecosystems are loose, temporary assemblages of species in which each behaves according to its own needs, depending on its specific physiology, morphology, demography, behavior, and dispersal capacity. "Because of a continual turnover of ecological conditions, local communities show a continual turnover of species, at one time gaining species because the scale of processes allows a certain type of trait, and at others losing them again because the same trait happens to have resulted in too great a risk of extinction. Biodiversity is both the result and expression of all sorts of adaptations of life to the environmental turmoils; it can only be maintained as long as this turmoil exists" (Hengeveld 1994). These new insights are the basis of managing dynamic ecosystems as a whole, recognizing the many different habitat structures found in nature (Oliver and Larson 1996).

Conserving this natural dynamism in the face of unnatural pressures such as fragmentation, invasive alien species, and climate change, is a major challenge for landscape managers, requiring judgments about the scale at which benefits are to be delivered to people. Because ecosystems are dynamic, highly complex, and unique to the site where they are located, it is not sufficient to conserve just one minimum viable population of a species, or just one example of an ecosystem. Instead, approaches are needed that not only conserve biodiversity but also recognize the dynamism of systems, the dependence of local people on their natural resources, and the need to build redundancy into the systems of protecting biodiversity (Daily and others 1997).

While previous suggestions highlighted the importance of providing economic incentives to farmers and reducing perverse incentives, it is also important to recognize that conserving agrobiodiversity at the landscape level can provide significant other benefits to farmers. In many mountainous regions, for exam-

Box 5.2
Ecoagriculture Strategies for Land and Resource Management

Ecoagriculture *increases wildlife habitat* in nonfarmed patches in agricultural landscapes, creating mosaics of wild and cultivated land uses, by:

- Creating new protected areas that also directly benefit local farming communities (by increasing the flow of wild or cultivated products, enhancing locally valued environmental services, or increasing agricultural sustainability)

- Establishing habitat networks and corridors in "in-between" spaces that are compatible with farming (such as hedgerows or windbreaks)

- Raising the productivity of existing farmland to prevent or reverse conversion of wild lands, along with explicit measures to protect or restore the biodiversity value of uncultivated lands.

Ecoagriculture *enhances the habitat quality* of productive farmlands, by:

- Reducing agricultural pollution through new methods of nutrient and pest management, and farm and waterway filters

- Modifying the management of soil, water, and natural vegetation to enhance habitat quality

- Modifying the mix and configuration of agricultural species to mimic the structure and function of natural vegetation.

ple, villages maintain forests above the village, as a means of providing both shelter from avalanches and various other goods and services. Forested watersheds help provide clean water to farmers. Many coastal villages find that maintaining healthy mangroves provides breeding ground for fisheries and protects them from the effects of typhoons or storm surges.

More generally, sound land management is a good investment in safety. For example, in October 1998, Hurricane Mitch was the worst natural disaster to strike Central America in 200 years. The damage to agricultural land was especially destructive, but farms using soil and water conservation methods and other agroecological practices survived better than those using conventional modern farming

methods. Based on results from 360 communities in Guatemala, Honduras, and Nicaragua, the sustainably farmed plots had 28-38 percent more topsoil and 3-15 percent more soil moisture than neighboring plots using conventional modern farming methods. Surface erosion was 2 to 3 times greater on conventional plots than on agroecological plots, which suffered 58 percent less damage in Honduras, 70 percent less in Nicaragua, and 99 percent less in Guatemala. While agroecological methods may not contribute to resilience in all conditions, it is clear that protecting the upper areas of the watershed can help reduce damage in the lower elevations; working at the farm level alone is insufficient (World Neighbours 2000).

Agrobiodiversity and Ecoagriculture

Conventional wisdom holds that modern farming is largely incompatible with conserving wild biodiversity. Thus policies to protect wild species and ecosystems typically rely on land use segregation, establishing protected areas from which agriculture is excluded (at least legally). Farmers are seen as sources of problems by those promoting this view of wildlife conservation. It is becoming apparent, however, that farming systems can make important contributions to biodiversity conservation, with forms of land use that support the objectives of protected areas rather than conflicting with them. These contributions can be enhanced by new approaches to resource management, supported by technical and policy research.

An essential strategy for conserving wild biodiversity, especially that found in highly populated, poor rural areas around the world, is to convert agriculture that is destructive of biodiversity into a new type of agriculture: "ecoagriculture" (McNeely and Scherr 2003). Ecoagriculture, which builds on the concept of "ecosystem management," refers to land-use systems that are managed both to produce food and to protect wild biodiversity. For ecoagriculture, enhancing rural livelihoods through more productive and profitable farming systems becomes a core strategy for both agricultural development and conservation of biodiversity. Ecoagriculture encompasses two sets of strategies for land and resource management, which are outlined in box 5.2.

To have a meaningful impact on biodiversity conservation at global or regional scales, ecoagriculture must be broadly promoted. In some cases, ecoagriculture systems can be developed by using available components and information from scientific and local knowledge, and by improving these through trial and error to design landscapes that address both local livelihood and conservation objectives. But in most cases, major scientific initiatives will also be required, using sophisticated methods and tools from various disciplines. Indeed, ecoagriculture is feasible now in large part because of the greater capacity to find synergies through scientific management. Advances in conservation biology, agricultural ecology, plant breeding, ecosystem monitoring systems, and modelling are revolutionizing the ability to understand and manipulate wildlife–habitat–agriculture interactions, to the benefit of both people and the rest of nature.

Conclusions

The people who use biological resources have many different needs, interests, cultures, and goals. The global industrial society that dominates the modern world has a tremendous appetite for the consumption of these resources as food, timber, fiber, fodder, and other commodities. Thus macroeconomic decisions taken in distant capital cities often determine the fate of biodiversity and of the way land is used. The people who live in the forested areas where species diversity is richest will themselves make decisions about resources that may sometimes result in the conversion of a forest into another form of land use or the local extinction of a species, although the evidence indicates that local people who have long lived on the land relatively seldom cause such extinctions.

Approaches being developed under many biodiversity-related international agreements and programs call for ecosystems to be managed to meet multiple national objectives, which include providing timber, forage, fiber, and energy; retaining options for future economic use; carrying out various ecosystem services; providing ethical and aesthetic values; and supplying that nation's share of global benefits (MA 2003). Achieving these sometimes conflicting objectives in a time of rising expectations and shrinking government budgets will require new approaches, such as those outlined in this paper.

These approaches are designed to encourage the development of technologies and practices that increase productivity and reduce degradation; reclaim, rehabilitate, restore, and enhance biodiversity, especially that which is relevant to agricultural development; and monitor the adverse effects of agriculture on biodiversity. Organic farming, integrated pest management, biological control, multicropping, crop rotation, and agroforestry are all approaches that can contribute further in this regard.

An essential component of any effort at sustainable landscape management is the economic viability of the various enterprises that are involved. While growing a crop is the most obvious money-earner from good agricultural land, many crops and methods of growing them are possible, with variable implications for biodiversity. Further, if local people can benefit financially from enterprises that depend on the biodiversity of the surrounding nondomestic land within which they live, then they might reasonably be expected to support the conservation and sustainable use of the ecosystem.

Converting the potential benefits of mainstreaming agrobiodiversity into real and perceived goods and services for society-at-large (and especially for local people) requires a systems approach that should include:

■ At the national level, an integrated set of protected areas, encompassing various levels of management and administration, including the national, provincial, and local governments, NGOs, local communities, and indigenous peoples, the private sector, and other stakeholders (McNeely 1999)

■ A fairly large geographical scale (sometimes called a "bioregion") for resource management programs, within which farms and pastures are considered as components in a diverse landscape, including protected areas, harvested forests, fishing grounds, human settlements, and infrastructures (Miller 1996)

■ Cooperation between private landowners, indigenous peoples, other local communities, industry, and resource users; the use of economic incentives, tax arrangements, land exchanges, and other mechanisms to promote biodiversity conservation; and the development of administrative and technical capacities that encourage local stakeholders, universities, research institutions, and public agencies to harmonize their efforts.

Managing for sustainable landscapes requires the development and actual implementation of sustainable production systems adapted to the different kinds of ecosystems. These should include, among others, the scientific, technological, economic, social, financial, and educational components that are required to ensure sustainability. The exact mix of goods and services to be provided from any particular landscape should be based on dialogue among farmers, industry, government, academics, hunters, local municipalities, and the environmental community, thereby bringing a measure of democracy to the landscape and enhancing the likelihood of sustainability.

The author thanks Sara Scherr, Norman Myers, and M.S. Swaminathan for their help in thinking through some of these issues; Frederik Schutyser for research support; and Wendy Price for secretarial support.

Endnote

1 IUCN (The World Conservation Union), Gland, Switzerland

References

Barzetti, V. ed. 1993. *Parks and Progress: Protected Areas and Economic Development in Latin America and the Caribbean.* Washington, DC: IUCN and Inter-American Development Bank.

Buskirk, J.V., and Y. Willi. 2004. "Enhancement of Farmland Biodiversity within Set-aside Land." *Conservation Biology* 18 (4): 987-94.

Chalise, M.K. 2001. "Crop Rating by Wildlife, Especially Primates, and Indigenous Practices for Crop Protection in Lakuwa Area, East Nepal." *Asian Primates* 7 (4): 4-9.

Clark, M.S., H. Ferris, K. Klonsky, W.T. Lanini, A.H.C. van Bruggen, and F.G. Zalom. 1998. *Agronomic, Economic, and Environmental Comparison of Pest Management in Conventional and Alternative Tomato and Corn Systems in Northern California.* Davis, CA: University of California, Davis.

Daily, G.C., G. Ceballos, J. Pacheco, G. Suzán, and A. Sánchez-Azofeifa. 2003. "Countryside Biogeography of Neo-Tropical Mammals: Conservation Opportunities in Agricultural Landscapes in Costa Rica." *Conservation Biology* 17 (6): 1814-26.

Daily, G.C., S. Alexander, P.R. Ehrlich, L. Goulder, J. Lubchenco, P.A. Matson, H.A. Mooney, S. Postel, S.H. Schneider, D. Tilman, and G.M. Woodwell. 1997. "Ecosystem Services: Benefits Supplied to Human Societies by Natural Ecosystems." *Ecology* 2: 1-16.

Daily, G.C., and B.H. Walker. 2000. "Seeking the Great Transition." *Nature* 403: 243-45.

Fleury, J.M. 1999. "Mountain Biodiversity at Risk." *IDRC Briefing* 2: 1-6.

Giovannucci, D. 2001. *Sustainable Coffee Survey of the North American Speciality Coffee Industry.* Washington, DC: World Bank.

Hengeveld, R. 1994. "Biodiversity: The Diversification of Life in a Non-equilibrium World." *Biodiversity Letters* 2: 1-10.

Heywood, V.J., and R.T. Watson, eds. 1995. *Global Biodiversity Assessment.* Cambridge, UK: Cambridge University Press.

Hilty, J.A., and A.M. Merenlender. 2004. "Use of Riparian Corridors and Vineyards by Mammalian Predators in Northern California." *Conservation Biology* 18 (1): 126-35.

Imhoff, D. 2003. *Farming with the Wild: Enhancing Biodiversity on Farms and Ranches.* San Francisco, CA: Sierra Club Books.

IPGRI (International Plant Genetic Resources Institute). 1999. *Annual Report: International Plant Genetic Resources Institute.* www.ipgri.cgiar.org/report/annualreport.asp?id=39.

IUCN (The World Conservation Union). 2003. *2003 Red List of Threatened Species.* Gland, Switzerland: IUCN. http://www.redlist.org.

Jackson, D.L., and L.L. Jackson. 2002. *The Farm as Natural Habitat: Reconnecting Food Systems with Ecosystems.* Washington, DC: Island Press.

Kleijn, D., F. Berendse, R. Smit, and N. Gilissen. 2001. "Agrienvironment Schemes Do Not Effectively Protect Biodiversity in Dutch Agricultural Landscapes." *Nature* 413: 723-25.

Lee, D., and C. Barrett, eds. 2001. *Tradeoffs or Synergies? Agricultural Intensification, Economic Development, and the Environment.* Wallingford, UK: CAB International.

Leung H., Y. Zhu, I. Revilla-Molina, J.X. Fan, H. Chen, I. Pangga, C. Vera Cruz, and T.W. Mew. 2003. "Using Genetic Diversity to Achieve Sustainable Rice Disease Management. *Plant Disease* 87 (10): 1156-69.

McNeely, J.A. 1999. *Mobilizing Broader Support for Asia's Biodiversity: How Civil Society Can Contribute to Protected Area Management.* Manila: Asian Development Bank.

McNeely, J.A., and S.J. Scherr. 2003. *Ecoagriculture: Strategies to Feed the World and Save Wild Biodiversity.* Washington, DC: Island Press.

MA (Millennium Ecosystem Assessment). 2003. *Ecosystems and Human Well-Being: A Framework for Assessment.* Washington, DC: Island Press.

Messmer, T.A. 2000. *The Emergence of Human-Wildlife Conflict Management: Turning Challenges into Opportunities.* Logan, UT: Utah State University.

Miller, K.R. 1996. *Balancing the Scales: Guidelines for Increasing Biodiversity's Chances through Bioregional Management.* Washington, DC: World Resources Institute.

Myers, N., and J. Kent. 2001. *Perverse Subsidies: How Tax Dollars Undercut the Environment and the Economy.* Washington, DC: Island Press.

Ntiamoa-Baidu, Y. 1997. *Wildlife and Food Security in Africa.* FAO Conservation Guide No. 3. Rome: Food and Agriculture Organization of the United Nations.

Oliver, C.D., and B.C. Larson. 1996. *Forest Stand Dynamics.* New York: John Wiley & Sons.

Pagiola, S., P. Agostini, J. Gobbi, C. de Haan, M. Ibrahim, E. Murgueitio, E. Ramirez, M. Rosales, and J.P. Ruiz. 2004. *Paying for Biodiversity Conservation Services in Agricultural Landscapes.* Washington, DC: World Bank.

Pagiola, S., and J. Kellenberg. 1997. *Mainstreaming Biodiversity in Agricultural Development.* Washington, DC: World Bank.

Pearce, D., F. Putz, and J.K. Vanclay. 1999. "A Sustainable Forest Future." Center for Social and Economic Research on the Global Environment (CSERGE). Working Paper GEC99-15, University of East Anglia, UK.

Perfecto, I., J. Vandermeer, P. Hanson, and V. Cartin. 1997. "Arthropod Biodiversity Loss and the Transformation of a Tropical Agro-Ecosystem." *Biodiversity and Conservation* 6: 935-45.

Pimm, S.L., and P. Raven. 2000. "Extinction by Numbers." *Nature* 403: 843-45.

Postel, S. 1999. *Pillar of Sand: Can the Irrigation Miracle Last?* New York: Worldwatch Books.

Ratcliffe, C.S., and T.M. Crow. 2001. "The Effects of Agriculture and the Availability of Edge Habitat on Populations of Helmeted Guinea Fowl (*Numida meleagris*) and on the Diversity and Composition of Associated Bird Assemblages in KwaZulu-Natal Province, South Africa." *Biodiversity and Conservation* 10: 2109-27.

Scherr, S.J. 1999. "Soil Degradation: A Threat to Developing Country Food Security by 2020?" IFPRI Food, Agriculture, and the Environment Discussion Paper 27, International Food Policy Research Institute, Washington, DC.

Scherr, S.J., A. White, and D. Kaimowitz. 2001. *Strategies to Improve Rural Livelihoods through Markets for Forest Products and Services.* Washington, DC: Forest Trends and the Center for International Forestry Research.

Seidensticker, J. 1984. "Managing Elephant Depredation in Agricultural and Forestry Projects." World Bank Technical Paper 16, World Bank, Washington, DC.

Stenseth, N.C., H.P. Andreassen, P.B. Bown, S.A. Davis, H. Leirs, R.P. Pech, M. Lima, R.M. Machangu, R.H. Makundi, D. Shi, G.R. Singleton, A. Skonhoft, X. Wan, and Z. Zhang. 2003. "Mice and Rats: The Dynamics and Bio-Economics of Agricultural Rodents Pests." *Front Ecol Environ* 2003 1 (7): 367-75.

Swaminathan, M.S. ed. 1994. *Eco-technology and Rural Employment.* Madras, India: MacMillan India.

———. 2001. *From Rio de Janeiro to Johannesburg: Action Today and Not Just Promises for Tomorrow.* Madras, India: East West Books.

Swingland, I.R. ed. 2003. *Capturing Carbon and Conserving Biodiversity: The Market Approach.* London: EarthScan.

Ten Kate, K. 2003. "Biodiversity: Towards Best Practice for Extractive and Utility Companies." Consultation document to accompany Insight's presentation to the World Parks Congress, September 13.

Ten Kate, K., and S.A. Laird. 1999. *The Commercial Use of Biodiversity: Access to Genetic Resources and Benefit-Sharing.* London: Earthscan Publications.

Tomich, T., M. van Noordwijk, S. Buddarsono, A. Gillison, T. Kusumanto, D. Murdiyarso, F. Stolle, and A. Fagi. 2001. "Agricultural Intensification, Deforestation, and the Environment: Assessing Tradeoffs in Sumatra, Indonesia." In D. Lee and C. Barrett, eds. *Tradeoffs or Synergies? Agricultural Intensification, Economic Development, and the Environment.* Wallingford, UK: CAB International, pp. 221-44.

Wambugu, F. 1999. "Why Africa Needs Agricultural Biotech." *Nature* 400: 15-16.

White, T.A., and A. Martin. 2002. *Who Owns the World's Forests?* Washington, DC: Forest Trends and Center for International Environmental Law.

Williams, M. 2003. *Deforesting the Earth: From Pre-History to Global Crises.* Chicago, IL: University of Chicago Press.

Wilson, C., P. Moura Costa, and M. Stuart. 1999. "Transfer Payments for Environmental Services to Local Communities: A Local-Regional Approach." International Fund for Agricultural Development Proposed Special Program for Asia. Rome: IFAD.

World Neighbours. 2000. *Lessons from the Field: Reasons for Resiliency: Toward a Sustainable Recovery after Hurricane Mitch.* Tegucigalpa, Honduras: World Neighbours.

WWF (World Wildlife Fund). 2000. *Lessons from the Field: What Does It Take to Make Conservation Work?* Washington, DC: WWF Biodiversity Support Program.

6. Mainstreaming Wildlife Conservation in Multiple-Use Forests of the Northern Republic of Congo

Paul Elkan and Sarah Elkan[1]

Increasing pressures around protected areas and expanding commercial wildlife trade have been well documented in recent years (Robinson, Redford, and Bennett 1999; Wilkie and Carpenter 1999; Ape Alliance 1998; BCTF 2001). However, thus far, few field-based initiatives have been undertaken to improve the situation. This paper describes the processes and systems developed for mainstreaming wildlife conservation principles into the management of a large timber concession in northern Republic of Congo, adjacent to the Nouabale-Ndoki National Park.

The initiative aims to mitigate the "bushmeat crisis" and promote sound wildlife conservation and management through collaborative efforts between the private timber industry, government, local communities, and an international nongovernmental organization (NGO). Detailed biological, socioeconomic, and law enforcement monitoring demonstrated that the initiative has had a significant impact across the landscape and neighboring protected area (Elkan and others, forthcoming). The lessons learned from this case study serve to inform similar conservation problems at multiple scales, address longer-term solutions such as private sector and community natural resource management, improve national policy on wildlife management in timber concessions, contribute to international certification of forests, and add to an understanding of mainstreaming.

Background

International Conservation Context

The arena of conserving and managing tropical forests and wildlife has long been identified as critical for focusing conservation effort on strategies that work in the context of the economic realities of developing countries (Strusaker 1997; Weber and others 2001; Fimbel, Grajal, and Robinson 2000). In an attempt to reconcile biodiversity conservation, revenue generation needs, and natural resource management objectives, the international community has sought to develop policies and incentives to conserve and manage tropical forests. These strategies have largely focused on the creation of protected areas and the promotion of "sustainable forest management" (SFM) practices (World Bank 2002; ITTO 1996).

Timber certification has provided an incentive leading to some progress in temperate forest management and forests in South America and Asia (Cauley and others 2001). The 109 million hectares (ha) of forest currently under some sort of certification (the surface area has doubled in the past two years with the expansion of several certification schemes), however, includes none of the Congo Basin forests (FSC 2002). More recently, the need to integrate wildlife conservation and management objectives into tropical forest management practices and certification schemes has been brought to the forefront of discussion (Robinson, Redford, and Bennett 1999; Bennett 2000; Ghazoul 2001; Cauley and others 2001).

Congo Basin

At present, the forests of the Congo Basin cover 2.05 million square kilometers (km^2), of which approximately 7.3 percent has been designated as protected areas (CARPE 2001). Much of the remaining forest is currently under commercial exploitation or destined for future timber, petroleum, or mineral exploitation by private industry. The economies of Congo Basin countries are largely based on natural resource extraction (World Bank 2002). Because resources are undervalued and there is insufficient regulation and monitoring of industry activities, there is little incentive for private industry to improve environmental management. In addition to representing an important source of timber revenue for developing countries, these forests support nontimber resources critical to livelihoods of local indigenous peoples, endangered and rare species, exploitable wildlife populations, and key ecosystem processes. Many production forest concessions are located in close proximity to protected areas.

Some species require large areas to support viable populations, and many timber concessions contain critical wildlife habitat (Elkan and others, forthcoming). The direct effects of selective logging in some Congo Basin forests may affect only a few large mammals species negatively (White 1992; Elkan and others, forthcoming). The direct effects of logging on birds, herps, small mammals, and other taxa have yet to be assessed. While selective logging, per se, may not drastically affect the abundance of some species, patterns in Cameroon, the Central African Republic (CAR), and the Republic of Congo indicate that the indirect effects of logging lead to increased hunting pressures and the decimation of wildlife (Wilkie, Sidle, and Boundzanga 1992; Elkan and others, forthcoming; P. Auzel, pers. comm.). There is a clear and critical link between the achievement of protected area objectives and the management of neighboring multiple-use forests.

Research over the past decade shows that hunting of wildlife in tropical forests is occurring at unsustainable levels (Robinson, Redford, and Bennett 1999; Fa, Peres, and Meeuwig 2002). Commercial hunting facilitated by the timber industry contributes directly to the systematic depletion of wildlife populations in large tracts of African forests (Wilkie and Carpenter 1999; Auzel and Wilkie 2000). Fa, Peres, and Meeuwig (2002) estimated that up to one million tons of bushmeat are consumed in Central Africa each year. The extinction of Miss Waldron's Colobus in Nigeria (Oates and others 2000) and increasing rates of great ape hunting have further raised international concern (Ape Alliance 1998). The critical link between sustainable use of wildlife, food security, and the livelihoods of local communities has been raised in international and national development strategy discussions (Davies 2002; Bennett 2002).

Throughout the Congo Basin, logging activities have led to a "domino effect" of increased access to the forest, population growth, influx of capital, increased demand for bushmeat, and escalating commercial hunting (Wilkie and Carpenter 1999; Robinson, Redford, and Bennett 1999). Forestry camps often create markets and staging points for commercial hunting in previously remote, undisturbed areas. The revenue generated by timber company communities attracts traders, commercial bushmeat traffickers, job seekers, and hangers-on, and contributes to rapid demographic growth. The pressures on wildlife populations and cultural hegemony associated with logging activities have an impact on local indigenous communities that depend directly on forest resources.

Northern Republic of Congo

The exploitable forest surface area of northern Republic of Congo is approximately 90,000 km^2, divided into 21 forestry management units (FMUs) in 1982. Throughout the 1970s, 1980s, and 1990s several of these concessions were selectively exploited for high-grade timber, predominantly *Entandrophragma sp.* While rich in valuable timber, the forests of northern Congo also hold some of the most important wildlife populations remaining in Central Africa, including forest elephants (*Loxodonta africana cyclotis*), lowland gorillas (*Gorilla gorilla gorilla*), chimpanzees (*Pan troglodytes troglodytes*), bongo (*Tragelaphus eurycerus*), buffalo (*Syncerus caffer nanus*), leopard (*Panthera pardus*), six species of duikers, and eight species of diurnal monkeys (Fay, Agnagna, and Moutsambote 1990).

Recognizing the ecological importance of the region, the government of the Republic of Congo upgraded the status of the Nouabale-Ndoki forest in 1993 from an FMU to a national park, thus preserving portions of a nearly undisturbed forest ecosystem. The Nouabale-Ndoki National Park (NNNP) is contiguous with the Dzanga-Ndoki National Park in Central African Republic and Lobeke National Park in Cameroon. Forest management units surround the NNNP: Kabo (300,000 ha) and Pokola (estimated at 560,000 ha) to the south have been exploited since the 1970s. Timber harvest in Loundougou (386,000 ha) to the east, and Mokabi (375,000 ha) to the north began in 2002. Complementing the three National Parks, the Kabo and Pokola FMUs support high densities of rare and endangered large mammals, making this landscape a high international conservation priority.

Traditional forest peoples (Bangombe and Benjele pygmies) and several Bantu groups have historically used the Kabo, Pokola, and Loundougou areas for hunter-gatherer livelihoods. Although the region has a relatively low human density (<1 per km^2), over the last three decades permanent settlements have been established along the Sangha River and near sawmills in Kabo and Pokola towns (Moukassa 2001). Development of the logging economy created a considerable export of game meat and uncontrolled hunting in many areas of Kabo and Pokola. In early 1997 a timber company called Congolaise Industrielle de Bois (CIB) acquired rights to Kabo and the neighboring Loundougou

concession in addition to Pokola, which it has been exploiting since the early 1970s. The arrival of CIB in Kabo immediately compounded old pressures on wildlife (such as revitalizing elephant poaching networks) and greatly increased new ones (systematic exporting of wildlife products). CIB rapidly expanded infrastructure and built a road to the Loundougou concession.

Methods and Process

In 1992, the government of the Republic of Congo and the Wildlife Conservation Society (WCS), with funding from the United States Agency for International Development (USAID), established the Nouabale-Ndoki National Park (NNNP), and in the late 1990s extended conservation efforts to the surrounding timber concessions. In 1998, WCS submitted a proposal to the government of the Republic of Congo for adoption of a land-use management plan for areas immediately surrounding the NNNP (Fay 1997). It included the establishment of "buffer zones" and extensions of park borders; however, the government rejected the plan because of a conflict between logging and conservation objectives. Instead, the government asked WCS to negotiate with CIB to develop a wildlife management and protection plan that reflected the government's goal of integrating conservation, while maintaining revenue generation from timber exploitation.

In June 1999, the Ministry of Forest Economy (MFE), CIB, and WCS finalized an agreement on the Project for Ecosystem Management of the Periphery of the Park. The objectives of the initiative were to design, implement, and monitor sustainable wildlife conservation and management systems in the Kabo, Pokola, and Loundougou concessions. The objectives of the initiative are highlighted in box 6.1. Activities focused on education and awareness, alternative activities and protein sources, wildlife management and hunting regulation, wildlife protection, socioeconomic and ecological research and monitoring, and geographic information system-based planning to improve forestry management. Efforts

Box 6.1
Objectives of the Project for Ecosystem Management of the Periphery of the Nouabale-Ndoki National Park (NNNP)

The objectives of the initiative were to:

- halt hunting encroachment and pressures around the NNNP

- extend protection to endangered and rare species across a large area of important habitat (the entire concession area of 1,200,000 hectares)

- establish a locally recognized and supported system of community hunting and no-hunting zones

- identify and protect key wildlife habitat areas (forest clearings) within the concessions

- create the conditions necessary for sustainable off-take of legally hunted game species in combination with alternative protein sources.

initially emphasized the reduction of hunting pressures in Kabo (closest to the park) and were gradually expanded to Pokola and Loundougou, depending on available resources and the adoption of regulations, and taking into account social volatility resulting from wildlife law enforcement.

WCS was responsible for development and administration of overall project activities in collaboration with the MFE. CIB modified its internal regulations and management to incorporate and promote wildlife conservation and management measures. WCS provided technical expertise and mobilized operational funding through its own funds and international sources. The government assigned protection personnel, facilitated ecoguard training, and oversaw law enforcement. The company initially provided support in the form of infrastructure (housing, guard posts, and a vehicle), diesel fuel, and other equipment for wildlife protection activities, later expanding to include direct funding of antipoaching and alternative protein activities. This amounted to 20-30 percent of the direct costs of alternative activities and wildlife protection components in the first years, with an increase to 30-40

percent in 2002 coinciding with expansion to Loundougou and efforts to address protein shortages in Pokola.

From 1999-2001, financial and institutional support increased and activities expanded, particularly with funding from the International Tropical Timber Organization (ITTO) in 2001. The level of effort grew steadily, with $300,000, $550,000, and $800,000 in the first, second, and third years, respectively, permitting expansion of activities to approximately 2,000 km^2, 4,000 km^2, and 6,000 km^2. In 2003, efforts were expanded to include the Loundougou concession as it was opened up to timber exploitation. Costs varied from $1.25 to $1.50 per hectare, with increased effort required in Pokola FMU due to hunting and human population pressures. After the establishment of initial infrastructure, wildlife protection costs were highest (40-50 percent), followed by research and monitoring (17-19 percent). Alternative activities received approximately 10 percent of outside assistance, in addition to direct CIB contributions (cold rooms, transport of domestic meat, construction of fish ponds, and so forth). Conservation education was cost-effective (10 percent) and reached a broad geographical region. International technical expertise was fundamental to efficient program development, training, and administration. In 2000, CIB embarked on the development of a long-term forest management plan. The project contributed to the wildlife management and conservation, and socioeconomic chapters of the plan, and advised on systems to reduce the direct impacts of exploitation.

Conservation and Management Activities

Conservation and management activities fall into the following five broad areas:

(1) Education and awareness
A conservation awareness campaign was the first step toward collaboration with the local communities and CIB employees on wildlife management measures. Conservation awareness of local villagers, hunters, women's groups, company employees, and

workers' unions was raised, and a dialogue established through individual contacts, films, meetings, and seminars. Over the course of the first two years of the project, every village in the Kabo and Pokola concessions participated in awareness meetings. New wildlife management interventions and principles were communicated and discussed to promote understanding, participation, and support. Nature clubs were established with the local schools in towns and camps closest to the park. Documentary films, a primary school protected-species education program, and individual and target group meetings improved conservation understanding at local, regional, and national levels.

(2) Wildlife management principles/regulations

Following awareness campaigns, steps were taken to modify internal company regulations legally, in order to integrate wildlife management principles. This process entailed two months of negotiations between WCS, MFE, and CIB representatives, and company employee labor unions (representing 1,500 employees). An agreement was concluded, integrating comprehensive wildlife conservation and management regulations and disciplinary measures for violations (scaled according to severity of violation). Unions agreed to these changes on the condition that alternative protein sources (beef importation, fish, poultry farms, and so forth) be developed as a substitute for bushmeat.

Specific measures incorporated in the company's administration and legal regulations included a wildlife management zoning plan based on studies of traditional community land tenure systems (Moukassa 2001). Zoning provided for community hunting zones and no-hunting areas, and prohibition of hunting in areas immediately surrounding the NNNP. Upon closure of safari hunting operations in 1999, the "safari zone" (150,000 ha) was maintained as a core "no-hunting" area.

Over the course of the first year, the zoning plan was discussed and adopted with each community concerned. Committees of five major and six smaller villages adopted regulations for community

---

Box 6.2
Key Regulations Integrated into Company Policy

- Prohibition of snare hunting (considered to be wasteful and the cause of unselective killing of non-target species)
- Prohibition of hunting of protected species (gorilla, chimpanzee, elephant, leopard, bongo, and so forth)
- Prohibition of export of bushmeat from sites (local consumption only, discouraging unsustainable and unmanageable commercialization)
- Establishment of conservation zones within the concessions where hunting was not allowed (particularly in forest clearings and other sensitive areas important for wildlife)
- Establishment of community hunting zones permitting legal hunting and local consumption
- Development of a system of community-based hunter associations to promote controlled legal exploitation
- Restrictions on transport of hunters and wild meat in company vehicles
- Prohibition of transport of commercial hunters and traffickers
- Specific regulations controlling subsistence hunting of forestry teams.

---

hunting zones. Local communities were often receptive to the opportunity to reinforce their traditional rights. Several villages formally requested assistance from the project to protect wildlife in their traditional areas from outside exploitation. Integrated into the company regulations (see box 6.2) in 1999, the zoning system has been recently completed for Loundougou concession and is being formally incorporated into the forest concession management plan.

Communities at CIB sites and traditional villages were encouraged to organize representative hunting committees. Committees acted as focal points for the resolution of wildlife management problems and were responsible for improving respect by members for hunting regulations (purchase of hunting permits, respect for zoning, collaboration with researchers, monitoring off-take, and so forth). These groups assisted in transforming an initially highly confrontational relationship (punctuated by at least two near-revolts in protest against wildlife controls) into functional collaboration. Collaboration was easier at the Ndoki 2, Kabo, and Pokola sites than the Ndoki 1 camp, which had an established history of commercial poaching.

(3) Alternative protein source development

Little alternative domestic protein was available prior to the initiation of the project, as local people traditionally hunt, fish, and gather forest products (Moukassa 1999). We designed the alternative protein source program to develop sustainable systems to supply protein substitutes for bushmeat, with an emphasis on the larger population centers. Priority was also given to creating revenue opportunities for local indigenous community members as an alternative to commercial hunting.

We quickly learned that local communities would not easily adjust their bushmeat exploitation patterns unless this became a necessity. The program identified and worked with local people on vegetable gardening, fishing, and traditional farming. Particularly motivated individuals were targeted for the introduction of new ideas, such as fish farming, improved chicken farming, and beef importation. Fishing associations were organized early on to assist traditional fishermen with appropriate materials. Chicken vaccination and technical assistance supported the development of farming. Guinea pig, porcupine, rabbit, and snail farming were piloted. Activities were focused on both company sites (camps and towns) and traditional communities, with a direct emphasis on reducing hunting pressures. Regular meetings were held with CIB employee unions to assess progress in relation to generating alternative activities and respect for internal company regulations on wildlife management.

Over the four-year period, company and local support for alternative protein increased dramatically. After relatively slow progress during the first two years, alternative protein became a strong preoccupation for local people and the company, as protection efforts reduced the supply of bushmeat to larger towns. By early 2002, the project and company had established two fish farms with 18 active basins, two butcher shops, one slaughter house, and five cold rooms to store imported produce. CIB further assisted local tradesmen with importation of more than 30 cattle per month and up to 15 tons of frozen produce every 2 to 3 months. Alternative sources of employment were encouraged through gardening, fishing associations, recruitment of ecoguards from local villages, and encouraging CIB to employ former commercial hunters from the local communities.

(4) Research and monitoring

Socioeconomic and ecological research and monitoring informed strategy development, assessed progress, and brought about adaptations to management interventions (Elkan and others, forthcoming). Bushmeat market and site entry surveys, household protein consumption investigations, studies of consumer taste and purchasing preference, and regularly updated censuses were undertaken at Kabo, Pokola, Ndoki 1, and Ndoki 2 sites. Forest reconnaissance surveys established and monitored baselines of large mammal relative abundance and distribution, and human activity in relation to protected and community hunting zones. Large mammal visitation of key forest clearings in proximity to roads and camps was monitored to detect and deter hunting perturbations.

In 2000, CIB and WCS jointly surveyed a high biodiversity area in the north of the Kabo concession known as the Goualogo triangle. Data confirmed earlier observations (Fay, Agnagna, and Moutsambote 1990; Morgan, personal observation) of pristine old growth mixed forest; little evidence of human use in the past 50 years or more; and chimpanzee, gorilla, red colobus, and other large mammals exhibiting "naïve" behavior, suggesting little or no contact with humans (Malonga, Glannaz, and Elkan 2000). Timber density was high, particularly in valuable mahoganies. WCS and CIB met regularly to discuss the Goualogo during 2000-1, and the World Bank included the issue in its dialogue with the government of the Republic of Congo. The president of the Republic of Congo learned of the conservation importance of the area during a visit to the WCS Congo Forest Exhibit at the Bronx Zoo in New York and instructed his government to find a solution to protect it. In July 2001, the government announced its decision to protect the 21,000 ha area by annexing it to the park.

WCS efforts to influence the placement of the Loundougou access road met with no success. Joint surveys investigated several road and dike construction scenarios at varying distances from the NNNP. The area was found to be generally flat, with swamp forests and drainage areas constraining road placement. A potential scenario with the road passing 17 kilometers southeast of the park would have required construction of twice the length of dike. Prioritizing long-term road maintenance concerns, CIB selected the most direct route, passing 5 kilometers from the park. The road will become the principal means of transport between the Likouala and Sangha provinces. Although the opportunity remains to relocate the road further from the park, the company has requested incentive development scenarios in order to share the costs.

(5) Wildlife law enforcement

Wildlife protection was initiated in Kabo in 1999, with a small mobile team of two MFE officers and eight ecoguards. Ecoguards recruited from local communities received training from the MFE, Congolese military, and WCS staff. Control posts were established at key vehicle circulation points, and mobile patrols surveyed key sectors of the forest. Activities were progressively expanded geographically, and rigor was increased in the application of regulations. The protection unit was expanded as funding became available, reaching 6 MFE officers and 25 ecoguards by 2001 (for coverage of greater than 600,000 ha), and was expanded to 40 guards in late 2002 (Elkan and others, forthcoming).

Protection activities initially focused on halting poaching of protected species and eliminating the use of wire snares. Enforcement of zoning and pro-

hibition of export from sites was implemented following the raising of public awareness. Hunters were encouraged to purchase hunting permits and register shotguns. Problems initially included protected species poaching, refusal by company drivers to collaborate with controls, and complicity of CIB employees in bushmeat export. Pressures to feed the large population center and potential social unrest required a more gradual approach to controlling the supply of bushmeat to Pokola town.

CIB applied its internal regulations for wildlife management through disciplinary measures, ranging from verbal reprimands for minor offenses to dismissal for more serious violations (such as protected species poaching). While significantly improving employee behavior with respect to wildlife management, key problems encountered included the following:

■ There was initial reticence to punish violators because of a fear that company operations would be disrupted (particularly with vehicle drivers).
■ Initially, several CIB managers perceived wildlife problems as the responsibility of WCS and the government, not that of the company.
■ Employees complained about the lack of protein availability and threatened labor strikes in protest against law enforcement actions.
■ Unions and employees objected to disciplinary measures for wildlife violations in the regional judiciary system.

High-level company management involvement was necessary to help address these problems, clarify the company's commitment to improving wildlife management, and communicate these principles directly to field managers and other concerned parties.

In addition to CIB systems, legal charges were submitted to the Regional Direction of Forestry Economy (RDFE) for legal processing. RDFE worked relatively efficiently in 1999, resulting in several substantial fines and the reinforcement of field activities. A change in administrators in 2000, however, limited legal pursuit of even the most serious violations. While this weakened field-based law enforcement, company disciplinary measures continued to provide significant support. Reinforcing and monitoring the legal processes in support of wildlife law enforcement will be fundamental to sustaining field conservation efforts.

Potential Gains and Risks

Formal and informal discussions with company management and employees, local hunters and community members, regional authorities, and government representatives elucidated various stakeholder goals and concerns. Potential long-term gains and risks in relation to wildlife management and conservation in timber concessions need to be considered in strategy development (see table 6.1).

Discussion

Under this program, relatively simple means were used to reduce the indirect (hunting) impact of timber exploitation on wildlife in an area of forest twice the size of and adjacent to a protected area of global biodiversity significance. The situation for wildlife management and conservation was greatly improved in much of the project area, and the process led to shifts in company and community involvement after only three years of interventions. Although problems still persist in several areas of the concession, and the sustainability of subsistence wildlife harvests is under investigation, the systems to address these problems have been firmly established. Based on this model, the government has modified forestry policy to require timber companies to support wildlife management and conservation in all concessions of the northern forest region of the country.

Key Factors and Difficulties

Personal relationships between organizational representatives, time invested in discussion of management issues, and frequent transparent communication all contributed to the establishment of the initiative and sustained progress. From the begin-

ning, high-level company management took a direct role in the process and communicated with employees and unions regarding company commitment to wildlife management. Direct and indirect company involvement and support increased greatly over the course of project implementation. Participation in the program has improved the company's image internationally, as well as its opportunities for certification. High-level government support was critical to the establishment of the program and the protection of the Goualogo. Low human-population density in the Kabo concession facilitated law enforcement and zoning of large no-hunting areas.

Some of the most difficult challenges to collaboration have been issues with the greatest potential impact on revenue (that is, set-asides of high biodiversity areas, and road and camp placement). Social conflict related to the reduction of the commercial bushmeat trade and pressures to feed the large town of Pokola challenged collaboration with local communities and were most complex to manage. In all cases, a joint process was undertaken to define the problem, study it, and propose and discuss solutions, taking into consideration the views of all parties.

Government officers indicated that the co-managed NGO-government structure fostered transparency, rigor, and accountability, alleviating many of these pressures. International involvement raised the profile of protection operations, encouraging the support and interest of high-level government and company representatives. Integration of wildlife rules into company regulations reinforced national laws and made up for slow or inefficient legal procedures. It was recognized that companies need to accept occasional temporary perturbations or delays in operations because of wildlife law enforcement (for example, as a result of dismissal of employees) as a cost of environmental management.

Issues of land and resource tenure are at the forefront of forest management problems in the Congo Basin. Wildlife management zoning can support traditional land-use patterns in the region, and recruitment of ecoguards exclusively from the local

Table 6.1

Potential Long-Term Gains and Risks of Wildlife Management and Conservation in Timber Concessions for Different Stakeholders in Northern Republic of Congo Forests

	Potential Gains	*Potential Risks*
Company	■ Improved international image and increased potential to obtain certification ■ Surveillance and controls result in fewer accidents, reduced immigration and nonemployee access, reduced theft of company property, and increased employee focus on work (not on hunting) ■ Shared technology and expertise improves forestry planning and reduces costs	■ Increased exposure of information about activities and potential for negative media attention ■ Increased pressure to undertake improved management and incur costs that competitors do not incur ■ Social problems related to wildlife management
Local Community	■ Reinforcement of traditional land tenure systems and reduction of outsider exploitation of local wildlife resources ■ Increased employment and economic opportunities for local indigenous communities (ecoguards and alternative protein source production) ■ Increased potential to secure long-term sustainable subsistence hunting for traditional forest communities	■ Loss of revenue from commercial hunting ■ Increased costs of respecting wildlife laws (hunting permits and shotguns instead of snares)
Government	■ Improved international image of country with continued revenue generation from timber exploitation ■ Reduced impact on ecosystem increases potential for development of multi-resource revenue generation activities (wildlife management, tourism, and so forth) ■ Managed buffer region resulting in protection and decreased management costs of neighboring PAs	■ Increased exposure of information and transparency ■ Increased pressure to remove areas from production and reduce the impact of road placement ■ Social problems related to wildlife management
Biodiversity Conservation	■ Protection of rare and endangered wildlife over a large area not normally designated as a PA with costs partially covered by private sector ■ Wildlife management measures promote sustainable use of game species across landscape ■ Managed buffer region resulting in protection and decreased management costs of neighboring PA	■ Criticism from some international environmentalists for working with the private sector ■ Potential nonachievement of specific goals where alternative strategies might have been effective (for example, halt exploitation and make the concession a PA)

Note: PA, protected area

communities can reinforce community "ownership" and support. A critical challenge to sustainable management of wildlife in these forests is control of secondary in-migration and access (Elkan and others, forthcoming; Auzel and Wilkie 2000). Sawmills and associated secondary industry opportunities lead to demographic booms that exacerbate social conflict over efforts to control the commercial wildlife trade. Placement of industrial development in existing populated centers away from forests should be central to regional-level planning and to international multilateral and bilateral dialogues and assistance. However, current government policies do not take this into account.

Hunting to feed company employees has long been the norm in many tropical timber concessions (Robinson, Redford, and Bennett 1999). Modification of company policy to integrate wildlife regulations creates a disincentive for employees, but sufficient alternative protein must also be available for this to be practically effective. CIB and labor unions in Kabo and Pokola eventually recognized their respective responsibilities and have begun actively to import beef, frozen fish, and chicken, and to support animal farming on a large scale. Policies need to be designed and clarified requiring companies to engage in this area at their camps and industrial sites. Once a private sector commitment is effective, international efforts and resources can then be shifted to emphasize work with traditional "non-company" communities, where the problem can more often be addressed through a combination of sustainable subsistence hunting and fishing, and the development of alternative revenue opportunities.

Alternative revenue is a key condition for traditional communities in the Congo Basin to be prepared to forego commercial hunting. Employment with timber companies conditional on adherence to wildlife regulations has the potential to provide an alternative to commercial hunting on a large scale. In addition, former hunters can be recruited as ecoguards and given priority in opportunities for alternative protein source provision. At present, many companies recruit skilled labor from capital cities (and even other countries) for convenience. This takes opportunities away from local communities and inevitably increases secondary in-migration. It is therefore in the long-term interest of companies, local communities, and wildlife for companies to invest in the training and development of a skilled, locally recruited workforce and to prioritize the recruitment of local indigenous peoples.

While the sustainability of wildlife harvests in the Kabo and Pokola concessions is currently under investigation, data indicate that clear progress has been made in control and management of hunting pressures (Elkan and others, forthcoming). The status of game populations, ability to spatially manipulate hunting pressures, and potential for species-specific regulations show significant potential for sustainable hunting programs in several areas with small communities (McCullough 1996; Robinson and Bodmer 1999; Eaton 2002; Elkan and others, forthcoming). Hunting and fishing alone cannot feed the large population centers, given current growth rates. Strict limits on hunting are therefore required in these areas to force demand for effective accompanying systems of alternative protein importation.

Research has shown that Kabo and Pokola are critical for wildlife ranging outside the NNNP, for protection of species that are not adequately represented in the park, and for conservation of rare and endangered species and forest clearing habitat (Elkan and others, forthcoming). Law enforcement has extended protection and management to a broad area of community hunting areas and strict no-hunting zones. Gorilla and chimpanzee were found to occur in high abundance in many areas (both logged and hunted) and demonstrated curious and calm behavior in the presence of humans. Further in-depth investigations will better understand the longer-term direct and indirect effects of logging on wildlife. As habitat is lost to deforestation, timber concessions in the Congo Basin will become increasingly important to wildlife populations, as has been the case in other regions of Africa and Asia.

Protection of the Goualogo triangle was a significant step for biodiversity conservation and set a precedent for set-asides as part of responsible forest management in the region. The government of the Republic of Congo has foregone timber exploitation of the NNNP and has yet to reap any direct benefits from park-based tourism. While several incentive mechanisms were explored, direct dialogue with the highest level of the government of the Republic of Congo and evolving company interest in certification contributed most directly to the decision to protect the area.

Attempts to influence the placement of infrastructure (roads and camps) generated little support from the government, which prioritized rapid development. Although CIB considered various road scenarios, there was little incentive to select options further away from the park. Many road development projects receive international assistance and a strong case is made for international subsidization to cover the incremental costs of environmentally sound public infrastructure placement. Planning of roads and infrastructure to minimize long-term impacts on protected areas in the Congo Basin should be a priority focus of multilateral processes.

Replication

Effective wildlife conservation and management in Congo Basin timber concessions requires investment in a comprehensive approach, including wildlife protection, alternative activities, education and awareness, and research/monitoring components. Undertaking one activity in isolation cannot effectively address the fundamental problems. Protection activities require the greatest number of personnel salaries (40 percent of staff), uniforms, diesel fuel, rations, vehicles, guard posts, housing, hospital care, and a personnel management structure. As these costs can make up more than 50 percent of the total budget, measures should be taken to reduce personnel needs and increase efficiency. Limiting access roads, avoiding ecologically sensitive areas, and minimizing camps can limit the medium- and long-term costs of wildlife protection and should therefore be incorporated in forestry planning and cost-benefit analyses.

If poorly developed, alternative activities programs can simply encourage further in-migration and increase hunting. The greatest pressures on wildlife originate from industrial sites, where companies need to incorporate alternative protein provision systems along with basic social obligations (schools, health care, water, and so forth). International funding can be useful in leveraging company funding and is essential for working with noncompany traditional communities in close proximity to protected areas. In addition to ensuring an adequate supply of domestic protein to company sites, policy and management should be carefully designed to restrict access to facilities in order to discourage secondary in-migration.

While private timber companies should be able to take on more wildlife program administrative and personnel management duties in the medium term, third party oversight helps foster transparency and is likely to be most effective in initial program establishment. The potential for corruption, the complexity of interventions required, and the need for coordination on multiple scales all require extensive technical knowledge and experience. Third party involvement (such as international or national NGOs, and so forth) will be critical to design, initiate and co-manage effective programs in the short term. This role can and should evolve toward a more technical advisory, research, and monitoring role as timber company managers and government officers take on increased responsibility for wildlife management oversight. Independent evaluations and certification schemes can play an important role in promoting objective evaluation of management efforts, ensuring transparency and maintaining pressure to improve. However, independent evaluations are a minor tool and are likely to be of little use to wildlife conservation if critical training and competent technical support are not available to companies and governments.

Figures from Kabo and Pokola indicate that effective wildlife management in the timber concessions of northern Congo would cost an estimated US$9.75 million per year (3 million ha with low pressures x US$1.25 per ha and 4 million ha with high pressures x US$1.50 per ha). Running costs of a 400,000 ha National Park in the region are currently about US$500,000 per year (US$1.25 per ha). Wildlife management costs in concessions are likely to decrease as serious threats are reduced, sustainable alternative protein systems are established, and research shifts from baselines to monitoring. Estimates show that this scenario could reduce expenses to US$0.90 per ha, or $6.3 million per year, for mainstreaming wildlife conservation in concessions across northern Congo.

The status of wildlife populations, biodiversity importance, human pressures and access, and proximity to existing protected areas all need careful consideration in prioritizing and catalyzing efforts in different concessions in the Congo Basin. A basic standard of wildlife management should be required in all concessions. Those concessions with high biodiversity, with important wildlife populations and habitat, and which act as buffer zones in contiguous landscapes for neighboring protected areas require immediate conservation intervention and support.

Implications for Landscape Conservation Strategy Development

Wildlife management efforts in the concessions around the NNNP provide an example of mainstreaming biodiversity conservation that has been subject to both praise and criticism. Criticism has included allegations of corruption of law enforcement units, complaints about restrictions on hunting rights for local communities, and appeals for the private sector to take on the full burden of the financial costs. Yet many parties have recognized the importance of this pioneering approach, and respect the rigor of its field implementation and monitoring. They have also recognized the concrete progress in bringing a catastrophic commercial bushmeat trade under control, stimulating private

sector involvement, and hence developing a model for replication.

New conservation approaches involving private industry require a high level of rigor and should be critically examined, tested, and evaluated. Detailed socioeconomic and ecological indicators and performance monitoring were used to assess progress and document engagements and improvements by the company (Elkan and others, forthcoming). Extensive internal control and personnel management systems were developed to reduce corruption in protection teams. Although law enforcement reduces potential commercial hunting revenue, wildlife management has reinforced traditional resource tenure systems. Employment opportunities with the timber company and conservation NGO have been created for local forest peoples. While much remains to be accomplished in the concessions, the level of progress achieved thus far has substantially improved the conservation situation for all species of wildlife over a large area.

One of the strengths of this approach is that many of the costs of wildlife conservation and management can eventually be passed on to the timber industry and the final consumer. While a strong

---

Table 6.2:
Summary of Key Factors and Challenges Affecting Wildlife Conservation and Management in the Kabo and Pokola Concessions, 1999-2001

Factors Contributing to Progress	Challenges to Progress
■ High-level government of the Republic of Congo support	■ Communication initially difficult and some resistance from mid-level company staff
■ Personal contacts and development of trust	■ Protection of high priority areas of the concession and major road and camp placement
■ Company orientation and interest in certification and improved image	■ Nutrition of employee population in Pokola
■ Practical, ground-based comprehensive approach	■ Clarification of responsibilities regarding alternative protein source development
■ Shared responsibility to address complicated problems	■ Demographic growth through immigration
■ Willingness to hold a dialogue on difficult issues and appreciate differing points of view	
■ Long-term experience in the region	
■ Large management area with one company	
■ Low human-population density in Kabo forestry management unit	
■ Written terms of obligations for involved parties	

move is needed in this direction, it will take time for companies to become willing to pay, for governments to adjust and implement policy, and for certification and other incentives to be operationalized. In the meantime, parks and reserves surrounded by industry are experiencing conservation crises and threats demanding immediate intervention on a landscape scale.

The urgency with which pressures are building up requires a stepwise approach with partial international support, in combination with funding and engagements from the private sector and Congo Basin governments. Technical expertise, training, and funding to assist governments to develop and implement wildlife management strategies, along with timber company support, are necessary to initiate effective programs. Interventions and targets for international support should be prioritized for those concessions with the most important buffer zone roles, wildlife populations, and habitat areas. If the commercial wildlife trade and systematic defaunation processes are to be stemmed and managed, this will come at high social costs, as the revenue generated is significant. Governments need to backstop field-based interventions with fully enforced national bans on commercial bushmeat traffic, clearly modified and publicly supported policies, and real prosecution of violators. Civil law enforcement, military and customs authorities, as well as transport agencies and private companies will play a critical role in the success of these efforts.

From a business perspective there is currently little incentive for the private sector to undertake wildlife conservation and management and improve forest management, for lack of an "even playing field" of enforced policy requirements. Forest certification provides the potential for private companies to gain market advantages as a direct result of improved environmental management. In March 2004, CIB announced its commitment to pursue Forest Stewardship Council certification of its concessions. However, certification criteria do not yet adequately address wildlife issues particular to the forests of the Congo Basin (Bennett 2002).

To shift from research to adaptive management, mandates must be developed to work directly with commercial and individual natural resource users in the landscapes surrounding and linking protected areas. Approaches such as field-based, private sector-NGO-government collaboration need to be carefully considered, designed, evaluated, and fully implemented where appropriate. Policy frameworks are lacking to support interventions in the field and create the incentive/disincentive climate necessary to encourage private sector engagement in sound wildlife and forest management. Finally, certification schemes must be clarified and consumers educated to take into account wildlife conservation concerns specific to the forests of the Congo Basin.

The authors thank the Ministry of Forestry Economy of the government of the Republic of Congo for its strong support for the work described in this paper. Jean-Marie Mevellec and Jacques Glannaz of CIB and Heinrich Stoll and Robert Hunink of TT Tropical Timber International, are thanked for their continued collaboration and efforts to integrate wildlife conservation in production forest management. The ITTO; the governments of France, Japan, Switzerland, and the United States; and the USAID; CARPE; USFW; USFS; Art Ortenberg and Liz Claiborne Foundation; and Columbus Zoo funded aspects of this conservation work. John Robinson, Mike Fay, Bill Weber, and Amy Vedder helped with the development of the initiative. Finally, this paper is dedicated to the memory of Frederic Glannaz, CIB Forest Management Planner.

Endnote

1   Wildlife Conservation Society, Brazzaville, Republic of Congo

References

Ape Alliance. 1998. *The African Bushmeat Trade: A Recipe for Extinction.* Cambridge, UK: Fauna and Flora International.

Auzel, P., and D. S. Wilkie, 2000. "Wildlife Use in Northern Congo: Hunting in a Commercial Logging Concession." In J. G. Robinson and E. L. Bennett, eds. *Hunting for Sustainability in Tropical Forests.* New York: Columbia University Press.

Bennett, E.L. 2000. "Timber Certification: Where Is the Voice of the Biologist?" *Conservation Biology* 14 (1): 921-23.

——. 2002. "Is There a Link between Wild Meat and Food Security?" *Conservation Biology* 16 (3): 590-92.

BCTF (Bushmeat Crisis Task Force). 2001. Bushmeat Crisis Fact Sheets. Washington, DC. www.bushmeat.org.

Cauley, H.A., C.M. Peters, R.Z. Donovan, and J.M. O'Connor. 2001. "Forest Stewardship Council Forest Certification." *Conservation Biology* 15 (2):311-13.

CARPE (Central Africa Regional Program for the Environment). 2001. *Taking Action to Manage and Conserve Forest Resources in the Congo Basin: Results and Lessons Learned from the First Phase (1996-2000).* CARPE Information Series. Washington, DC: CARPE Biodiversity Support Program.

Davies, G. 2002. "Bushmeat and International Development." *Conservation Biology* 16 (3): 587-89.

Eaton, M.J. 2002. Subsistence wildlife hunting in a multi-use forest of the Republic of Congo: monitoring and management for sustainable harvest. M.S. Thesis, University of Minnesota.

Elkan, P.W., S.W. Elkan, A. Moukassa, M. Ngangoue, and J.L.D. Smith. Forthcoming. "Management of Bushmeat Hunting in a Timber Concession in Northern Republic of Congo." In W. Laurence and C. Peres. *Emerging Threats to Tropical Forests.* Chicago, IL: University of Chicago Press.

Fa, J.E., C.A. Peres, and J. Meeuwig. 2002. "Bushmeat Exploitation in Tropical Forests: An Intercontinental Comparison." *Conservation Biology* 16 (1): 232-37.

Fay M., M. Agnagna, and J.M. Moutsambote. 1990. Surveys of the Nouabale-Ndoki Region, Northern Congo. Report to USAID and WCS.

Fimbel, R., A. Grajal, and J.G. Robinson, eds. 2000. *Wildlife-logging interactions in tropical forests.*

FSC. 2002.

Ghazoul, J. 2001. "Barriers to Biodiversity Conservation in Forest Certification." *Conservation Biology* 15 (2): 315-17.

ITTO (International Tropical Timber Organization). 1996. *Annual Report and Assessment of the World Tropical Timber Situation.* Yokohama, Japan: ITTO.

Malonga R., F. Glannaz, and P.W. Elkan, 2000. *Wildlife and Timber Surveys in the Goualogo Triangle, Kabo Forest.* New York: Wildlife Conservation Society.

McCullough, D.R. 1996. "Spatially Structured Populations and Harvest Theory." *Journal of Wildlife Management* 60 (1): 1-9.

Moukassa, A. 1999. Reconnaissance ecologique de la zone est de la rivière Ndoki UFA Kabo. Report for PROGEPP-WCS.

——. 2001. *Etude demographique et socio-economique dans la Zone Périphérique du Parc National Nouabale-Ndoki (Kabo, Pokola, Loundougou, Mokabi).* New York: Wildlife Conservation Society.

Oates, J.F., M. Abedi-Lartey, W. Scott McGraw, T.T. Strusaker, and G.T. Whitesides. 2000. "Extinction of a West African Red Colobus Monkey." *Conservation Biology* 14 (5): 1526-32.

Robinson, J. G., and R. E. Bodmer. 1999. "Toward Wildlife Management in Tropical Forests." *Journal of Wildlife Management* 63 (1): 1-13.

Robinson, J.G., K.H. Redford, and E.L. Bennett. 1999. "Wildlife Harvest in Logged Tropical Forests." *Science* 284 (5414): 595-96.

Strusaker, T.T. 1997. *Ecology of an African Rain Forest: Logging in Kibale and the Conflict between Conservation and Exploitation.* Gainesville, FL: University Press of Florida.

Weber, W., L.J.T. White, A. Vedder, and L. Naughton-Treves, eds. 2001. *African Rainforest Ecology and Conservation.* New Haven, CT: Yale University Press.

White, L.J.T. 1992. Vegetation history and logging disturbance: Effects on rain forest mammals in the Lope Reserve, Gabon (with special emphasis on elephants and apes). PhD Thesis, University of Edinburgh.

Wilkie, D.S., and J.F. Carpenter. 1999. "Bushmeat Hunting in the Congo Basin: An Assessment of Impacts and Options for Mitigation." *Biodiversity and Conservation* 8 (7): 927-55.

Wilkie, D.S., J.G. Sidle, and G.C. Boundzanga. 1992. "Mechanized Logging, Market Hunting, and a Bank Loan in Congo." *Conservation Biology* 6: 570-80.

World Bank. 2002. A Revised Forest Strategy for the World Bank Group, October 31. World Bank, Washington, DC.

Part 3.

Challenges and Opportunities in Mainstreaming

7. Achieving Sustainable Landscapes: A Calculus for Trade-Offs between Conservation and Human Use

Kent H. Redford[1]

If the turn of the century has left us with a single conclusion, it is that humans are now the major actors on planet Earth. Measures of our hegemonic ecological role are now well known, and can be seen in usurpation of the majority of surface water, primary productivity, and large oceanic fish (Sanderson and others 2002). Even jet contrails, the sign of distant human passage, have been shown to affect climate (Boucher 1999).

The past 40 years have produced a growing understanding of the impacts that humans are having on the Earth and its other inhabitants. In response, in what some have called the largest planned land-use decision ever made by humans, an increased and now significant portion of the Earth's surface has been assigned to one of a number of categories of protection.

Unfortunately, it has become clear in the last decade that these protected areas, even if well managed and adequately supported, will not be able to survive the vagaries of human action on their own in order to succeed at their assigned task of conserving all biological diversity (Brandon, Redford, and Sanderson 1998; McNeely 1997). This unsettling conviction has been built on a number of observations:

- Many of the protected areas are too small either to conserve sufficiently large populations of wide-ranging animals or to maintain the ecological processes on which their fauna and flora depend.

- Most protected areas were not established in the right places for preserving the Earth's biodiversity. One major underlying factor responsible for this mismatch is the dedication of areas with richer, arable soils to human agriculture, with their resultant conversion, making them largely unavailable for biodiversity protection.
- Many of the forces responsible for biodiversity loss and attenuation are not stopped by the boundaries of protected areas (such as invasive species and fire caused by humans).
- Climate change may produce impacts on biodiversity that decrease the effectiveness of protected areas in carrying out their protective role.
- Finally, there has been a growing, vocal critique of protected areas, with some advocating the dissolution of the entire protected area estate.

To those with a conviction that humans cannot live productive, fulfilling lives without biodiversity, the lesson is clear: Protected areas, by themselves, will never be able to maintain biodiversity. Conservation of biological diversity will only succeed if this conservation takes place in virtually all parts of the Earth's surface.

The Imperative of Mainstreaming

Overall, 83 percent of the land's surface, and 98 percent of the area where it is possible to grow rice, wheat, or maize, is directly influenced by humans (Sanderson and others 2002). In another analysis,

Freese (1998) pointed out that 56 percent of the terrestrial realm and over 95 percent of the marine realm are neither fully protected nor converted into built environments, but can be classified as multiple-use natural or seminatural ecosystems. By anyone's calculations, vast areas of the Earth's surface are affected by humans. If biodiversity conservation is to succeed, and if protected areas are to play their part, then conservation activities, too long considered to take place only in parks, must extend into the human-dominated landscape.

The extension of conservation activities into such landscapes can be termed "mainstreaming." According to the Cape Town workshop on Mainstreaming Biodiversity in Production Land-scapes and Sectors, the objective of mainstreaming biodiversity is: "to internalize the goals of biodiver-sity conservation and the sustainable use of biological resources into economic sectors and development models, policies and programmes, and therefore into all human behaviour." Discussions of mainstreaming emphasize those economic sectors directly related to natural resource use and manage-ment—agriculture, forestry, fisheries, invasives con-trol, wildlife utilization, mining, and tourism. This list must be extended to include protected areas so con-servation can be moved from its stronghold in pro-tected areas and extended to encompass the entire surface of the globe.

Before mainstreaming can succeed, a critical step must be taken to acknowledge explicitly the costs of human activity to biodiversity. Too much fuzzy thinking and a lack of precision have allowed the current permissive "win-win solution" climate, which enables many to believe that development can take place without any significant cost to the natural world. Costs must be acknowledged before intelligent, a priori discussions can begin as to how to apportion these costs and how to ensure that conservation has a chance to succeed.

This paper lays out a proposal for developing sustain-able landscapes (in the sense of Robinson 1994), based on an "unpacked" definition of biodiversity

Box 7.1
A Definition of Biodiversity

Biodiversity refers to the natural variety and variability among living organisms, the ecological complexes in which they naturally occur, and the ways in which they interact with each other and with the physical environ-ment. Climate, geology, and physiography all exert con-siderable influence on broad spatial patterns of biotic variety; local ecosystems and their biological components are further modified by environmental variation (such as local climatic and stream-flow fluctuations) and interac-tions among native biota. This natural variety and vari-ability is distinguished from biotic patterns or conditions formed under the influence of human-mediated species introductions and substantially human-altered environ-mental processes and selection regimes.

Source: Adapted from Redford and Richter (1999).

and an explicit method of calculating the precise impact of different land uses on biodiversity. This planning "calculus" can be used to inform the trade-offs that are made between potential conservation benefits, as well as the inevitable trade-offs between the often conflicting imperatives of conservation and development. The calculus thus informs the develop-ment of a sustainable landscape consisting of a mosaic of different land uses, urban zones, and fully protected areas. Such a mosaic would be designed in order to maximize conservation of all the existing components and attributes of biodiversity, while allowing people to practice sustainable livelihoods.

A Comprehensive Definition

Before a coherent and strategic discussion can be held on mainstreaming biodiversity, it is essential to work with a comprehensive definition of biodiver-sity. The definition in box 7.1 is drawn from Redford and Richter (1999), based upon references listed therein.

Biological diversity can be measured in terms of dif-ferent components (genetic, population/species, and community/ecosystem), each of which has compositional, structural, and functional attributes. Composition refers to the identity and variety of elements in each of the biodiversity components. Structure refers to the physical organization or pattern of the elements. Function refers to ecological and evolutionary processes acting among the elements. Table 7.1 is a modification of the matrix presented in Noss (1990), presenting some of the measurable attributes of compositional, structural,

and functional diversity for the three components of biodiversity, with a focus on those measures that would be most useful in determining potential effects of human use on biodiversity.

The three components of biodiversity are defined below, together with an indication of how the attributes (composition, structure, function) might be measured:

Table 7.1
Attributes of Each Biodiversity Component, Emphasizing Those Measures Useful in Determining Potential Effects of Human Use

Biodiversity Component	Composition	Structure	Function
Genetic	Allelic diversity; presence of particular rare alleles, deleterious recessives, or karyotypic variants	Effective population size, heterozygosity, chromosomal or phenotypic polymorphism, generation overlap, and heredity	Inbreeding depression; outbreeding rate; rate of genetic drift; gene flow; mutation rate; and selection intensity
Population/species	Abundance, biomass, or density; frequency, importance, or cover value	Dispersion (micro-dispersion); range; metapopulation spatial configuration; and population structure	Demographic processes (such as fertility, recruitment rate, survivorship, dispersal, mortality); metapopulation exchange rates; and individual growth rates
Community/ ecosystem	Presence, richness, frequency, and relative abundance of patch types, guilds, and species; proportions of endemic, exotic, threatened and endangered species; proportions of generalists and specialists; and life form proportions (C_4:C_3)	Patch size-frequency distributions; patch spatial configuration and connectivity; trophic structure; vegetation physiognomy; seral stage diversity and areal extent; stream channel form; and abundance and distribution of structural elements	Extent/spread, frequency/ return interval, predictability, timing, intensity and duration of disturbance processes; patch turnover rates; energy flow rates and patterns; nutrient delivery and cycling rates; biomass productivity; herbivory; parasitism and predation rates; pollination success; geomorphic processes; and water chemistry and temperature variation

Source: Redford and Richter (1999), after Noss (1990).

Table 7.2
Effects of Human Alteration, from Heavily "Built" to Unaltered "Natural," on the Components and Attributes of Biodiversity

Biodiversity component attribute	Human alteration			
	Built	Cultivated	Managed	Natural
Genetic				
function	o	o	X	XX
structure	o	o	X	XX
composition	o	o	X	XX
Population/species				
function	o	o	X	XX
structure	o	o	X	XX
composition	o	o	X	XX
Community/ecosystem				
function	o	X	XX	XX
structure	o	X	XX	XX
composition	o	o	X	XX

Note: XX, completely conserved; X, partially conserved; o, not conserved.

Source: Hunter (1996); redrawn from Redford and Richter (1999).

- *Diversity of the genetic component* refers to the variability within a species, as measured by the variation in genes within a particular species, subspecies, or population. Composition of this component might be measured through allelic diversity, structure through heterozygosity, and function through gene flow.
- *Diversity of the population/species component* refers to the variety of living species and their component populations at the local, regional, or global scale. Composition of this component might be measured through species abundance, structure through population age structure, and function through demographic processes such as survivorship.
- *Diversity of the community/ecosystem component* refers to a group of diverse organisms, guilds, and patch types occurring in the same environment or area, and strongly interacting through trophic and spatial biotic and abiotic relationships. Composition of this component might be measured through relative abundance of species and guilds within a community; structure through spatial geometry and arrangement of patch types; and function through disturbance regimes (such as fire and flood) and flows of water, nutrients, chemicals, and organic matter.

Calculating the Costs of Use

With a definition of biodiversity in terms of components and attributes, it is then possible to look in greater detail at the impacts of different human uses on biodiversity. At a first approximation, the world can be divided into four general categories (adapted from Hunter 1996): natural, managed, cultivated, and built; and the general condition of the attributes and components of biodiversity can be assessed in each one of these (table 7.2, redrawn from Redford and Richter (1999)). As is clear, on average, in built environments there is virtually no con-

Table 7.3
Effects of Resource-Use Systems on the Components and Attributes of Biodiversity

Biodiversity component and attribute	Types of use						
	Irrigation supply reservoirs	Hydropower dams	Intensive fishing on coral reefs	Grazing in historically ungrazed forests	Water diversion	Harvesting nontimber forest products	Wilderness river-running
Genetic							
function	o	o	o	X	X	X	XX
structure	o	o	o	X	X	X	XX
composition	o	o	o	X	X	X	XX
Population/species							
function	o	o	o	X	X	X	XX
structure	o	o	o	X	X	X	XX
composition	o	o	o	X	X	X	XX
Community/ecosystem							
function	o	X	X	X	XX	XX	XX
structure	o	X	X	X	XX	XX	XX
composition	o	X	X	X	X	XX	XX

Note: XX, completely conserved; X, partially conserved; o, not conserved.

Source: Adapted from Redford and Richter (1999)

servation of the components and attributes of biodiversity, whereas in natural environments, both are fully conserved.

What is important for this analysis is that the intermediate categories show differential effects. The "cultivated" environments partially conserve only the function and structure attributes of the ecosystem component, whereas the "managed" environments fully conserve these, while only partially conserving all other attributes and components. Admittedly, this is a caricature of human impact on biodiversity, but it begins to suggest ways of building pieces to assemble in sustainable landscapes. It seems that the ecosystem component may be more robust in relation to human use than other components, and that function and structure attributes may be more robust than composition.

At a finer scale, it is possible to examine the ways in which specific human uses can affect biodiversity

components and attributes. Table 7.3 (redrawn from Redford and Richter (1999)) demonstrates this sort of analysis on a set of human uses, ranging from those with greater impact on the left-hand side (irrigation supply reservoirs) to those with little impact on the right-hand side (wilderness river running). As this analysis demonstrates, the impact of human use on biodiversity is not a one-dimensional variable, with some uses being benign and others being "bad" for biodiversity, but rather a complicated mix of greater and lesser impact on different components and attributes of biodiversity. This scale of analysis shows similar trends to those at the broader scale. Once again, there are types of use that conserve few, if any, components and attributes, while other, nonconsumptive, uses exert few, if any, costs on biodiversity. The many intermediate uses between these two extremes show that attributes and components vary in their sensitivity to human use, but the ecosystem component seems most robust.

Finally, this way of looking at the impact of use on biodiversity components and attributes can be extended to a comparison of different ways of implementing the same type of use. There are clearly several ways of implementing the same type of human use. Figure 7.1 (from Putz and others 2000) demonstrates an analysis of the impact of different forest uses on the components of biodiversity (this analysis adds "community" and "landscape" components and scores using "mostly conserved," "affected," and "mostly lost"). There are marked differences in the impacts of these different general "forest uses," ranging from nontimber forest product harvesting, which has the least impact on biodiversity components and attributes, to logging followed by enrichment planting, which has the greatest impact. Once again, it seems that the ecosystem component is the most resilient in the face of human use, and the genetic component is the least resilient. These conclusions seem broadly in agreement with other studies (Freese 1998, for example). Any conversation about how a given land use type may contribute to an overall sustainable landscape must specify what specific version of that land use is being considered.

A Calculus to Inform Biodiversity Trade-Offs

With an understanding of the ways in which different human uses affect the components and attributes of biodiversity it is possible to begin to develop the concept of a sustainable landscape (in the sense of Robinson (1994)). Such a sustainable landscape would consist of a mosaic of different land uses, urban zones, and fully protected areas designed in such a way as to conserve all the existing components and attributes of biodiversity, while allowing people to practice sustainable livelihoods.

The key factor in this concept of sustainable landscapes is that it allows a planning calculus that includes all of the land uses, rather than just single types of human use. This calculus, or method of calculation, is based on the evaluation of individual land uses outlined earlier and a determination of

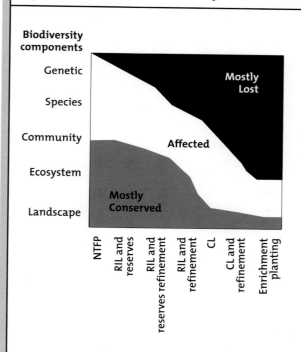

Figure 7.1:
Expected Effects of a Range of Forest Uses on the Components of Biodiversity

NTFP: Non timber forest products

RIL: Reduced-impact logging

Reserves: Protected areas within logged units

Refinement: Silvicultural treatments such as liberation of future crop trees from competition, which can substantially change the physiognomy, composition, and trophic structure of forest stands which are applied to increase volume increments and relative densities of commerical timed species

Enrichment planting: Increasing the stocking of commercial species by planting seedlings (or seeds) in logging gaps or along cleared lines

CL: Conventional logging

Source: Putz and others (2000).

which attributes and components of biodiversity can be maintained under that land use. Table 7.4 presents a simplification of this process that, in its full elucidation, would require multiple dimensions to allow for proper scoring of each land use in a three-by-three matrix. But this table allows appreciation of

Table 7.4:
Examples of Ways in Which Different Land Use Types Could Contribute to Achieving Comprehensive Conservation of Biodiversity Configured in a Sustainable Landscape*

	Composition	Structure	Function
Genetic	Fully protected areas	Grazing on natural grasslands	Traditional fishing on coral reefs
Population/species	Mixed farming such as found in European cultural landscapes	Water diversion	Trophy hunting
Community/ecosystem	Ecotourism	Selective logging	Traditional agroforestry

* Placement assumes well-executed versions of the specified land use types.

the way that multiple land uses within a single landscape can be evaluated simultaneously.

Virtually every type of use has an unavoidable impact on some attribute or component of biodiversity, no matter how well configured it may be. This is the inevitable result of redirecting goods and flows from ecosystems to humans, and must be accepted and incorporated as a cost of use. However, most types of use also have the intrinsic potential to maintain—even though only partially—some component or attribute of biodiversity. Some even have the potential to restore various components or attributes of biodiversity. Therefore, an important part of developing a sustainable landscape is recognizing what can potentially be conserved under a given use regime, and putting into practice the particular form of that use that most effectively conserves the target attribute/component. Calculating the potential costs to and/or conservation of specific attributes and components is thus a useful tool in informing decisions in land-use planning and management.

The concept of sustainable landscapes is a multiscalar one, with the upper end being the entire globe. Recent efforts to promote broader scale conserva-

tion, such as the African Heartlands, Conservation Corridors, and Living Landscapes, are based on similar types of thinking (Redford and others 2003). In fact, this thinking can also be seen in the bioreserve (or biosphere reserve) concept, with its core and buffer zones, and the more general concept of zoning. What is being offered here is a way of both operationalizing these concepts, explicitly considering all of the components and attributes, and developing a standard currency that can be used to make trade-offs in a spatially explicit, comprehensive calculus. For the purposes of this proposal, the spatial scale of a sustainable landscape must be constrained by the feasibility of management.

It is important to point out that the existing system developed by IUCN (The World Conservation Union) for classifying the world's protected areas includes categories ranging from limited to no usage (Category 1) to those managed to ensure long-term protection and maintenance of biological diversity, while also providing a sustainable flow of natural products and services to meet community needs (Category 4). This range spans Hunter's "natural" and "managed" categories, and provides an internationally recognized framework to classify the ways in which protected areas can contribute to sustainable landscapes, and allows escape from the sterile arguments on protected areas currently taking place.

Trade-Offs and Sustainable Landscapes

Trade-offs between conservation and human use are an integral part of all conservation and development activities. Despite this obvious fact, both conservation and development communities have preferred to draw the curtain on this inevitable part of their work. Ignoring the need for trade-offs does not make it go away, and in fact makes the decision-making process more difficult. In front of the curtain it is possible to make generous promises of win–win solutions, equal consideration for all stakeholders, and cost-free solutions. When such fanciful solutions prove impossible to deliver, blame is heaped on everyone for failed project execution, whereas what actually failed was project conception. In the context of accounting, such reasoning would be grounds for a charge of deliberate fraud by "cooking the books."

It is therefore essential to discuss the different types of trade-offs associated with the concept of sustainable landscapes. Trade-offs are implicit both in determining which components/attributes are conserved in one land use and not another, and in determining which manifestation of a given land use most effectively conserves the relevant component/attribute. Both of these calculations involve trade-offs between components and between attributes within components.

There are also trade-offs between sustainable landscapes. For reasons due to biophysical factors, human history, and the management constraints of individual landscapes, not all of the biodiversity in a given region can be conserved within a single sustainable landscape. A process will therefore be necessary to create a comprehensive mosaic of sustainable landscapes that collectively achieve conservation objectives.

Table 7.5: Relative Reliance of the Poor on the Direct Use of Different Components of Biodiversity

Biodiversity component	Poverty in Different Settings		
	Urban dwellers	Rural intensive farmers	Low-density forest dwellers
Genetic	o	o	*
Population/ species	o	*	**
Community/ ecosystem	*	*	**

Note: o , little reliance; * , some reliance; ** , great reliance.

The types of trade-off outlined earlier feed into broader trade-offs between conservation and human use. Both types are mute on the subject of power. This issue is outside the scope of the current paper, but it is important to point out that there are trade-offs inherent in deciding who gets to make the decisions concerning biodiversity trade-offs. The interests of biodiversity itself are often underrepresented in discussions. Poor people, and those engaged in resource extraction that falls outside the modern notion of production, are also often left without an adequate voice. This is particularly true for extensive (but less significant) resource extraction activities such as nontimber forest product extraction or extensive grazing. Political and economic elites are often favored at the expense of these groups.

Finally, there is a growing realization of the importance of trade-offs between more developed and less developed countries. The existing set of resource flows from developed countries to help support biodiversity conservation creates a challenge for the "closed" model of sustainable landscapes discussed earlier. If resources from very distant sites are changing the dynamics in a given landscape, then these need to be taken into explicit consideration. These remote resources are themselves also often favoring certain components of biodiversity and certain ecosystems—witness the ways in which funding is increased by the existence of appealing vertebrate species and the favoring of tropical forests and coral reefs over grasslands and inshore marine grass beds.

Poverty Alleviation and Conservation

It is worth pointing out that poverty alleviation has become a siren's call in discussions of combining conservation and development. In the past few years a renewed interest in alleviating poverty has drawn attention and money away from pressing conservation challenges. Part of this move has been an often implicit assumption that improving the lot of the world's poor would in and of itself bring about conservation benefits (Sanderson and Redford 2003). This unproven assumption has complicated the important effort to incorporate concerns for the world's poor properly into consideration of mainstreaming biodiversity. Table 7.5 is a first attempt to show how the approach outlined in this paper might be used to begin such a complicated task.

Conclusions

In addition to conserving biodiversity, in the past couple of decades protected areas began to be assigned a multitude of other tasks, including livelihood generation for local peoples, generation of support for regional and national economies, democratization, and, most recently, poverty alleviation. Protected areas should never be expected to carry the weight of humanity's efforts to achieve sustainable development. They play a vital role in protecting those components/attributes most susceptible to human use that are hard to conserve in a landscape of use. But in many cases they are not configured to be able to achieve even this.

The attention of the conservation community must be broadened to include the vital tasks of biodiversity conservation on the majority of the Earth's surface that is affected by human use. The concept of mainstreaming has the potential to play a key role in the repositioning of conservation efforts. Mainstreaming must be used in a way that addresses the trade-offs between use and conservation across all components and attributes of biodiversity and across all categories of human use. These trade-off calculations can then be reassembled to help create sustainable landscapes that may offer a chance to improve the lot of people and the lot of the biodiversity that share a single Earth.

Endnote

1   WCS Institute, Wildlife Conservation Society, New York, USA

References

Boucher, O. 1999. "Air Traffic May Increase Cirrus Cloudiness." *Nature* 397: 30-31.

Brandon, K., K.H. Redford, and S.E. Sanderson, eds. 1998. *Parks in Peril: People, Politics, and Protected Areas.* Washington, DC: Island Press.

Freese, C. 1998. *Wild Species as Commodities.* Washington, DC: Island Press.

Hunter, M.L. Jr. 1996. *Fundamentals of Conservation Biology.* Cambridge, MA: Blackwell Science.

McNeely, J.A. 1997. "Conservation and the Future: Trends and Options toward the Year 2025." IUCN Biodiversity Policy Coordination Division, IUCN (The World Conservation Union), Gland, Switzerland.

Noss, R.F. 1990. "Indicators for Monitoring Biodiversity: A Hierarchical Approach." *Conservation Biology* 4: 355-64.

Putz, F. E., K.H. Redford, J.G. Robinson, R. Fimbel, and G.M. Blate. 2000. "Biodiversity Conservation in the Context of Tropical Forest Management." World Bank Environment Department Papers. Biodiversity Series–Impact Studies, No. 75, Washington, DC.

Redford, K. H., and B. Richter. 1999. "Conservation of Biodiversity in a World of Use." *Conservation Biology* 13 (6): 1246-56.

Redford, K.H., P. Coppolillo, E. W. Sanderson, G. A.B. da Fonseca, E. Dinerstein, C. Groves, G. Mace, S. Maginnis, R.A. Mittermeier, R. Noss, D. Olson, J.G. Robinson, A.- Vedder, and M. Wright. 2003. "Mapping the Conservation Landscape." *Conservation Biology* 17 (1): 116-31.

Robinson, J.G. 1994. "Carving up Tomorrow's Planet: An Interview with J.G. Robinson." *International Wildlife* 24 (January-February): 30-7.

Sanderson, E.W., M. Jaiteh, M.A. Levy, K.H. Redford, A.V. Wannebo, and G. Woolmer. 2002. "The Human Footprint and the Last of the Wild." *BioScience* 52 (10): 891-904.

Sanderson, S.E., and K.H. Redford. 2003. "Contested Relationships between Biodiversity Conservation and Poverty Alleviation." *Oryx* 37(4): 389-90.

8. Mainstreaming Biodiversity through South Africa's Bioregional Conservation Programs: Top-Down and Bottom-Up

Trevor Sandwith,[1] Kristal Maze,[2] Mandy Barnett,[3] Sarah Frazee,[4] and Mandy Cadman[5]

South Africa ranks as one of the most biologically diverse countries in the world, with plant diversity estimated at nine percent of the world's total. The Cape Floristic Region, for example, contained entirely within South Africa's borders, is the smallest and richest of the world's six floral kingdoms. These biological resources play a vital role in meeting basic human needs through their direct and indirect use and the delivery of ecosystem services. Despite their value, these resources have been compromised and remain under threat. This is the result of continuing processes of conversion and degradation of natural habitat, by agriculture and rangelands; inappropriate fire management; rapid and insensitive urban infrastructural development; over-exploitation of terrestrial, freshwater, and marine resources; infestation by invasive alien species; and the pervasive effects of pollution and climate change.

While understanding that there are several root causes of these problems, there is also an acknowledgment by governmental and nongovernmental role-players in South Africa that fragmented institutional mandates and organizational incapacity inhibit an appropriate response. The country has recognized the urgent need to address these problems, and has therefore enabled large-scale bioregional conservation programs to coordinate the efforts of governmental and nongovernmental organizations (NGOs) at both regional (for example, biome and/or bioregion) and local (site) levels. The explicit goal of these programs is to conserve a representative sample of the biodiversity pattern and processes of the

bioregion, through a suite of enabling as well as site-based conservation measures, supported through a process of mainstreaming conservation into the production sectors—particularly agriculture, water, forestry, fisheries, mining, and tourism. The underlying challenge is to manage these resources strategically in support of the country's reconstruction, growth, and sustainable development goals, and in accordance with national commitments to the United Nations' Millennium Development Goals, and the Convention on Biological Diversity's (CBD) Programme of Work on Protected Areas.

The approach is not new, as the concept of defining political and/or jurisdictional boundaries based on biophysical elements has been explored and debated over centuries (Fall 2003). Miller ((1999), cited in Fall (2003)) reviewed the origins of the "bioregion" concept, identifying famous references in the work of geographers Friedrich Ratzel in 1897 and Paul Vidal de la Blanche in 1903. Miller concluded that bioregions could be defined not only by the biological resources in a particular area, but also by the cultural, societal, institutional, and political elements represented there. More recently, the application of the ecosystem approach, guided by the CBD (see www.biodiv.org), has resulted in the extensive development of bioregional as well as ecoregional conservation programs in many parts of the world. The ecosystem approach is a strategy for the integrated management of land, water, and living resources that promotes conservation and sustainable use in an equitable way. It is based on the application of appropriate scientific methodologies, focused on levels of biological organization that encompass the essential processes, functions, and interactions among organisms and their environments. It recognizes that humans, with their cultural diversity, are an integral component of ecosystems.

Examples of these bioregional/ecoregional programs are the biodiversity hotspots recognized by Conservation International, the Global 200 Ecoregions identified by the World Wildlife Fund (WWF), the African Heartlands proposed by the African Wildlife Foundation, and the extensive development of transboundary protected areas worldwide (Olson and Dinerstein 1998; Sandwith and others 2001). The growth in such programs is partly due to the recognition that ecosystems are not bound by anthropogenic definitions, jurisdictions, and management regimes, but also to the fact that factors affecting ecosystems can operate at an extremely large scale (such as the effects of climate change and habitat transformation). It emphasizes more than ever before that to achieve effective conservation requires the spatial integration and linkage of different elements of the landscape—such as mountains, lowlands, wetlands, rivers, and oceans— but also the integration and linkage of biodiversity with institutional frameworks, economic opportunities and impacts, communities, and other social structures and political imperatives.

The Emergence of Bioregional Conservation Programs in South Africa

Over the past decade, several large-scale conservation and development programs have been proposed and formulated in South Africa, based on an initial understanding of South Africa's biodiversity priorities. These programs include the Greater St. Lucia Wetland Park and Maloti-Drakensberg Transfrontier Conservation and Development programs in KwaZulu-Natal (Sandwith 2003), the GRASS Initiative straddling the boundaries between

Mpumalanga, Free State and KwaZulu-Natal (Jarman 1999), and several other transboundary conservation programs (Peace Parks Foundation 2000), most notably the Great Limpopo Transfrontier Park.

Since 2000, however, three smaller-scale bioregional conservation programs, informed by the analysis and evaluation of biodiversity, social, economic, and institutional considerations, have undergone extensive development and implementation in three priority bioregions. These are the Cape Floristic Region Cape Action for People and the Environment (C.A.P.E.), the Succulent Karoo Ecosystem Programme (SKEP), and the Subtropical Thicket Ecosystem Programme (STEP) (see http://cpu.uwc.ac.za/). Through these analyses, and particularly through an appreciation of how the root causes of biodiversity loss could be addressed by existing and proposed program interventions, the designers and implementers of these programs identified situations where the linkage of biodiversity priorities to key development processes had resulted in win–win situations.

At a workshop convened at Giant's Castle in early 2001 (Pierce and others 2002), case studies from these programs were examined to assess not only whether they constituted effective examples of mainstreaming biodiversity into development processes, but also whether the process of mainstreaming itself could be characterized, and therefore replicated. One of the conclusions was that mainstreaming could be deemed to have occurred when:

- Biodiversity considerations were incorporated into policies governing sectoral activities.
- There were simultaneous gains in biodiversity and an economic sector (the "win–win" scenario).
- Sectoral activity was recognized as being based on, or dependent on, the sustainable use of biodiversity.
- Where situations resulted in which sectoral activities produced overall gains for biodiversity exceeding biodiversity losses (Sandwith 2002).

The implementation progress of the C.A.P.E., SKEP, and STEP bioregional programs provides further evidence of these processes of mainstreaming. The following sections attempt to characterize these processes by considering examples of emergent properties from the early implementation of these bioregional conservation strategies at three scales, namely national, bioregional/provincial, and local/project scales, and considering whether these processes constitute mainstreaming as described earlier. Also examined are the extent to which these processes are dependent upon top-down, bottom-up, and cross-sectoral approaches. This is followed by discussion of how these processes are drawn together in a bioregional conservation program—to enable replicability both within and beyond the program, to promote sustainability beyond the program interventions, and to capture and disseminate lessons learned.

The National-Scale Enabling Environment

National Policy and Legislation

In 2004, South Africa enacted legislation to provide for the management, conservation, and sustainable use of biodiversity, in the form of the National Environmental Management: Biodiversity Act (Act No. 10 of 2004) (Republic of South Africa 2004). The legislation promotes an ecosystem and programmatic approach to the management of biodiversity, which takes into account the need for key social transformation and developmental goals to be met. It specifically provides for the preparation and adoption of a national biodiversity framework that will ensure an integrated, coordinated, and uniform approach to biodiversity management by organs of state in all spheres of government, NGOs, the private sector, local communities, other stakeholders, and the public. It also provides for the identification of bioregions, and the preparation of bioregional plans and biodiversity management plans. The promulgation of this legislation is a significant milestone in South Africa's legislative reform process, in that it marks the first time that biodiversity has been explicitly recognized, and that measures to secure an

ecosystem approach to biodiversity management have been introduced in South African law.

Although there were many factors influencing the preparation of this legislation, the need for comprehensive laws was highlighted in the legal and institutional analysis conducted in the preparation of the C.A.P.E. Strategy (CSIR 1999). The C.A.P.E. Strategy noted that biodiversity conservation was promoted in a number of policies and laws, but argued that for these to be effective, national legislation was required in order to draw together and focus biodiversity conservation policies from different sectors (Younge 2000). The then National Minister of Environmental Affairs and Tourism, Valli Moosa, in introducing the C.A.P.E. Strategy in September 2000, noted that the government's priority was implementation, to be guided by a National Biodiversity Strategy and Action Plan (NBSAP), and that because of its global significance and vulnerability to threat, the Cape Floristic Region would be a high priority in this plan. He noted further that the C.A.P.E. Strategy provided an important example of how the government would go about implementing its priorities. The Biodiversity Act (Republic of South Africa 2004) and the Protected Areas Act (Act No. 57 of 2003) (Republic of South Africa 2003) prepared by this minister, are evidence of this commitment to the implementation of the strategy, and of enabling other similar processes countrywide.

Subsequently, the government has also completed a National Spatial Biodiversity Assessment (Driver and others 2005) and is rapidly concluding the preparation of the NBSAP. The National Spatial Biodiversity Assessment has, without doubt, benefited from the world-class conservation planning that was developed through C.A.P.E., STEP, and SKEP (Cowling and others 2003a; Cowling and others 2003b; Driver and others 2003). The resultant priorities for South Africa reflect all of the key bioregions described above. Perhaps more important, the need for systematic conservation planning and the identification of explicit and measurable targets was asserted by these planning exercises; and these have subsequently become requirements in law, as expressed in provisions regarding bioregional plans in the Biodiversity Act. Since the act binds all organs of state in the national, provincial, and local spheres of government, it can certainly be regarded as a prerequisite for mainstreaming of biodiversity in all sectors.

Bioregional Program Responsibilities

In the absence of national laws governing the implementation of bioregional conservation programs, more informal mechanisms were introduced by the three pilot programs to ensure vertical (from national and enabling levels through to local level) and horizontal (cross-sectoral) integration of Implementing Agency activities. Linked to the C.A.P.E. Strategy, for example, the national and provincial lead ministries entered into a memorandum of understanding to cooperate in implementing the provisions of the strategy and ensuring alignment of the key Implementing Agencies. This led to the placement of the C.A.P.E. Coordination Unit in the National Botanical Institute (NBI) as program management agency for C.A.P.E.

The promulgation of the Biodiversity Act has resulted in the expansion of the NBI to become the South African National Biodiversity Institute (SANBI), and provides for the national minister to mandate SANBI to advise him, among other things, on matters pertaining to the identification of bioregions and the contents of any bioregional plans. Since this time, SANBI has become involved in the Grasslands Initiative and the coordination of STEP, and is preparing to host the coordination of SKEP. In this way, biodiversity programs that had their foundations in NGO-moderated planning exercises have become a core element of environmental governance in South Africa, and a new statutory agency has been mandated to nurture and expand the programs, ensuring horizontal and vertical integration between the Implementing Agencies. It remains for the regulatory provisions in the legislation to be prepared, and this could elicit a strong reaction across sectoral interests as the power of this new legislation becomes apparent.

Coordination and Implementation Mechanisms

The Bioregional/Provincial-Scale Coordination and Implementation Mechanism

The three pilot bioregional programs, C.A.P.E., SKEP, and STEP, provide the basis for conserving globally significant biodiversity, while ensuring that people benefit from the sustainable use of natural resources. The high-level goals of the three programs are fundamentally similar (box 8.1), and their geographical domains overlap. They focus targeted conservation intervention in priority areas identified through systematic conservation planning across the landscape, as well as through enabling systemic and institutional interventions.

The key interventions in each case are captured in a strategy based on extensive public consultation, representing consensus among Implementing Agencies, and providing a means to facilitate

---

Box 8.1
Objectives of C.A.P.E., SKEP, and STEP

Cape Action for People and the Environment (C.A.P.E.)
By the year 2020, the natural environment and biodiversity of the Cape Floral Kingdom will be effectively conserved and restored wherever appropriate, and will deliver significant benefits to the people of the region in a way that is embraced by local communities, endorsed by government, and recognized internationally.

Succulent Karoo Ecosystem Programme (SKEP)
The people of the Succulent Karoo take ownership of and enjoy their unique living landscape in a way that maintains biodiversity and improves livelihoods, now and in perpetuity.

Subtropical Thicket Ecosystem Programme (STEP)
The people of the Thicket Biome take custodianship of their unique living landscapes and work together to conserve, enhance, and use their natural resources to ensure sustainable ecological processes and livelihoods, now and in the future.

alignment and cooperation. These agreements have been formalized in C.A.P.E. and STEP by means of a memorandum of understanding entered into by key political and implementation partners. The C.A.P.E. Implementation Committee has met every quarter since May 2001, with representation from all key sectors involved in implementing the C.A.P.E. Strategy, to agree on priorities for funding, to seek alignment and facilitate partnership arrangements, and to build the capacity of Implementing Agencies to undertake their responsibilities.

Moving beyond the usual sectoral fragmentation of effort and impact, these programs encourage collaboration among different sectors such as conservation, agriculture, and land-use planning. Within this enabling context, they coordinate and channel effort for focused on-the-ground impact. A key advantage is that this coordinated management model offers a flexible and replicable method of facilitating collective effort at the site level, supported by the agreed high-level vision and strategy. It manifests itself in new partnerships that bridge the gaps between governmental and nongovernmental organizations, and between conservation and social development agencies and the private sector; and assists in securing and financial and institutional effort and focusing it on priorities. The memorandum of understanding provides an example of an action at a higher as well as broader (cross-sectoral) institutional scale that has enabled more focused and coordinated site investment and action.

This level of programmatic coordination is attractive to both large and small funders, as it ensures that investments are buffered by strong institutional support and committed cofinancing, including in-kind contributions. For the three programs mentioned, over US$30 million in donor funding has been committed to planning and implementation over the next six years. This has leveraged approximately US$100 million in cofinancing by Implementing Agencies in the region, anxious to show delivery on key social and environmental commitments. A valuable spin-off is that there has been a growth in the capacity of all the institutions involved to plan and implement collaborative programs.

In each case, the programs have also invested in capacity within the coordination units to assist with fundraising, project development, communication, and monitoring and evaluation. The coordination units have been found to provide a suite of services that are essential for setting direction and maintaining momentum.

Perhaps the most important contribution has been the mediation and facilitation/brokering role that the coordination mechanisms have engendered among Implementing Agencies, and how this has stimulated alignment with the central strategies. CapeNature, a statutory nature conservation agency, adopted the C.A.P.E. Strategy as its own strategy, and reoriented the entire thrust of the agency's approach to be an "agent of rural development" in the Western Cape Province. This has been well received by provincial leadership and augurs well for cross-sectoral collaboration on such social priorities as addressing rural poverty, youth development, and community health, providing evidence of the mainstreaming of biodiversity into these sectors (Western Cape Nature Conservation Board 2002).

At the provincial level in the Western Cape, a Provincial Spatial Development Framework (PSDF) is in the process of being prepared. The political will and commitment associated with the implementation of the C.A.P.E. and SKEP strategies in the Western Cape have made it a relatively straightforward process to ensure that biodiversity priorities inform the preparation of the PSDF. There are also province-wide development processes that have come under scrutiny, such as the rapid development of golf courses and polo estates in critical coastal lowlands. The availability of information on spatial biodiversity priorities and a well-mobilized NGO sector have made it possible not only to advocate a position regarding the importance of biodiversity in these landscapes, but also to ensure that the analyses of options explicitly incorporate biodiversity considerations.

Subregional Coordination and Implementation Mechanisms

Because of the enormous extent of the bioregions, the coordination of these programs has been further devolved in each case to the subregional scale. Within SKEP, the subregional coordination teams have focused on capacity building and project development with key stakeholders in the SKEP priority areas. The teams have concluded that in each priority region, a large anchor project and several smaller projects will provide a focus for implementation, supervised by multi-stakeholder steering committees. Within C.A.P.E., subregional coordination is provided by steering committees that address the development of large conservation corridors and priority lowland landscapes. Here, too, there are usually large flagship projects, such as the Baviaanskloof Mega-reserve, which is coordinated by the Baviaanskloof Steering Committee, representing key stakeholders in that region and ensuring effective integration and governance at the subregional scale. The STEP program has not yet reached the stage where a comprehensive subregional implementation plan can be rolled out, and the approach has been to focus on one subregion and a cluster of projects within it, building on key provincial and NGO initiatives.

The Local Site-Scale Implementation Mechanism

One of the most pervasive weaknesses of conservation and development interventions is their "project focus," resulting in short-term interventions, often managed by short-lived project teams without any inter-project integration, and limiting the sustainability of project impacts. By developing and adopting bioregion-wide strategies, it has been possible for the programs to provide a region-wide context for individual projects. In this way, the pitfalls of ad hoc project development and implementation, a major downfall of many conservation and natural resource management interventions could have been avoided (see, for example, Wells and Brandon 1993;

Infield and Adams 1999; Adams and Hulme 2001; Mahanty 2002; Sayer and Campbell 2004). The following section includes examples of interventions that illustrate how the implementation method reinforces the mainstreaming outcomes.

Integrating Biodiversity into Land-Use Planning and Decision Making in the Municipal and Agricultural Sectors

Several projects in the bioregional programs are piloting approaches for incorporating fine-scale spatial biodiversity priorities into local-level decision making by municipalities and other land use decision makers, such as the department of agriculture and provincial environmental affairs and land-use planning departments.

(1) Supporting municipal planning and development

Integrating biodiversity priorities into local government planning and decision making is a cornerstone of all three bioregional programs, as well as a key strategy in the country's NBSAP. At the local level, every municipality in South Africa must produce an integrated development plan (IDP) that includes a spatial development framework (SDF). This presents an opportunity to integrate spatial information on biodiversity priorities into cross-sectoral spatial plans at different spatial scales, so that biodiversity priorities inform decision making at local level and development is directed into nonpriority areas.

In the City of Cape Town, an integrated environmental management framework incorporates a biodiversity policy that emphasizes a network of important biodiversity nodes and corridors. By focusing on specific nodes, such as the Edith Stephens Wetland Park on the Cape Flats, the Cape Flats Nature partnership (between the City of Cape Town, Table Mountain Fund, SANBI, and the Botanical Society of South Africa) has engaged with very poor local communities to undertake greening initiatives in local schools and training of emergent conservation managers from previously disadvantaged social groups. Most important, the partnership has secured support from adjacent local communities for the protection and recreational use of these areas. One indication of successful mainstreaming is that the City of Cape Town has guaranteed the extension of contracts for project workers to maintain and expand this program, thereby sustaining employment. Another indication is that local community members who had been trained to deal with fire that threatens their own security, have stepped in on several occasions to put out fires that threatened important biodiversity sites.

In the Eastern Cape Province, the STEP program has produced a suite of planning and decision-support tools, including the STEP Conservation Priority Map, the STEP Conservation Framework, and the STEP Handbook and Mapbooks for Municipalities. All of these tools were designed to assist decision makers in integrating biodiversity priorities into land-use planning and decision-making processes (at both the development control and forward planning ends of the spectrum). The STEP Handbook and Mapbooks (authored by Shirley Pierce) represent a groundbreaking way of illustrating how both the social and economic sectors are dependent on the environmental sector, thus empowering municipal decision makers to make wise and informed choices about land use and sustainable development. These planning tools have been effectively mainstreamed through a number of stakeholder participation workshops conducted during the planning phase of STEP, as well as more recently through the SANBI-WESSA Mainstreaming Biodiversity into Planning and Development Project funded by the Development Bank of Southern Africa.

Indicators of successful mainstreaming of these tools include that: (a) the provincial Department of Economic Affairs, Environment, and Tourism (DEAET) has made it mandatory for the STEP planning tools to be used in all Environmental Impact Assessment and scoping reports submitted with applications for land use change and for development control purposes; (b) a number of municipalities have made it mandatory for the STEP data

to be incorporated into the SDFs and Strategic Environmental Assessments that have to be completed as part of the Integrated Development Planning process; and (c) STEP data have been successfully integrated into numerous SDFs and SEAs (Strategic Environment Assessments), whether or not it has been a requirement of the municipality.

(2) Facilitating sustainable agriculture in the Slanghoek Valley

The provincial department of agriculture in the Western Cape and farmers in the Slanghoek Valley, when faced with difficult decisions regarding development that would affect natural ecosystems, requested maps of biodiversity priorities. C.A.P.E., through the development of a small Critical Ecosystem Partnership Fund (CEPF)-funded project, was able to support the mapping of biodiversity priorities in the valley, to map the existing agricultural lands within the valley, and to generate overlays of proposed development. This clearly indicated where proposed transformation would affect priority biodiversity, and enabled the authorities to steer development toward less critical areas.

Of major importance was the degree of cooperation this engendered among authorities who often deal with conflicting priorities, enabling them to take a more strategic approach, and reinforcing this form of collaboration among these agencies in other areas of their jurisdiction. For example, in the Agulhas Plain, the Department of Agriculture, South African National Parks, CapeNature, and district and local municipalities are collaborating to achieve the integration of biodiversity priorities generated by fine-scale planning with agricultural resource priorities, through "area-wide planning" that will ensure that key biodiversity sites and ecosystem linkages are maintained in the landscape.

Involving Communities and the Private Sector in Conservation Activities

(1) Biodiversity and wine initiative
The location of the best agricultural soils for the

cultivation of table wine grapes coincides with South Africa's most threatened lowland ecosystems. The challenge is to guide the expansion of vineyards in a way that avoids further transformation of priority biodiversity areas. The Biodiversity and Wine Initiative seeks to influence environmental management within vineyards and in adjacent areas. There are two main mechanisms, one involving the stewardship by estate managers of priority biodiversity resources on these lands, and the other involving the promulgation and adoption of industry-wide guidelines and standards for land management and wine production, avoiding such negative impacts as water abstraction and pollution through run-off of agrichemicals. The industry has now incorporated the biodiversity guidelines into their Integrated Production of Wine guidelines and is exploring the potential marketing benefits of using the biodiversity of the Cape Floristic Region as a unique selling point for South African wine.

(2) Sustainable harvesting of wild flowers

The harvesting of wild fynbos for international flower markets has been a traditional activity on the Agulhas Plain for decades. Changing land-use practices and a highly seasonal market have had an impact on farm viability, resulting in the sale of properties and the replacement of wild harvesting by other more lucrative, but damaging, land uses such as flower cultivation or viticulture (Privett and others 2002). At Flower Valley, an experiment is in progress to determine sustainable yields of wild-harvested flowers, coupled with the certification of socially and environmentally sustainable farm management practices. Early results have been the development of niche markets for certified flower products, and the engagement of the private sector in developing viable year-round production and sales. The approach has also tested an emergent partnership between an NGO, a private company, and the local community, and is providing important lessons for similar initiatives in the region. It is coupled with the development of the highly successful Walker Bay Conservancy and the emergence of skilled tourism operators who have the means not only to interpret the unique biodiversity for visitors, but also to train

and develop unemployed community members in horticulture using indigenous plants, improving their prospects of gainful employment.

(3) Biodiversity and mining (SKEP)

Mining is one of the key economic activities in the Succulent Karoo hotspot (Myers and others 2000). The entire northern extension of the Succulent Karoo is mineral-rich, and, with various mining applications pending throughout the region, transformation from mining operations represents a significant pressure on biodiversity. Certain types of mining result in irreversible loss of natural habitat across large areas. Where mineral deposits are located in biodiversity-rich areas, this inevitably results in competing land-use needs between mining and conservation. In most cases the conditions for mining approval have been weak and of little value from a biodiversity conservation point of view.

To address this, the SKEP program is engaging proactively with the mining industry to improve the biodiversity management performance of existing as well as new operations through several means. A mining and biodiversity forum of corporate and small-scale mining enterprises is being established to discuss and develop mechanisms for addressing biodiversity concerns. With the support of the CEPF, the SKEP program is also investing in pilot projects in Bushmanland as well as the Namaqua Coast, aiming to incorporate mine-owned lands into multi-ownership protected area initiatives. The aim here is to encourage mines to contribute to conservation targets as well as regional development objectives. So far the program has been successful in encouraging certain mining companies to see themselves as custodians of biodiversity rather than as threats to biodiversity, and to view themselves as positive contributors to conserving biodiversity in priority areas.

(4) Community-based ecotourism

There are several emergent ecotourism ventures associated with the bioregional programs. The large-scale conservation corridors and anchor projects seek to attract investment in the expansion of a tourism economy based on the unique selling points of world heritage sites and other key attractions. Their explicit goal, however, is to generate local benefits, an elusive goal for such ventures in many parts of the world. Some progress has been made, however, with investment in highly participatory ecotourism planning involving local communities and municipalities in the Nieuwoudtville area, where an annual display of wild flowers attracts visitors from far afield. Using a participatory tourism workshop, local stakeholders were able to assess the tourism resource base of the area and plan several linked facilities that will be implemented with the support of the local municipality and tourism organizations.

Similarly, in the Greater Cederberg Biodiversity Corridor, a community living in a fairly remote part of the area is working with the Cederberg Coordination Unit to develop a donkey trail, using an existing access road on the boundaries of the wilderness area, both to open up tourism opportunities and to provide local employment. It is unlikely that the local community would be able to develop and sustain a viable ecotourism product without the critical mass provided by the combination of these factors—the listing of the Cederberg as a component of the Cape Floristic Region World Heritage Site, local entrepreneurs who already run successful tourism operations, and the support of the corridor initiative.

Assessing Progress

Bioregional conservation programs have the explicit purpose of conserving biodiversity and sustaining benefits to society, and these examples of coordination and implementation at a variety of scales serve to illustrate the range and complexity of approaches being undertaken in South Africa. There are indications that the programs are making progress in achieving their goals, in that further areas (both terrestrial and marine) are being set aside for conservation, the management of sites on both public and private land is improving, a greater number of stake-

holders is involved in the programs, and important changes have been made in the legal, institutional, and organizational environment. The programs are however, primarily exploratory, in that neither the best process nor the outcomes can be predicted with any certainty.

It is clear, though, that lessons are being learned from their implementation, and the programs are providing a focal point for the sharing and exchange of lessons within and across the programs. In the case of C.A.P.E., the Fynbos Forum, a long-standing association of researchers and managers of biodiversity in the Cape Floristic Region, has continued to flourish and has become an important annual "State of the C.A.P.E." review mechanism. In addition, the C.A.P.E. program has invested in an annual C.A.P.E. Partners' Conference to ensure that the emergent insights and lessons learned from implementation are translated into recommendations for the further adaptation and roll-out of the program, and project-level monitoring and evaluation has been initiated. In the STEP program, an annual Thicket Biome Forum will be held, and it is hoped that this will serve to generate similar momentum; while in SKEP, participatory reviews of program implementation have been undertaken together with project partners, serving to adapt the coordination and implementation program to emerging realities.

The key question that remains is whether these programs can be considered to be achieving the broader objective of mainstreaming biodiversity into the development process, as evidenced by the presence of the key characteristics of mainstreaming outlined earlier. It is clear that biodiversity considerations are being incorporated into several sectoral policies and programs, and that there is a far greater appreciation that many economic opportunities, especially in rural contexts, can be supported by the biodiversity resource base. An explicit attempt is also being made to ensure that options for achieving win-win solutions are actively explored and characterized. Perhaps the greatest unknown, however, is whether these efforts are sufficient to arrest the declining status of biodiversity in these regions, and to ensure the long-term persistence of their globally significant biodiversity. The programs do, at least, provide a baseline for long-term monitoring of their progress against explicit goals.

It is somewhat easier to identify what approaches have been productive for the mobilization of political and institutional stakeholders, and for coordination and communication among stakeholders, and where difficulties and challenges remain. Some of the key ingredients for success and replication of bioregional approaches to conservation and development have been:

- The participatory development of an agreed common vision and strategy for a recognizable bioregional entity, consistent with national biodiversity and development priorities
- The preparation of a clear program of action, with dedicated roles and responsibilities among Implementing Agencies
- The identification and proactive development of key policies and legislation that resonate with social priorities and reforms
- The engagement of Implementing Agencies at all levels in a nonthreatening coordination mechanism that allows for peer review, analysis and discussion, as well as the celebration of successful initiatives and an honest appraisal of less successful ones
- The identification of key institutional and community champions, who are prepared to undertake leadership roles and to work across institutional boundaries in a spirit of cooperation
- The opportunity to reflect on and analyze lessons learned and to capture and disseminate insights widely within and between programs
- The use of catalytic funding, which leverages additional cofinancing and in-kind support and commitment
- Fair and effective systems of governance and accountability, including the independent and objective review of proposals and results
- A combination of top-down and bottom-up approaches.

Challenges that remain include:

- The continuing need to assert the fundamental value of biodiversity conservation for sustainable livelihoods in the face of the enormity of social challenges in the region, such as poverty and the HIV/AIDS pandemic, and the depredation caused by short-term exploitation of scarce natural resources
- The need to ensure that sufficient resources are made available by government at all levels to secure the persistence of biodiversity resources in functional ecosystems, with the assistance of functional public institutions
- The need to develop capacity to manage complex interventions involving multiple stakeholders in diverse institutional and social settings, while also ensuring the redress of apartheid legacy distortions in opportunity and capacity development
- The continuing need to ensure the effectiveness of implementing institutions, and their ability to work across institutional boundaries.

Conclusions

Although the bioregional conservation programs in South Africa are relatively young, there are emerging demonstrations of positive impact in line with program aspirations and objectives. The enhanced coordination of conservation activities at the bioregional scale, engendered by the agreed goals, strategies, and action plans, has resulted in greater site-level impact through improved communication and cooperation among Implementing Agencies, and certainly between government and civil society at large. These programs have been very successful in involving a broad range of stakeholders, and in attracting and retaining an ever-expanding group of professionals from an increasingly diverse range of skills and backgrounds in direct implementation. The levels and diversity of participation in conservation activities have increased. This is especially evident in the new types of partnership that have been formed, bridging gaps between governmental organizations and

NGOs, and between conservation and social development agencies and the private sector.

There remains a need to evaluate the extent to which these planning processes have actually achieved biodiversity gains on the one hand, and social and economic development on the other. First, however, there is a need to identify and agree on what exactly is required and how to measure the status and trend of these impacts and outcomes. Coupled with this is the need to analyze which implementation options are best suited to specific contexts and why, as a means of improving efficiency and effectiveness. Fundamentally, if one reflects on the rate of degradation of the natural resource base and the cost of reversing this trend, there is a need to evaluate whether the current investment and effort is capable of achieving the goals in the expected time frames, and of securing biodiversity in the long term.

In compiling this analysis, the authors benefited greatly from discussions with Mark Botha, Mandy Driver, David Daitz, and Amanda Younge. Richard Cowling provided valuable comments on a draft version of the paper. They also gratefully acknowledge the financial support provided to the programs through the GEF (via the World Bank and United Nations Development Programme), the Table Mountain Fund, and the Critical Ecosystem Partnership Fund.

Endnotes

1 Cape Action for People and the Environment

2 South African National Biodiversity Institute

3 Cape Action for People and the Environment

4 Conservation International, South Africa

5 South African National Biodiversity Institute

References

Adams, W.M., and D. Hulme. 2001. "If Community Conservation Is the Answer in Africa, What Is the Question?" *Oryx* 35 (3): 193–200.

Cowling, R.M., R.L. Pressey, M. Rouget, and A.T. Lombard. 2003a. "A Conservation Plan for a Global Biodiversity Hotspot: The Cape Floristic Region, South Africa." *Biological Conservation* 112 (1–2): 191–216.

Cowling, R.M., A.T. Lombard, M. Rouget, G.I.H. Kerley, T. Wolf, R. Sims-Castley, A.T. Knight, J.H.J. Vlok, S.M. Pierce, A.F. Boshoff, and S.L. Wilson. 2003b. *A Conservation Assessment for the Subtropical Thicket Biome*. Terrestrial Ecology Research Unit Report No. 43, University of Port Elizabeth, South Africa.

CSIR (Council for Scientific and Industrial Research). 1999. *Cape Action Plan for the Environment: An assessment and review of the current policy, legal, institutional, socioeconomic and financial situation affecting the conservation of biodiversity in the Cape Floristic Kingdom*. Parts 1 and 2. CSIR Report No. ENV-S-C 99130A. Prepared for WWF-SA.

Driver, A., P. Desmet, M. Rouget, R.M. Cowling, and K. Maze. 2003. *Succulent Karoo Ecosystem Plan: Biodiversity Component Technical Report*. Cape Conservation Unit Report No. CCU 1/03, Botanical Society of South Africa, Cape Town.

Driver, A., K.E. Maze, M. Rouget, A.T. Lombard, J. Nel, J.K. Turpie, R.M. Cowling, P. Desmet, P. Goodman, J. Harris, Z. Jonas, B. Reyers, K. Sink, and T. Strauss. 2005. National Spatial Biodiversity Assessment 2004: Priorities for Biodiversity Conservation in South Africa. *Strelitzia* 17, South African National Biodiversity Institute.

Fall, J.J. 2003. "Planning Protected Areas across Boundaries: New Paradigms and Old Ghosts." In U.M. Goodale, M.J. Stern, C. Margolius, A. Lanfer, and M. Fladeland, eds. 2003. *Transboundary Protected Areas: The Viability of Regional Conservation Strategies*. New York: Food Products Press.

Infield, M., and W. Adams. 1999. "Institutional Sustainability and Community Conservation: A Case Study from Uganda." *Journal of International Development* 11: 305–15.

Jarman, J. 1999. "Revitalizing South Africa's 'Forgotten' Grassland." http://www.changemakers.net/studio/.

Mahanty, S. 2002. "Conservation and Development Interventions as Networks: The Case of the India Ecodevelopment Project, Karnataka." *World Development* 30 (8): 1369–86.

Miller, K.R. 1999. "What Is Bioregional Planning?" In *Integrated Planning: International Perspectives,* Battleby, Scotland 7–9 April 1999, IUCN and Scottish Natural Heritage.

Myers, N., R.A. Mittermeier, C.G. Mittermeier, G.A.B. da Fonseca, and J. Kent. 2000. "Biodiversity Hotspots for Conservation Priorities." *Nature* 403: 853–58.

Olson, D.M., and E. Dinerstein. 1998. "The Global 200: A Representation Approach to Conserving the Earth's Most Biologically Valuable Ecoregions." *Conservation Biology* 12: 502–15.

Peace Parks Foundation. 2000. Interactive Map of Transfrontier Conservation Areas. www.peaceparks.org/.

Pierce, S.M., R.M. Cowling, T. Sandwith, and K. MacKinnon, eds. 2002. *Mainstreaming Biodiversity in Development: Case Studies from South Africa*. Washington, DC: World Bank.

Privett, S.D.J., B.J. Heydenrych, and R.M. Cowling. 2002. "Putting Biodiversity to Business on the Agulhas Plain." In S.M. Pierce, R.M. Cowling, T. Sandwith, and K. MacKinnon, eds. 2002. *Mainstreaming Biodiversity in Development: Case Studies from South Africa*. Washington, DC: World Bank.

Republic of South Africa. 2003. National Environmental Management: Protected Areas Act (Act No. 57 of 2003). *Government Gazette* 26025, 2003: Government Printer.

———. 2004. National Environmental Management: Biodiversity Act (Act No. 10 of 2004). *Government Gazette* 26436, 2004: Government Printer.

Sandwith, T.S. 2002. "Introduction." In S.M. Pierce, R.M. Cowling, T. Sandwith, and K. MacKinnon, eds. 2002. *Mainstreaming Biodiversity in Development: Case Studies from South Africa*. Washington, DC: World Bank.

———. 2003. "Overcoming Barriers: Conservation and Development in the Maloti-Drakensberg Mountains of Southern Africa." In U.M. Goodale, M.J. Stern, C. Margolius, A. Lanfer, and M. Fladeland, eds. 2003. *Transboundary Protected Areas: The Viability of Regional Conservation Strategies*. New York: Food Products Press.

Sandwith, T., C. Shine, L. Hamilton, and D. Sheppard. 2001. *Transboundary Protected Areas for Peace and Cooperation*. Best Practice Protected Area Guidelines Series No. 7. Gland, Switzerland: IUCN (World Conservation Union).

Sayer, J., and B.M. Campbell. 2004. *The Science of Sustainable Development: Local Livelihoods and the Global Environment.* Cambridge, UK: Cambridge University Press.

Western Cape Nature Conservation Board. 2002. *Annual Report 2001-2002.* www.capenature.org.za.

Wells, M.P., and K.E. Brandon. 1993. "The Principles and Practice of Buffer Zones and Local Participation in Biodiversity Conservation." *Ambio* 22 (2/3): 157-62.

Younge, A. 2000. *Cape Action Plan for the Environment: A Biodiversity Strategy and Action Plan for the Cape Floral Kingdom.* WWF.

9. Mainstreaming Biodiversity in Rural Development Programs in Mexico

Carlos Toledo[1]

The objective of this paper is to present a review of some experiences in mainstreaming biodiversity in marginalized rural areas in Mexico and to discuss the principles and practices that have emerged. Over the past few years a group of projects, designed from different points of view and with interesting new approaches, has been established with the aim of achieving biodiversity conservation beyond the boundaries of protected areas.

These projects were initiated to address the needs and challenges of the zones surrounding the reserves, where small peasant farmer communities are often located. A central aim of these projects has been to integrate conservation criteria into development programs carried out by government agencies in the marginalized rural zones. Although these projects are still in operation, and despite their small size, they have already produced important lessons and experiences that deserve to be documented. These lessons may contribute to the discussion of new strategies for biodiversity protection by the Global Environment Facility (GEF), highlighting the large area of land with biological wealth outside of protected areas.

The Focus of Analysis: Marginalized Rural Zones where Small Peasant and Indigenous Farmers Live

The projects discussed in this paper are situated in the isolated outer zones of rural Mexico, with the following features:

■ These are inaccessible zones, because they have not had communication media, or because they are topographically complex.

■ These zones contain important areas of natural vegetation with great biological value, and more or less intact habitats. Mexico is a very diverse country, but the biological wealth is concentrated in these marginalized zones, where natural vegetation is more abundant.

■ These are regions where small peasant farmers live. These farmers produce mostly maize for their own consumption, since they have little access to markets.

■ These regions are also home to indigenous peoples, who have historically been marginalized from the central zones. Their cultural heritage includes a great folk knowledge about nature and ways of managing and preserving it.

■ In general, the population of these regions is among the poorest sectors of Mexican society.

So, there is a significant coincidence of areas with great problems of poverty and those of high biological diversity. These regions are currently being threatened by the horizontal expansion of peasant activity, which, although it is occurring at a slower rate than urban expansion, does present an important demographic shift. The expansion of peasant activity is causing a continuous process of deforestation, and does not bring about a significant improvement in peasant incomes or living standards. The destruction of ecological richness and continuing rural poverty are two important characteristics of these marginalized regions.

This situation creates an ongoing cycle of poverty and the destruction of biodiversity—a cycle that characterizes countries other than Mexico as well, and reflects the structural conditions of our contemporary world. Most of the rural population in developing countries consists of small peasant farmers. Such small farmers and peasants also tend to coincide throughout the world with zones of important biodiversity. Most of the countries with the greatest biodiversity are tropical developing countries, and most of the habitats where this great biological wealth can be found are located at the periphery of the rural societies in these countries.

Meanwhile, most of the world's food production is carried out by super-intensive agricultural systems, mainly in developed countries. These systems are based on unsustainable methods, and often place considerable risks and have negative impacts on the environment and human health. This occurs in a range of ways: a high use of fossil fuels, intensive use of chemical products (such as fertilizers, pesticides, hormones, and so forth), excessive use of water, the use of hybrids, and genetic modification. Peasant producers are isolated geographically and economically from national and international markets, which are dominated by super-intensive agriculture. As a result, horizontal expansion of production appears to be the only option for peasant farmers, leading to the continual loss of biodiversity.

The inequity that small rural producers face thus constitutes a structural factor in the destruction of biodiversity. The inadequate relationship between peripheral rural zones, which are not incorporated and fully integrated into modern development, and central urban-industrial areas of developed countries can also be seen as reflecting an inadequate global relationship between society and nature.

In the case of the marginalized rural regions of Mexico, mainstreaming would imply the development of an integral policy of regional and sustainable development that addresses biodiversity conservation, poverty alleviation for rural peasants, and increasing the sustainability of production activ-

ities. For such a policy to be successful would require changes to the structural conditions at a national and international level which keep these regions marginalized and underdeveloped, and lead to the destruction of biodiversity.

Protected Areas and Small Peasant Producers

During the past 15 years, Mexico has considerably advanced in the consolidation and expansion of a national system of protected natural areas. The area of land under protection has been increased by 17.9 million hectares, which represents 9.1 percent of Mexican territory. In addition, reserves have been provided with proper personnel and equipment in order to implement proper management plans. Nevertheless, most of these protected areas are located in marginal zones of the countryside and are frequently under tremendous amounts of pressure from the expansion of poor peasants and their activities.

The teams of biologists or ecologists who manage these reserves, whose concern is to halt environmental deterioration processes, have to deal with small producers who view reserves as one more factor affecting and restricting their already limited production possibilities. Most reserves in Mexico are governed by federal or state-level legislation, and this situation is perceived by peasant producers as a restriction imposed by central authorities. It is also important to mention that protected areas in Mexico are established without modifying the tenure regime of land. Half of Mexico's territory has social forms of tenure, constituted by agrarian communities and *ejidos*, which are collective forms of property. Within marginalized zones, these communal forms of land tenure are present in about 80 or 90 percent of the territory.

Because of trends in population growth, a strategy of conservation based on ecological reserves alone is not viable if it does not address the social and economic problems of small poor farmers who live in or near such reserves. Mainstreaming biodiversity needs to provide alternatives for communities of poor farmers, in order to address deep inequalities. Reforms are needed to correct the imbalances and integrate rural communities into modern development.

The Projects Analyzed in This Study

During the past decade, a number of projects have been initiated in poor peasant zones rich in biodiversity. These projects have involved various strategies to incorporate peasant and indigenous communities into conservation and development. One of the most important objectives is to conserve biodiversity outside the ecological reserves. The projects have been operating at the interface between the conservationist aims of protected areas, and the development programs of different sectoral institutions. Although these projects have been created from different perspectives, all of them share some characteristics: a participatory character, an aim to work with peasant communities, an integrated approach promoted by the environmental sector, the objective of achieving inter-institutional coordination, the search for sustainable production alternatives, and international financial support, mainly from the GEF.

Each of the five projects is described in the following section, followed by an analysis of the principles, strategies, challenges, and achievements of each program.

Sustainable Development Programs in Marginalized Indigenous Regions (PRODERS)

This program was established with the creation of the Ministry of Environment, Natural Resources, and Fisheries (SEMARNAP) in 1995—an environmental institution that raised environmental matters to a ministerial level and joined various sectoral policies with environmental ones, mainly the fishing, forestry, and water policies.

The main objective of Sustainable Development Programs in Marginalized Indigenous Regions (PRODERS) is to promote sustainable development in poor peasant regions by trying to stop environmental deterioration, improving productivity, and fighting against poverty. It also has the goal of articulating ecological and conservation policies with those of economic growth and improvement of living standards, with a decentralized focus, through a medium-term plan (SEMARNAP 2000). This program has been operating with financial resources from the Mexican government.

To achieve these objectives, PRODERS used two lines of action: the transformation of management mechanisms in the development of marginalized zones, and the promotion of sustainable production alternatives.

In the first case, the aim is to strengthen the capacities of poor regions by promoting decentralization, participation in decisions, and regional autonomy. This enables the public programs of both the environmental sector and other sectors to address development issues in accordance with long-term regional programs that have biodiversity conservation as a priority. Regional councils have also been promoted to lead the development process, with broad participation by regional stakeholders. There is also a monitoring and evaluation scheme (SEMARNAT 2003).

A second action line promotes specific changes in production patterns by sustainable transformation of small farmer communities using a planning framework. Strategic sustainable production projects are also designed and operated in order to increase economic activities and join these communities with markets.

Since 2001, this program has been run by the National Commission of Natural Protected Areas (CONANP), and it is now more closely related to protected areas.[2] The program has achieved important successes in demonstrating a participatory and decentralized approach to regional development. In the late 1990s, a successful scheme of institutional coordination was implemented, with the National

Box 9.1
Components of the Mexico Mesoamerican Biological Corridor

The components of CBMM are:

- Participatory design of the corridors and of a monitoring system that includes sustainable development programs and plans based on land-use planning, elaborated on in the focal areas with participation of the local population, and mechanisms to monitor the state of biodiversity

- Actions aimed at reorienting public policies and budgets toward the goals and objectives defined in the planning of each corridor

- Specific actions of sustainable production projects

- Coordination and administration.

Programme of Support for Priority Regions (PROAREP). Eight government ministries participated in this project, which was documented in a World Bank study (World Bank 2000).

Overall, however, the PRODERS program has been a small one, and its achievements have been limited to a few areas.

Mexico Mesoamerican Biological Corridor (CBMM)

This is the Mexican part of a regional project that includes several Central American countries. It is supported by the GEF through the World Bank and managed by the National Commission for the Knowledge and Use of Biodiversity (CONABIO).[3]

The main objective of the Mexico Mesoamerican Biological Corridor (CBMM) is to link a number of protected areas in the southeast of Mexico with nature reserves in the Central American countries, thus creating corridors in which the sustainable use of natural resources is promoted by allowing various species to flow through them.

Conservation and sustainable use of biodiversity is promoted in five biological corridors, with eight

focal areas in four states of southeastern Mexico. This is to be done by means of introducing biodiversity conservation criteria into governmental budgets and through local planning and development practices with strong community participation.

The CBMM was formally established in 2000, and started its activities in 2002 (see box 9.1 for its main components). It has a projected duration of seven years and a budget of $US90 million, including $US14.8 million from the GEF, and a contribution from the Mexican government (through various sectoral programs) of $US66 million.

CBMM has established a national advice council and four state advice councils with the participation of federal, state, and municipal institutions, as well as representatives of civil society (such as social and producer organizations, NGOs, scientists, and business enterprises). These councils have been constituted and are currently working, although their formation was a slow and complicated process due to political problems in the selection of the social representatives.

The Indigenous and Community Biodiversity Conservation Project in Mexico (COINBIO)

Communidades Indigenas y Biodiversidad (COINBIO) is a project based on the idea that indigenous and peasant communities can establish mechanisms of biodiversity conservation and sustainable use by themselves, given the necessary support. These conservation mechanisms could complement or even be more efficient than the formal protected areas established by governmental environmental authorities, which often lack the consensus of communities.

Project initiatives emerged directly from the indigenous forest communities of Sierra Norte, a region in Oaxaca state, which constitute an important successful example of environmental conservation, social development, and sustainable communal forest management. In these communities, as in a range of others, it has been demonstrated that communal management of forests is a real alternative for their sustainable use and conservation.

The objective of the project is to conserve areas of high biodiversity, through strengthening and promoting communal conservation initiatives in lands of communal (or *ejido*) property, in a high-priority group of ecological zones in the states of Oaxaca, Michoacán, and Guerrero. The conservation actions are based on traditional management practices and positive cultural values developed by the communities since ancient times.

COINBIO is a project funded by GEF through the World Bank and is operated by the state bank, Nacional Financiera, with the technical supervision of the National Forest Commission (CONAFOR) and the environment ministry (National Commission on Natural Protected Areas (SEMARNAT)). The agreement was signed at the beginning of 2001, although it began to operate in 2002. It is planned to have a duration of 7 years and have a total budget of $US18.7 million, with a GEF contribution of $US7.5 million. Box 9.2 outlines the components of COINBIO.

The project is operating in about 100 communities in the three states. An important mechanism has been established for technical assistance, through which communities are given resources directly to pay external technicians hired by communal representatives instead of governmental institutions, making the process of generating technical outputs more efficient.

Forest Conservation and Management Project (PROCYMAF)

Forest Conservation and Management Project (PROCYMAF) emerged at the initiative of the environment ministry (SEMARNAT), together with the creation of public support programs for the forest sector. The forest sector in Mexico has, over the past few decades, lacked financial support, in contrast with the subsidies received by the farming sector. The disparity in financial support between the two sectors is an important factor in stimulating

---

Box 9.2
Components of the Indigenous and Community Biodiversity Conservation Project (COINBIO)

The project has four components:

1. *Strengthening local capacity and setting up participatory organizations.* The project has integrated state committees in each of the three states where it works, which lead project operation in a participatory and decentralized way. These committees have federal and state governmental representation, but it is interesting to note that most of their members are representatives of their own communities, nongovernmental organizations (NGOs), and academia. These committees make the fundamental decisions that are carried out by a state unit headed by a coordinator.

2. *Conservation and sustainable use subprojects.* Financial resources are given directly to communities for operating four action lines:

   ■ Biodiversity inventories, communal land-use planning, and other actions aimed at strengthening conservation planning
   ■ Training and capacity building
   ■ Community investments for conservation areas and sustainable use
   ■ Community "green" venture funds.

3. *Monitoring and evaluation*

4. *National coordination.*

---

the change of land use and has led to deforestation and the consequent loss of biodiversity. When SEMARNAT was created and the forestry policy was located within the ministry, several forest programs were established in order to allocate more financial resources to this activity. Among these were the Forest Development Programme (PRODEFOR), to support the sustainable use of natural forests through subsidies to owners, and the National Forest Plantation Programme (PRODEPLAN), to support the establishment of commercial forest plantations in deforested zones.

PROCYMAF is similar in structure to a pilot project that also had its origin in the successful experiences of the communities of Sierra Norte in Oaxaca

> **Box 9.3**
> **Objectives of the Forest Conservation and Management Project (PROCYMAF)**
>
> The project has the following objectives:
>
> - To strengthen technical capacities and social capital, and to develop strategies for community management of natural resources
> - To undertake technical capacity building in order to offer better technical and professional services to forest producers
> - To promote diversification of the use of natural resources through the design of strategies for use of nontraditional forest products
> - To strengthen public institutions in their functions of regulating and promoting the use and conservation of forest resources.

state. This project was designed to support indigenous and small farmers in forest communities, in order to strengthen their capacities to manage their own forest in a sustainable way and so conserve biodiversity. The objectives of the project are outlined in box 9.3.

The project has the support of a World Bank loan of $US15 million and, after an initial five-year period, began a second stage in 2004. The pilot project was at first restricted to Oaxaca State, but later it was extended to Michoacán and Guerrero. In its second stage it is operating in three additional states: Jalisco, Durango, and Quintana Roo.

Integrated Ecosystems Management Project in Three Priority Eco-Regions (MIE)

This project arose from the experience of PRODERS, with the aim of building a planning process in peasant and indigenous communities in or surrounding ecological reserves or high biodiversity sites without formal protection. The Integrated Ecosystems Management (MIE) project is today operating in these regions: Montaña in Guerrero state (dry tropics and temperate zone), Los Tuxtlas in Veracruz state (rain forest zone), and la Chinantla in

Oaxaca state (also rain forest zone). The agreement was made in 2000 and the project was implemented from 2002.

The project is supported by a GEF grant through the United Nations Development Programme (UNDP), of approximately $US15 million to be spent over eight years. The basic idea is to support a selected group of communities that will carry out planning actions addressing the sustainable use of their natural resources, by means of community land-use planning. An intensive educational campaign will also be implemented in order to define conservation zones within the territories. The new community conservation areas would then increase the total area under protection in practice. An essential concept of this project is to build conservation schemes through bottom-up processes with the participation of farmers and indigenous communities. Two of these three regions do not have any formal protected areas.

Discussion Points about Principles and Lessons

In the experience of the Mexico Sustainable Development Network with the five projects mentioned in the previous section, the following broad conclusions can be drawn:

1. The first aspect that must be highlighted as an important conclusion is that *integrated conservation and development projects,* carried out with participatory and decentralized planning mechanisms in regions with small-scale farmers and high biodiversity in developing countries, are a successful and effective tool for including conservation criteria in development policies. For this reason, such projects should be a priority for both international organizations and national and sectoral policies.

Adequate articulation of small peasant regions with high biodiversity into the national and international economies is a structural need that can help assure long-term biodiversity conservation. It is not possible to conserve biodiversity effectively without taking into consideration the need for better livelihoods and economically and socially sustainable development for the rural poor. Hence the future of biodiversity is strongly tied up with the future of millions of poor farmers on our planet.

2. Mainstreaming biodiversity in the case of peripheral rural areas is more effective when *environmental institutions have significant influence* within the arrangement of national governmental institutions. This also applies to international organizations and to subnational levels.

3. *International financial resources* applied to these kinds of projects, especially those of the GEF, are very important supports for building an integrated conservation and development policy for poor regions. All reviewed projects show important elements of success, despite their small size compared with other governmental programs. The financial support provided by the GEF, UNDP, and the World Bank allows such projects to exist and to have an important demonstration effect. Without this international aid, the possibilities for mainstreaming would be significantly smaller. International support plays an important role in strengthening environmental institutions, including protected areas, allowing them to increase their influence over other sectors through improved negotiating conditions. These financial resources work as seed resources and attract other sectoral budgets to conservation goals.

4. *Local, decentralized, and participatory planning* is an important factor that facilitates and allows mainstreaming of biodiversity. Planning instruments at a local level—such as long-term plans or programs, community or microregional land-use planning, and sustainable strategic production projects—constitute valuable elements for achieving an adequate integration of sectoral policies with biodiversity conservation.

Local programs and plans constitute basic elements for policy integration. These planning tools enable conservation policies to consider social and economic needs, and ensure that social and economic

strategies contain pertinent criteria for maintaining biodiversity. One of the most important causes of deforestation and loss of biodiversity is the horizontal expansion of production activities. So a change in techniques must be carried out, in order to achieve sustainable intensification and diversification. With these changes, impacts and threats can be diminished, while simultaneously improving productivity and social conditions.

Local planning must take into account the need for meaningful participation and buy-in by the community and the primary stakeholders. Technicians and facilitators need to ensure high-quality products and effective communication with stakeholders.

5. A very important planning instrument is *community land-use planning*, a basic component for local management of development and conservation. Community land-use planning is an essential point in the strategy of the five revised programs mentioned earlier, and it is the most important planning instrument for achieving integrated natural resource management at local level. It consists of participatory planning for the use of communal land, with the help of modern instruments such as geographic information systems, to generate agreements about the use of land, taking into account ecological characteristics, level of conservation, agricultural methods, and market opportunities.

As well as being based on adequate technical studies such as good cartographical analysis, it is important that land-use planning expresses a real understanding and commitment by the producers of the community. A frequent problem is the cultural relationship between the technical group, with its sophisticated cartographical tools, and the community, which frequently has a low educational level. The experience of the analyzed projects has demonstrated that the land-use planning scheme must effectively express the community's vision and the basic agreements reached, as a solid foundation for sophisticated technical work. This requires an adequate communication strategy between the technical group and the community, through interviews, workshops, and other instruments for ensuring an effective public participation process. Running training sessions on the use of maps and cartographic techniques is also important in ensuring meaningful community participation.

6. The *participation of all important regional actors*, such as environmental NGOs and small peasant producers, is an essential element for achieving mainstreaming. All the analyzed projects include mechanisms to incorporate local participation in their operation through committees or councils. Building participation spaces is crucial for the purpose of mainstreaming, because when there is effective social participation there are better conditions for the introduction of environmental criteria.

Involvement of local communities in basic decision making for development, including spending of public resources, is a way to empower rural society. This can contribute to the changes and reforms that build up a society that keeps its biological wealth.

7. Creating *relationships, mechanisms of information exchange and communication*, and networks between the integrated conservation and development projects carried out in different areas are important ways of sharing experience and building political and technical capacities.

8. Regional integrated conservation and development projects promote *inter-institutional coordination*, and such coordination at the national level, in turn, permits operation of the projects.

Inter-institutional coordination is an essential requirement for mainstreaming. The integration of public policies that integrate social, economic, and political criteria requires coordination between the sectors that develop them. In Mexico there are widely differing points of view and operating rules between the sectoral programs, which are often implemented in the rural areas in an uncoordinated way and may leave important needs unattended to. The efficiency of the programs could be greatly improved through adequate inter-institutional coor-

dination. The experience of the PRODERS project, which integrated eight national ministries and formed the basis of the National Programme for Attention to Priority Regions, shows that integrated conservation and development projects can catalyze inter-institutional coordination.

At an international level, the relatively weak influence of environmental organizations and the lack of coordination between agencies constitute important limitations on mainstreaming. Better articulation is required between environmental agencies on the one hand and rural poverty alleviation policies and food security projects on the other, to help bring about the required integration between conservation and development.

9. *Decentralization of development programs and policies*, not just from national to state level, but also to the local government level, can help the poor regions achieve autonomy, and promote their empowerment. Decentralization of programs and policies helps local decision making, enabling conservation actions to be articulated with the objectives and strategies of local planning.

10. Mainstreaming biodiversity into socioeconomic development should be accompanied by the corresponding process of *incorporating economic and social issues into environmental policies*. Protected areas are frequently managed using exclusively environmental criteria, and their policies fail to recognize the needs of poor communities. Social and economic criteria must be incorporated into conservation policies to integrate environmental actions with other social needs.

11. Communities of *small peasant producers are key actors* in the marginalized rural zones, and must be considered in the design of development and conservation policies. Peasant villages are social units that are united through tradition and cultural heritage, with deep history. Indigenous traditional communities and their forms of agriculture have a natural tendency toward conservation. In Mexico, these links are strengthened by the communal land tenure of *ejidos* and agrarian communities, but in all

countries conservation policies must consider small villages as important actors.

12. The experience of these projects shows that actions taken at a single scale are not enough, and effective mainstreaming requires a *combination of scales of activity*. Local actions have the advantage of allowing for community participation, specific sustainability projects, experimentation with sustainable technology, and educating individual producers. International policies can assist national environmental institutions to incorporate conservation into their governments. At the same time, international factors, such as market forces, can be negative for biodiversity conservation, because they stimulate economic activities that cause deterioration, or because they do not allow for the articulation of sustainable activities by small producers with international markets.

Mainstreaming Biodiversity and Reforming the Development Model toward Sustainability

It is incorrect to assume that mainstreaming means simply adding an element to existing development policies, because incorporating biodiversity conservation criteria into development implies significant changes in how society as a whole is organized. This idea is related to one of the points of Agenda 21 that calls for the transformation of production and consumption patterns.

The idea is not just to take one or another policy or program and add a conservation component, but rather to incorporate conservation criteria into the *mainstream* where decisions about global development are taken. This involves the transformation of development models to include the concept of sustainability.

The case of rural zones in Mexico provides an illustrative example of the influence of development models on the possibility of achieving integrated conservation and development, as well as the possibility of successfully mainstreaming biodiversity conservation. From the 1950s to the late 1970s,

Mexico followed a model of economic development called the "stabilizer model," which used tariff barriers to promote industrialization that successfully achieved import substitution and price stability. During this era, the "green revolution" and agrarian reform promoted an increase in both agricultural productivity and the area of land under cultivation. The economic crisis of the late 1970s saw a shift to an "open model" or "neo-liberal model" of economic development, which set as top priorities macroeconomic stability, the removal of trade barriers, and selling off of state-owned enterprises. This policy has generated huge structural changes in the national economy, aimed at making Mexico competitive in the global arena.

In the countryside, the application of an open model brought deep and significant consequences. The application of trade liberalization resulted in deeper rural polarization, because only a small part of the sector was able to take advantage of export opportunities. Without protection, many small and medium-size producers were simply unable to compete with the specialized producers who dominate international markets, and faced economic ruin. The pure economic logic of competition takes into account neither the historic value of peasant and indigenous cultures, nor the value of Mexico's enormous agrobiodiversity. According to the logic of the open model, small peasant farmers will eventually be replaced by modern agents who can compete in the international market. For this reason, rural development policies since the 1980s have focused mainly on financial compensation directly to families, without any relation to production projects, and certainly with no biodiversity conservation criteria. So direct subsidy programs like Procampo or Temporary Employment try to assist poor farmers migrate to urban areas, or to change activities; some stop producing maize and become producers of other goods and services.

This vision of the future of poor farmers that exists in Mexico, and which is common among economic policy designers worldwide, fails to acknowledge that almost a third of the world's population is made up of such small farmers, who cannot simply be wished away or easily assimilated into already over-stretched urban areas. Although this vision has been the dominant one underpinning rural economic development policy in Mexico, it has not been the only one. In practice, different visions coexist in the universe of programs and policies. The projects analyzed here are informed by a different vision—one of integrated development and conservation, in which poor small-scale farmers have an economic and social future based on their villages and regional development. This vision also takes into account their cultural and agrobiological wealth and their natural patrimony, including a rich biodiversity.

It is clear that the open model is predominant in the planning strategies for national economic policies, and this factor operates against the success of projects like those analyzed in this study. The model also generates obstacles to the introduction of biodiversity conservation criteria into governmental programs that are designed merely as compensatory actions. An adequate economic and general development policy must have as one of its fundamental strategies the sustainable development of marginalized zones; and sectoral programs must be designed to contribute to building local integrated conservation-development projects. This would be an important factor in helping the analyzed projects to achieve effective mainstreaming of biodiversity conservation.

Those engaged in mainstreaming, however, also need to engage with other development policies and the mainstream of political and economic decision making, particularly in countries with great biodiversity. A major review of development policies should be undertaken in order to incorporate effective biodiversity conservation criteria. This should include the promotion of integrated conservation and development projects in all of the marginalized regions where small-scale and indigenous farmers live, and where so much valuable biodiversity is located.

Endnotes

1 Mexico Sustainable Development Network (Red para el Desarrollo Sostenible; RDS México), Mexico City, Mexico

2 National Commission of Natural Protected Areas (CONAND) at http://conanp.gob.mx/proders/.

3 National Commission ... Biodiversity (CONABIO) at http://www-wds.worldbank.org/servlet/WDSContentServer/WDSP/IB/1999/09/24/000094946_99092405342163/Rendered/PDF/multi0page.pdf

References

SEMARNAP. 2000. *Programas de Desarrollo Sustentable de Regiones Marginadas Campesinas e Indígenas (PRODERS). Logros y Retos para el Desarrollo Sustentable* 1994-2000. Secretaría de Medio Ambiente Recursos Naturales y Pesca, México.

SEMARNAT. 2003. *La deforestación en 24 Regiones PRODERS*. Comisión Nacional de Áreas Naturales Protegidas. Secretaría de Medio Ambiente y Recursos Naturales, México.

World Bank. 2000. *Mexico: Institutional Coordination for Regional Sustainable Development*. Report No. 19870-ME. Environmentally and Socially Sustainable Development Sector Management Unit, Washington DC.

Web sites

http://conanp.gob.mx/proders/

http://www-wds.worldbank.org/servlet/WDSContentServer/WDSP/IB/1999/09/24/000094946_99092405342163/Rendered/PDF/multi0page.pdf

10. Mainstreaming Biodiversity in Transition Countries: UNDP-GEF Experiences in Project Development in Eastern Europe, CIS, and Asia

Tehmina Akhtar[1] and Jeffrey F. Griffin[2]

The concept of mainstreaming biodiversity conservation and sustainable use in production sectors and landscapes is gaining more attention from the international conservation community. Social and economic transition in Eastern Europe, the Commonwealth of Independent States (CIS), and Mongolia has provided fertile ground for the development of an unusually high number of United Nations Development Programme (UNDP)-Global Environment Facility (GEF) projects in recent years concerned with mainstreaming approaches. Attempts are being made in these countries to view biodiversity in a more integrative and cross-sectoral manner and to move beyond narrow protection-based approaches. The new approach considers the role and value of biodiversity within a broader context in production systems and landscapes, as well as ways to generate greater value from its sustainable use.

This study reviews six projects from six countries that are attempting to mainstream biodiversity within production: Bulgaria, Croatia, Hungary, Mongolia, Russia, and the Slovak Republic. The methodology included a review of project documents, related guidance notes and supporting materials, as well as the authors' knowledge of the history and development of the projects. In addition, each project also used a standardized questionnaire to gather data. The findings were compared across projects and analyzed for lessons to be applied to GEF's ongoing discussion about mainstreaming.

The study analyzes the experience of these six projects in the design and implementation of mainstreaming approaches within production activities for agriculture, forestry, water management, fisheries, tourism, and other related sectors.[3] The study looks at project characteristics, the extent to which they have been able to secure commitment from stakeholders, how they will measure success in achieving mainstreaming outcomes, to what extent they seek to cover or mitigate against potential economic costs, and how they plan to replicate and disseminate the lessons generated.

The study considers how the transition process in the region provides an enabling context for new project strategies to be adopted, how UNDP's experience over the past 12 years has led to more mainstreaming approaches being taken, how the strategies of these case study projects may be assessed against the guidance provided by GEF for its strategic priority on "mainstreaming biodiversity within production sectors and landscapes," and whether these earlier projects help to validate this guidance. The study also highlights a number of discussion points and lessons learned, to inform ongoing discussions and future mainstreaming practice.

Case Studies in Mainstreaming Biodiversity

The six case study projects considered are outlined in this section.

Bulgaria—Conservation of Globally Significant Biodiversity in the Landscape of Bulgaria's Rhodope Mountains

The focus of this five-year project run by the Bulgarian Ministry of Agriculture and Forestry is on the landscape of the Rhodope Mountains of southern Bulgaria.[4] The Rhodope is an ancient, European cultural landscape where productive uses of forestry and agriculture predominate and protected areas are small and scattered. The project applies landscape-scale conservation practice and perspective to the production landscape as a whole and in relation to the protected areas. The change process associated with privatization, land restitution, and European Union (EU) accession provided an opening for more comprehensive approaches to biodiversity conservation within the Rhodope landscape in order effectively to conserve the mosaic of forest, agricultural land, and grassland habitat.

Croatia—Conservation and Sustainable Use of Biodiversity in the Dalmatian Coast through Greening Coastal Development (PDF-B)[5]

This three-year project of the Croatian Ministry of Environmental Protection, Physical Planning, and Construction focuses on key sectors in the landscape/seascape of the Dalmatian Coast, which constitutes a unique patchwork of marine, coastal, island, terrestrial, and agricultural ecosystems. The biodiversity has been well conserved in comparison with other Mediterranean regions, but is threatened by unsustainable development in tourism, agriculture, industry, fishing, and transport.

The project is designed to work at several levels: national—by promoting reform of policy and legal frameworks and by integrating biodiversity concerns into development planning; sectoral—by working with government sectors to integrate biodiversity into sector planning and with the private sector to adopt biodiversity friendly practices; and local or country—by seeking to improve the investment climate for biodiversity friendly, profitable enterprises, and to increase compliance by strengthening enforcement capacity, mobilizing public pressure, and developing economic incentives.

Hungary—Conservation and Restoration of the Globally Significant Biodiversity of the Tisza River Floodplain through Integrated Floodplain Management

The main focus of this three-year project of Hungary's Ministry of Environment and Water is on catalyzing effective change within agricultural and water management areas of the Tisza floodplain, where globally significant biodiversity results from its unique geological and meteorological conditions and from centuries of distinctive management practices that integrated flood control, agriculture, and natural resource management. Over the past 150 years much of this biodiversity has been lost, through large-scale flood control and agricultural development projects.

In the past decade floods, declining agricultural competitiveness, and the EU accession process have radically altered the government's management objectives for the floodplain. With EU support, the government is set to implement well-funded plans to control floods, to reform the agricultural sector, and to promote rural development. The project is designed to complement these sectoral developments by encouraging alternative approaches that include biodiversity considerations within flood control, agriculture, and rural development programs in pilot sites. The project will also work to influence sector agencies and decision makers at the national level to ensure that the results of local level demonstrations are integrated into government policies.

Mongolia—Community-Based Conservation of Biological Diversity in the Mountain Landscapes of Mongolia's Altai Sayan Mountains

This five-year project of Mongolia's Ministry of Nature and the Environment has as its focus the production landscape and protected areas that encompass Mongolia's Altai Sayan ecoregion. In the mountainous landscape of the Altai Sayan, semi-nomadic herders live in family groups and graze their animals on surrounding state grassland and forestland. Animals and plants adapted to large, open spaces also characterize this landscape.

The project's strategic approach to securing the sustainable long-term conservation of biodiversity in these mountains is to apply landscape-scale conservation practice and perspective to the production landscape as a whole and in relationship to the protected areas. To do this, the project focuses on empowering local stakeholders to integrate biodiversity conservation and sustainable use practices and priorities into grassland and forest management. The project is designed to mitigate threats to biodiversity and conserve biodiversity by: integrating biodiversity conservation objectives into sustainable natural resource use policy, programs, and practice, and linking traditional protected area management to the landscape around each area, including cross-border cooperation.

Russia—Conservation and Sustainable Use of Wild Salmonid Biological Diversity in Russia's Kamchatka Peninsula

The first phase of this project, being run over four years by the State Fisheries Committee (Kamchatrybvod), focuses on a group of at least 11 salmonid fish species and the fishery management sector in four river systems on Russia's Kamchatka Peninsula. Five of these 11 salmonid species are commercially fished; the other 6 are noncommercial species, 1 of which is the endangered "steelhead" sea-run rainbow trout.

The project is designed to develop and pilot diversity-friendly commercial fishing practices and sport-fishing ecotourism, forge new partnerships among local and international stakeholders, protect crucial salmonid habitat by establishing protected areas and participatory management regimes, establish a diversity information baseline by conducting field surveys, and lay the foundation for long-term financing. Because half of the salmonid species of concern were commercial, the project had to focus on the fishery production sector, requiring different partners and approaches than those used in a traditional conservation project.

Slovak Republic—Integration of Ecosystem Management Practices into Land and Water Management of the Slovak Republic's Laborec-Uh Lowlands (PDF-A)[5]

This project, due to be started by the Hydromelioration Authority of the Slovak Republic's Ministry of Agriculture, aims to facilitate a transition by water managers, farmers, and other resource managers in the Eastern Lowlands region from conventional water and agricultural management techniques to integrated ecosystem management practices. In so doing, resource managers would conserve globally significant biodiversity and reduce nutrient loading of Europe's largest transboundary river, the Danube.

The project focuses on a wetlands area between the Laborec and Uh Rivers, characterized by its traditional rural landscape of meadows, wet meadows, tilled land, small waterbodies, and forests. It has been affected by a Soviet-era, energy-intensive, mechanized system that was built to drain wetlands for conventional tillage agriculture, regardless of the economic or environmental costs. With the Slovak Republic's market-oriented transition, the real environmental and economic costs of these measures are becoming more evident and the government is seeking ways to reduce these costs, improve water management, and encourage appropriate agricultural practices. The design of this project capitalizes upon

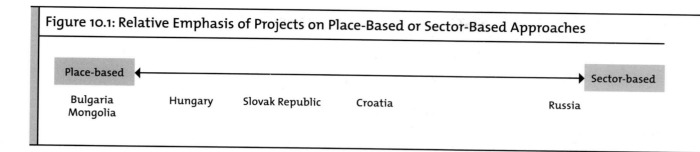

Figure 10.1: Relative Emphasis of Projects on Place-Based or Sector-Based Approaches

this need by demonstrating how to apply a scientific understanding of ecosystem function and services in order to produce economic benefits for farmers, while generating water quality, biodiversity, and other environmental benefits.

Integrating Biodiversity into Production Sectors

In analyzing the ways in which UNDP has applied the concept of integrating biodiversity into production sectors, seven questions are considered:[6]

(1) Have the projects been mainly place-based or sector-based?
(2) What is the range of strategic approaches used?
(3) What implications has integrating biodiversity into nontraditional sectors had for project design?
(4) What mainstreaming results have been achieved during the project development phase?
(5) How will success be measured and what barriers are projects being designed to overcome?
(6) How will projects cover or mitigate the potential economic costs of adopting the mainstreaming approach?
(7) What strategies are applied for replicating these projects?

1. Have the projects been mainly place-based or sector-based?

While most of the six case study projects described earlier started out as place-based projects, they have become hybrids of the place-based and sector-based approaches. Figure 10.1 shows the range that these six projects represent—from Bulgaria and Mongolia, which are very spatially oriented, with sector-based integration tools applied to a range of production activities across their landscapes, to Hungary, the Slovak Republic and Croatia, which are 50-50, to the Russia Salmonids project, which tips over to a predominantly sector-based orientation. An interesting point here is that this is not a time line, as the Russia Salmonids project is the oldest one in this subset of projects.

Primary and Secondary Sectors within Each Project's Integration Efforts

Tables 10.1a and b present sectors of focus of the six projects, including both government and industry/commercial sectors. Sectors containing or impacting on biodiversity that are thus directly targeted by each project are characterized as "primary" (P), while sectors that are indirectly or incidentally affected are considered "secondary" (S).

The following broad points can be made about sectoral involvement:

■ Agriculture, as the largest sector in most countries in which UNDP-GEF works, is addressed most in all the projects.
■ There are some viable opportunities for future projects to focus on other sectors. Projects have begun to address mainstreaming within the water sector, and are only just beginning with forestry, fisheries, tourism, planning, and integrated development.
■ Five of the six projects listed rural development as being a sector of secondary focus. This reflects

Table 10.1a Government Sectors

	Agriculture	Forest	Tourism	Water	Fishery	Infrastructure	Rural Development	Planning	Integrated Development
Bulgaria	S	P	S	S	—	S	S	—	—
Croatia	S	—	P	—	S	—	—	P	P
Hungary	P	—	—	P	—	—	S	—	—
Mongolia	P	S	S	—	—	S	S	S	—
Russia	S	S	S	—	P	S	S	—	—
Slovak Republic	P	—	S	P	S	S	S	—	—

Note: P, primary; S, secondary.

Table 10.1b Industry/ Commercial Sectors

	Agriculture	Forest Products	Tourism	Water	Fishery	NTFP	Transport/ Shipping	Infrastructure	Lending	Sport-hunting
Bulgaria	S	P	S	—	—	S	—	—	—	—
Croatia	S	—	P	—	S	—	S	—	P	—
Hungary	P	—	—	P	—	—	—	—	—	—
Mongolia	P	S	S	—	—	—	—	S	S	P
Russia	P	S	P	—	P	—	—	S	—	—
Slovak Republic	P	—	S	—	P	—	—	—	—	—

Note: NTFP, nontimber forest products; P, primary; S, secondary.

the history of UNDP-GEF projects and their incorporation of the "sustainable development baseline" with the proposed GEF alternative to secure global biodiversity benefits.

■ The six projects are largely focused on working with government sectors, by considering sector plans and policies, laws, regulations, and institutional structures. However, almost all include state-run as well as private sector enterprises and specific activities to work with private sector actors.

In the case of Mongolia, private sector involvement is largely limited to local family-based or community-based small-scale enterprises. In Russia, the project targets the fisheries sector, which is a combination of government and private ownership, and the private ecotourism sector. In Bulgaria, a vibrant, fledgling private sector has expressed considerable support and interest in the project's objective. Small and medium enterprises concerned with organic agriculture, ecotourism, medicinal plants, and other nontimber forest products (NTFPs) are mostly involved. The project will support forest certification and eco-labelling of organic produce to help develop niche markets.

In Croatia a broader range of private sector actors is likely to be involved in the project— from small family-run enterprises, to large hotel and fishery enterprises at the central level. Here the project is likely to focus both on the development of specialized niche markets (ecotourism) and on improving and increasing the effectiveness of environmental impact assessment (EIA) and other environmental management guidelines for enterprises to ensure conservation of biodiversity.

Working with the private sector poses different challenges to working with government. The projects working in government sectors are focusing on influencing the legal and regulatory frameworks that guide production activities. They seek to build institutional and individual capacity with sector agencies, and to develop relationships with an array of partners, including environment agencies, protected areas, nongovernmental organizations, and the private sector.

The private sector projects are focusing on supporting the development of biodiversity friendly products through capacity building of small and medium-sized enterprises, for example, in the area of medicinal plants. Projects look at sustainable harvesting, marketing, and processing, as well as improving production processes (in farming, livestock, and forestry, for example). Projects are also attempting to support niche markets for certain products (such as certified timber in Bulgaria), and to promote greater compliance and corporate responsibility in the private sector (as in the tourism sector of Croatia).

Working effectively with the private sector will challenge UNDP, since coordinating private sector involvement requires ongoing stimulation from key UNDP staff and consultants, and since project development must proceed more quickly in order to maintain the interest and motivation of the private sector.

2. What is the range of strategic approaches used?

The strategic approach of the Russia Salmonids project is to target a very specific biodiversity group—salmonids, and a specific sector—fisheries. It is not "sector-specific" per se, because the place (the Kamchatka peninsula) and its salmonid biodiversity are central to the project's design and justification. But the project's work has much relevance for the entire fishery sector in Russia and indeed worldwide, as it seeks to move beyond protection and combine "traditional" habitat conservation work with new and innovative efforts to reorient fishery management practices. In so doing, the project seeks

to leverage the power of the fishery sector through relatively small-scale investments in local pilots, new partnerships, and conservation.

The project is working with the government and private fishing industry to define just what "biodiversity-oriented salmonid fishery management" means, and exactly what mainstreaming would entail in this context. It considers how this approach will affect quotas for fish catch, timing, and the methods used. Pilot sites are an important part of the project's strategic approach, seeking to leverage change in the commercial fishery sector. At the same time, the project is designed to clarify and fine-tune these changes at the local level by piloting reoriented fishery management practices in four specific river systems at the local Kamchatka level.

The project is one of the first GEF projects worldwide to be based within a fishery management agency. Due to the visionary support of key stakeholders, the project was ensconced in the State Fishery Management Agency's regional office in Kamchatka. Diversity-oriented salmonid fishery management requires more information to be applied in decision making more frequently, and a broader definition of the value of the salmonid fishery. These tasks require that new partnerships be built, involving government, academia, the private sector, and local communities.

The strategy of the Croatia Dalmatian Coast project is to modify development practices in a few key sectors, especially tourism, fisheries, integrated development, planning, banking, and shipping/transport, and to modify their plans, programs, and management practices to become "greener" or more biodiversity friendly. The project will work in three or four demonstration sites, which are to be selected not for the highest levels of biodiversity (hotspots), but in areas with high visibility and high levels of conflict, where the "greening" approaches can be effectively demonstrated. There is a lot of emphasis on improving EIA for the tourism industry and demonstrating integrated coastal management.

The project will thus work at a number of levels—at the national level to influence planning and decision making, at the provincial level to support integrated planning and integrated coastal management, at the sector level to influence the behavior of key sectors, and at the local level, within pilot sites, to demonstrate sustainable practices and management measures within tourism, fisheries, and other local enterprises.

The overall strategy of both the Bulgaria (Rhodope Mountains) and Mongolia (Altai Sayan) projects is to catalyze change in resource management and administrative governance systems in ways that benefit biological diversity. Both projects are focused on particular landscapes. Both are designed to complement and catalyze change. In Mongolia, this includes administrative decentralization and community-based grassland management. In Bulgaria, this includes forest and agricultural land restitution and evolving regional development priorities. The strategic approach of the Bulgarian project is to work across the local, provincial, and national levels on mainstreaming-related activities. In Mongolia, the approach is much more focused on the local-level stakeholders and institutions.

In both landscapes, relatively small protected areas scattered throughout large areas required a more integrated and larger-scale approach to secure conservation over the long term. In Bulgaria, this means working with the national forest administration to reorient in subtle (but significant) ways how forests are managed, and what criteria and considerations are applied to key decisions within forest management. It means working with newly privatized forest owners to pilot forest certification, with extra time and attention paid to biodiversity concerns within the certification process. It also requires working with farmers, agricultural policymakers, and water managers.

Achieving all this meant establishing an umbrella institution—a nature park —to serve as the primary intersectoral coordination body for national-level ministries and their local-level offices, as well

as municipalities, tourism, and water management enterprises.[7] A primary focus of the Bulgarian project is on reorienting and leveraging large-scale agroenvironmental and rural development programs to support biodiversity mainstreaming in the key sectors of forestry, agriculture, and tourism.

In Mongolia, it involves focusing on the local level, which is of central importance to piloting mainstreaming efforts, and also central to planning and policy making, and institution and partnership-building, in order to improve local governance and bring decision-making authority closer to the people who are using the resources. In Mongolia, much of the project's focus is on strengthening local herder communities in order to enable and empower local people to manage grasslands and forest resources in ways that reduce pressure on natural resources and keep in reserve key habitats for targeted communities of wildlife and plants.

The strategic approach of the Hungary Tisza Floodplain Management project is to catalyze effective change in the water management paradigm along the Tisza, one of Hungary's largest rivers. To do this, the project is one large demonstration of best practices for this changing paradigm—from an engineering-intensive, mechanized approach to flood control and wetlands management—to an approach that restores ecosystem function and services related to natural flood control, clean water, and wildlife habitat.

The project intends to work across the vertical cross-section of the sectors—from national policies in the agriculture and water sectors to local farmers applying improved practices. At the local level in seven pilot sites, the project will build institutional capacity for assessment, planning, and management, by providing guidelines and training to local stakeholders to implement holistic floodplain management. At an intermediate or provincial level, the project will establish institutions to help support the local initiatives. At the national level, the project will make recommendations for integrating biodiversity considerations into the national flood control and agroenvironmental programs.

The project also seeks to review and change the incentive structures, for example, to enable farmers who provide flood control services to benefit from water withdrawals rather than being charged for them under existing perverse incentives. The project will advocate necessary changes in pricing structures, land-use planning guidelines, and environmental requirements, in order to facilitate these changes.

3. What implications has integrating biodiversity into nontraditional sectors had for project design?

Mainstreaming appears to require the involvement of a broader array of stakeholders and sectors than traditional biodiversity projects. In protection-oriented projects, the environment-related government institution usually takes the lead, with other sectors and stakeholders playing a more peripheral role (see table 10.2). In mainstreaming, the array of stakeholders can be much broader and more diverse, and the environment agency may not be the lead player.

A project's Executing Agency, or lead agency, is one indicator of how projects are being designed to involve new "nontraditional" stakeholders. A review of the Executing Agencies for the case study projects revealed that half of them are located within a ministry other than the ministry of environment, which is the usual GEF focal point institution. In

Table 10.2
Key Agencies Involved in Projects

Project	Executing Agency	Other Key Agencies
Bulgaria—Conservation of Globally Significant Biodiversity in the Landscape of Bulgaria's Rhodope Mountains	Ministry of Agriculture and Forestry	Ministry of Environment and Water
Croatia—Conservation and Sustainable Use of Biodiversity in the Dalmatian Coast through Greening Coastal Development (PDF-B)[5]	Ministry of Environmental Protection, Physical Planning, and Construction	Ministry of Agriculture, and Ministry of Tourism
Hungary—Conservation and Restoration of the Globally Significant Biodiversity of the Tisza River Floodplain through Integrated Floodplain Management	Ministry of Environment and Water	Ministry of Agriculture and Rural Development, State Secretariat for Water Management, and Water Management Boards
Mongolia—Community-Based Conservation of Biological Diversity in the Mountain Landscapes of Mongolia's Altai Sayan Mountains	Ministry of Nature and the Environment	Ministry of Agriculture
Russia—Conservation and Sustainable Use of Wild Salmonid Biological Diversity in Russia's Kamchatka Peninsula	State Fishery Agency (Glavrybvod)— Northeastern Branch (Sevostrybvod)	Ministry of Natural Resources
Slovak Republic—Integration of Ecosystem Management Practices into Land and Water Management of Slovakia's Laborec-Uh Lowlands (PDF-A)[5]	Hydrometeorological Authority (within the Ministry of Agriculture)	Ministry of Agriculture, and Ministry of Environment

Note: See endnote 5 for an explanation of funding levels for projects designated as PDF-A, and PDF-B.

Table 10.3a
Extent of Agreement during Project Development

Types of changes	Extent of Agreement Prior to Implementation		
	Significant	Moderate	Very little to none
Law and polices	—	R,S,H,M,B	R,C,M,B
Institutional reorganization	B	M,	R,S,H,C,M
Resources leveraged	R,S,M,B	H,C	—
New partnerships	—	R,S,C,M,B	—
New practices	—	R,S,M,B	C

Table 10.3b
Extent of Commitment during Implementation

Types of changes	Extent of Agreement Prior to Implementation		
	Significant	Moderate	Very little to none
Law and polices	R,H,C,M	R,M	—
Institutional reorganization	C,M,B	H	—
Resources leveraged	R,H,C,M	—	—
New partnerships	R,M,B	C	—
New practices	R,H,M,B	C	—

Note: B (Bulgaria), C (Croatia), H (Hungary), M (Mongolia), R (Russia), S (Slovak Republic)

During project design, efforts have been made in several cases to put in place some checks and balances by designing benchmarks that track progress in joint collaboration with other sector agencies.

4. What mainstreaming results have been achieved during the project development phase?

Tables 10.3a and b show the extent to which projects have been able to secure agreements prior to implementation, and the extent of commitment to broad changes, the details of which would be worked out during project implementation.

From tables 10.3 a and b it is apparent that, while a moderate level of stakeholder agreement to changes has been achieved during project development, securing actual commitment and buy-in for most mainstreaming changes is being left to the project implementation stage. This is for good reason, as often specific changes to be brought about by these projects are still not clear. For example, the government of Mongolia agrees to the concept of mainstreaming biodiversity into grassland management, but the specific changes that will be required are not yet known, and so it is impossible to achieve agreement on these prior to project implementation. The same is true for all of the case study projects. Mainstreaming is essentially about changing practices, rather than drawing lines on a map or building new infrastructure for a protected area. These projects show that it is difficult to anticipate the final outcome until initial steps are taken.

5. How will success be measured and what barriers are projects being designed to overcome?

Table 10.4 shows an average (among the projects) of the extent to which different indicators are being measured. It shows that a high percentage of the indicators included in the projects relates to building institutional and individual capacity. This confirms what is also seen in the field—that very little existing capacity in the production sectors to support

four out of six cases, the choice of the Executing Agency was an obvious and appropriate one, whereas in two projects (Hungary and Mongolia) the choice was less obvious, and the agriculture ministry could have played a lead role, had the project not started out with environment.

It is worth noting that even where the ministry of environment takes the lead role, the projects include expanded roles for other sector agencies, and a strong focus on intersectoral coordination. This is a first step that not been particularly easy, because in many cases the situation is complicated by difficulties in interministerial coordination. Project implementation will test how effective intersectoral collaboration is in reality, compared with what has been proposed.

biodiversity mainstreaming. It also shows that institutions are changing and new skill sets are needed in the region, given the transition context.

Another interesting finding of this analysis is that projects frequently focus on measuring impact with respect to institutional capacity, changes in practice, and actually establishing programs and infrastructure. These three are the most frequently measured results, with changes in practice measured at 23 percent and changes in both institutional capabilities and the establishment of programs and infrastructure with an average of 19 percent of the indicators. These indicators include measuring impact with respect to establishment or effectiveness of public-private partnerships. In fact, the creation of new partnerships to support the integration of biodiversity into nontraditional sectors is a common thread that runs through most, if not all, of these projects.

Projects are constrained by not knowing exactly what impact mainstreaming will have on biodiversity, and so at this point, indicators are measuring changed human and institutional behavior, rather than improved status of biodiversity. With respect to impact upon biodiversity, changes in biodiversity are measured by an average of 10 percent of the indicators, the fifth most frequently measured impact among 10 types of indicators.

6. How will projects cover or mitigate the potential economic costs of adopting the mainstreaming approach?

Approaches of the various projects to covering the costs of mainstreaming are outlined in table 10.5.[8]

Some of the interesting points which can be concluded from table 10.5 are as follows:

■ *Most projects assume that there will be additional costs associated with mainstreaming.* The only exception is Hungary, which argues that in some cases there will be no additional costs and in other cases there will be additional costs. This result speaks well to the maturity and rigor of project develop-

Table 10.4
Frequency of Use of Types of Indicator

Types of indicator	Average percent
Changes in individual capacity and/or knowledge	11.0
Changes in institutional capabilities	19.0
Changes in law or policy	8.0
Changes in biodiversity condition or number	10.0
Changes in practice	23.0
Reduction in level of threats	2.5
Programs, PAs, and infrastructure established	19.0
Changes in awareness	2.0
Mainstreaming specifically mentioned	3.5
Participation	2.0

Source: Authors' calculations.
Note: PA, protected areas.

ment work. Hungary's win-win position is that there will be no additional cost associated with mainstreaming in floodplain lands, as traditional agriculture currently practiced in the project site is not competitive and the project area is economically depressed. By converting the land to different uses (such as wetlands and bird refuges) and producing different types of products (tourism experiences, and so forth), mainstreaming would not reduce levels of production, but change the type of production to one of higher value. However, the project acknowledges that there will be additional costs to changing the way land and water will be managed in terms of new infrastructure, skills, and equipment, and makes provision for applying government subsidies (largely from EU programs) to offset these costs.

■ *All projects assume that stakeholders will absorb the extra costs.* This includes absorbing the unquantified and even unspecified costs associated with mainstreaming. For example, the Mongolia project's strategy is to mainstream biodiversity into production sector practices, thereby "piggybacking" conservation on production sector investments. Principal investments in land-use and resource-use management over the long term

Table 10.5
Approaches to Covering the Costs of Mainstreaming

Key elements of the solution	Bulgaria	Hungary	Mongolia	Russia	Slovak Republic
The project assumes no additional cost for mainstreaming.	N	Y/N	N	N	N
The project assumes the stakeholders or other sources of funding will absorb the cost.	Y	Y	Y	Y/N	Y/N
The added cost is quantified.	Y/N	N	N	Y/N	Y/N
The solution is accompanied by cost-benefit analysis or other supporting rationale for mainstreaming.	N	N	N	N	N
The project includes specific provisions/ commitments for covering the additional cost of mainstreaming.	Y	Y	Y	Y	Y
The project relies on unquantified or unqualified assumptions in presenting the mainstreaming solution.	Y /N	Y	Y	Y	Y
The solution seeks to qualify and quantify ecosystem services.	Y		Y	Y	Y

will have to come from reoriented development expenditures. The project recognizes that there will be additional ongoing, recurrent costs associated with mainstreaming biodiversity into production sector practices. In the Bulgaria project, forest certification is seen as a potential win–win solution, where newly privatized forests are able to access new, higher-priced markets and yet better manage the resource and biodiversity at the same time. Of course, this potential solution is based on the assumption that certified forests in the Rhodope region will be able to find suitable buyers and markets.

■ *Three projects quantify the additional costs involved, but these are rough estimates.* Two projects do not quantify any of the costs. The Mongolia project attempts to quantify some of the costs involved, but again, this is a rough estimate. The project assumes that the Mongolian Environmental Trust Fund (METF) will be fully operational and funded by 2009, in time to be able to cover a relatively modest US$30,000 per year of the total estimated US$90,000 in recurrent costs associated with landscape-scale biodiversity conservation in the Altai Sayan. The remaining approximately US$60,000 in estimated recurrent costs will be absorbed into government and large

sectoral program budgets as a matter of normal agricultural and program practice.

■ *No project includes a cost-benefit analysis.* Hungary comes close when it asserts that mainstreaming-inspired changes to existing agricultural practices will actually add value to the local land, but this assertion is not backed up with even a basic cost-benefit analysis. Doing such an analysis would be difficult at this stage, given the level of ambiguity regarding mainstreaming changes and their costs.

■ *All case study projects seek to find ways of covering the additional costs associated with mainstreaming.* This finding shows that these projects are on the right track and are being proactive about this issue. However, more information is needed about whether or not the projects are succeeding in helping stakeholders to secure this additional funding. For example, the Bulgaria Rhodope Mountains project relies heavily upon EU/government of Bulgaria program funding that has yet to be leveraged by local stakeholders. The project has arranged these programs and secured their agreement to participate, but it remains to be seen whether or not it succeeds. The Russia Salmonids project assumes there will be additional costs for mainstreaming or reorienting practice, but these costs are mixed up with the increased costs for enhanced conservation activities, and these costs were loosely estimated. The project seeks to establish a trust fund to cover many of these costs, but the trust fund is meant primarily to cover the expenses of managing the new protected areas and conducting an ongoing enhanced level of research and monitoring. So the Russia Salmonids project blurs the line between mainstreaming within production practice and traditional conservation work.

- *All projects rely on unquantified or unqualified assumptions regarding the costs and who will pay for the mainstreaming solution.* This result highlights the immaturity of these mainstreaming projects. By this we mean that UNDP-GEF is just beginning to gain experience in mainstreaming with respect to what works and what does not, what projects can reasonably expect to achieve, and so on.

- *All projects recognize ecosystem benefits and seek to understand them better.* This result is promising, and the experiences of projects in quantifying ecosystem benefits and successfully integrating this way of thinking into decision making processes must be closely monitored. For example, the Hungary project notes that the floodplain provides flood control services, and that oxbows perform extremely important ecological functions (spawning, rearing, feeding, resting and staging, aquifer recharge, aquatic species "banks," and habitat connectivity). The project will seek to influence policy- and decision makers as well as the public with respect to these ecosystem services.

- *Some projects were designed to achieve win-win outcomes by handling smartly some inevitable economic imbalances.* Some projects are exploring direct payment schemes. For example, the Laborec-Uh project will work with the ministry of agriculture in the Slovak Republic to pilot agroenvironmental programs that will establish contracts with farmers to alter the way they manage grasslands, wetlands, and forested areas. The project will help stakeholders develop guidelines and codes by which farmers would manage their lands in line with wetlands-compatible land uses defined by the agroenvironmental program. It is unclear yet whether the payments will be sufficient to cover

the costs incurred or the benefits foregone by farmers. But this approach will generate interesting lessons for the integration of biodiversity into agroenvironmental frameworks.

7. What strategies are applied for replicating these projects?

The following four approaches to replication were considered:

Bottom-up: scaling up from local pilots to national, regional, and sector plans and programs

All six case study projects utilize local pilots to test and flesh out mainstreaming concepts and to use these results either to influence regional and national policy or simply to influence other local actors in other places. The Bulgaria Rhodope Mountains project is designed to demonstrate new approaches at the "bottom level," with the intention of influencing regional and national programs. Here one begins to see some of the differences in approach between the projects. Mongolia seeks to use pilots largely to influence other local actors; Bulgaria, to influence national programs that will, in turn, influence local actors. The Croatia Dalmatian Coast project is also being designed to draw lessons from three or four demonstration sites, where greening of local level sector-based activities and enterprises can be demonstrated, to show how coastal development can proceed in a sustainable manner. Lessons derived in these sites are to be scaled-up to influence management practices and policies within sector agencies and the private sector.

Top-down: Starting at high policy level and moving toward ground implementation

Three of the six projects included a top-down approach to replication of mainstreaming. The Russia Salmonids project dedicates significant resources to devising practical recommendations for conservation of salmonid diversity. Funding was earmarked for annual lessons learned roundtables, which will seek to facilitate adoption of lessons learned at higher administrative levels. The Hungary Floodplain project aims, by influencing national policies and programs, to create conditions that support the replication of project lessons to other parts of the floodplain.

Horizontal: Extending mainstreaming to other sectors

This approach is used by three of the six case study projects. The Russia Salmonids project, which has a primary focus on commercial fisheries, will support work to integrate biodiversity conservation criteria into road building and sport fishing practices in Kamchatka. The Laborec-Uh project in the Slovak Republic will focus on mainstreaming in three sectors: water, agriculture, and fisheries. Mainstreaming in multiple sectors is an integral part of Bulgaria's Rhodope Mountains project approach—agriculture, water, forestry, rural development, and tourism.

Horizontal: Expanding geographical coverage to other specific places

This approach is included in five of the six projects, but is fairly weak in each. Projects support outreach and training activities but lack a clear strategy to achieve their goal of expanding geographical coverage. The Russia Salmonids project will hold roundtables to discuss and disseminate best practices on an annual basis, and will organize an international symposium and workshop at the end of the project to share lessons learned and best practices. Perhaps the strongest approach to expanding geographical coverage is included in the Laborec-Uh project in the Slovak Republic, which will work with stakeholders to develop a systematic dissemination and replication plan, identifying other areas in the country where such an approach would work, and organizing catalytic training and lessons learned exercises for stakeholders from these areas. Another approach that makes sense is included in the Hungary Floodplain project, which aims to link up with and support ongoing programs that are monitoring and reviewing EU policy on nature protection, farming, and agriculture in a broader context.

UNDP's Current Understanding of Mainstreaming

This concluding section examines how the experiences of these six projects have contributed to UNDP's better understanding of mainstreaming, by exploring three areas—the context of transition, UNDP's experience, and guidance from the GEF on its Strategic Priority 2 for biodiversity.

The Regional Context of Transition

The ongoing social and economic trends in transition countries have produced fertile ground for cultivating a wide range of mainstreaming approaches.[9] These trends include decentralization, land restitution, privatization, certification, the growing influence of the EU in terms of production sector/ environmental programs, and growing markets for "green" timber and natural resources. The resulting processes of transformation have included formulation of new laws, reorganization of institutions, emergence of private sector actors, greater market influences, and social and political changes, all of which have provided entry points for approaches to integrate biodiversity conservation needs within economic sectors and production activities.

The six case study projects were developed within a social and economic context that was and is characterized by change, which has created many problems for conservation but new opportunities and challenges as well. The projects responded to these opportunities by seeking to catalyze this change, to make the new laws and institutions more cognizant of biodiversity, to seek out new partners, and to develop new partnerships. The projects address all levels of capacity development—systemic, institutional, and individual—and have been able to work across an array of these levels, partly as a consequence of the change process.

Mainstreaming is facilitated by the decentralization process in Mongolia, by the social and economic changes in Croatia and the Russian Far East, and by the changes inspired by the accession of several Eastern European countries to the EU. In the case of the EU accession countries, Bulgaria, Hungary, and the Slovak Republic, the accession process has acted as an "enabler" for mainstreaming approaches. It remains to be seen, however, to what extent the experience and lessons of these countries would be relevant to other contexts. The fact that the other three projects included in this study are from non-EU accession countries shows that astute project development work may be able to identify appropriate enabling processes and supportive strategic directions in many countries.

UNDP's Mainstreaming Experiences in Transition Countries

Twelve years of experience in developing and implementing more "traditional" biodiversity projects has influenced how UNDP-GEF projects have understood and begun to apply the concept of mainstreaming. Looking back at these projects with the concept of mainstreaming as it is currently articulated, one can see an evolution of mainstreaming approaches.

Prior to the emergence of the strategic priorities in the Biodiversity Focal Area in 2003, the GEF emphasized conservation of specific places and their biodiversity. For the most part, UNDP/GEF projects have sought to conserve biodiversity in one or more protected areas and/or ecotypes. To do so, projects have been designed to assess the threats to this specific biodiversity and their root causes, and design a project to remove those root causes and thereby the threats. The focus of these projects has been on "traditional" conservation— strengthening environmental laws, building capacity of organizations, establishing and strengthening protected areas, working with local communities to promote community-based management of biodiversity, and so forth.

Mainstreaming-related work, if it appeared in UNDP projects, most often appeared under the guise of "sustainable development," and was one tool used to reduce pressure on the specific biodiversity resource. For example, if existing agricultural practices threatened biodiversity, the project would seek a way to help local stakeholders modify these practices and thereby mitigate the threat. A "Special Study on Mainstreaming Biodiversity Conservation" prepared by UNDP for the *GEF Biodiversity Program Study 2004* (UNDP 2004) analyzed a subset of eight fairly mature GEF projects. The study found that these older projects focused on two types of approaches to mainstreaming: improving sustainable resource management (largely at the local level) and creating an enabling environment for conservation by strengthening laws, institutions, and so forth (largely at national or subnational levels).

In more recent projects, such as those analyzed in this study, the standard analyses of threats and root causes began to point the UNDP-GEF in new directions. In more and more situations, when we asked the question "What does the biodiversity of concern need in order to be protected?," the answer pointed not just to traditional protection measures or strengthened protected areas, but to new governmental and commercial sectors, and new partners and approaches. We began looking beyond protected areas at larger landscapes, related sectors, and production practices. Our case study analysis shows a range of approaches and levels of complexity being applied by these six projects to achieve specific "mainstreaming" targets.

UNDP-GEF's understanding of "mainstreaming," as evidenced by the analysis of these six projects, is informed by the following aspects:

- Mainstreaming is inherently practical in its purpose and concept, and so we are striving to focus on impact, or just what "mainstreaming" means to the biodiversity of interest and, equally as important, to the average practitioner in the target sector(s).
- Mainstreaming, for our purposes, integrates biodiversity conservation and sustainable use into "non-green sectors" that are largely production-oriented. The practice is not only relevant to sectors that utilize or extract natural resources

(forestry, agriculture, mining, oil and gas), but also to those with an impact on biodiversity (tourism, planning, construction, transportation, and so forth).

■ The term "production sectors" (or "non-green sectors") is preferred in this context, rather than "economic sectors," for two reasons: The term "economic" is restrictive and does not account for the full range of social and cultural benefits produced by various sectors; and because protected areas can be (and are also) economically productive uses of the land and/or seascape.

■ Mainstreaming strategies can be effectively applied at a range of different levels—local, provincial, and national. In these case study projects, all three levels have been targeted in order to influence the different levels of decision making that have an impact on biodiversity.

UNDP's Contribution to Interpreting the GEF Secretariat's Guidance on SP-2

The *GEF Biodiversity Program Study 2004* (Dublin and Volonte 2004) and the Second Overall Performance Study (OPS2) (GEF 2002) noted that the GEF biodiversity portfolio has predominantly emphasized support for protected areas, with less emphasis on systemic capacity building, setting up sustainable financial instruments, education and awareness, and participatory management involving local stakeholders. Sustainable use, mainstreaming, and private sector initiatives were identified as areas requiring further emphasis. This was broadened with the development of the four new strategic priorities in 2004, particularly Strategic Priority 2 (SP2) focusing on mainstreaming biodiversity within production sectors and landscapes.

UNDP-GEF experiences in project design, as represented by the six projects analyzed in this study, are relevant to SP2's objective and help to validate it, through directions already being prioritized in the process of project design prior to the emergence of the strategic priorities. Furthermore, this case study analysis highlights the importance of the natural resource-based sectors mentioned in GEF's objec-

tive—specifically agriculture, forestry, fisheries, and tourism—to biodiversity mainstreaming approaches. However, these projects also indicate the importance of a range of other sectors that are not natural resource-based but have the potential to have negative impact on or provide opportunities to positively benefit biodiversity, such as infrastructure, urban development, rural development, coastal development, planning, and banking.

The six projects considered in this paper use approaches that are in line with the kinds of activities suggested by the GEF (GEF 2003)—developing the capacity of stakeholders, developing market incentive measures, and undertaking demonstration projects. All projects place a strong emphasis on creating an "enabling environment" for biodiversity by focusing on legislation and policy change; building institutional capacity of government agencies and other stakeholders; developing partnerships between stakeholders; and developing knowledge, guidelines, and management procedures that help to integrate biodiversity conservation needs. Though a lesser emphasis is placed on market-incentive measures, at least five of the six projects include specific activities to support certification, development of codes of conduct, engagement of private sector stakeholders, and small and medium-sized enterprise development. Finally, demonstration is a key element of all projects, with a number of different strategies being employed for replication of project approaches, as indicated above.

In addition, several of the projects analyzed also indicate the importance of carefully tailoring project design within the overall strategic directions taken by countries. The effectiveness of some of these project design experiences stems from the fact that projects were clearly designed to support new directions, and were thus able to obtain buy-in and interest from government and private stakeholders engaged in these change processes. This has helped to obtain greater leverage of GEF resources by integrating biodiversity within the strategic reform of laws, policies, institutional mandates and capacity, role of stakeholders, and jurisdictions over land and resources. Linking projects with larger governance and sector changes may also have important implications for assuring greater sustainability of project impacts in the longer term. However, the overall success of these initiatives will also be affected by the degree to which stakeholders ultimately buy in to these new approaches and apply new practices, and the degree to which these new overall policy directions succeed.

Conclusions

In conclusion, there are a number of key discussion points arising out of the analysis of the six UNDP projects. These are as follows.

Sector-Related Issues

- Mainstreaming biodiversity is important not just in natural resource-specific sectors, but also in other areas such as planning, transportation, and development.
- Mainstreaming requires new partners and new approaches—and in many cases more intensive management activities (that is, additional and enhanced data, information, monitoring requirements, as well as often greater local community involvement).
- There is a shift from standard approaches to improving limited resource use at the local level, to more complex and comprehensive efforts to integrate biodiversity into production sectors.
- While all projects include agriculture as a key sector, there are some real opportunities for future projects to focus on nonagricultural sectors. Projects are currently addressing mainstreaming in the areas of agriculture and water, and are starting to address forestry, fisheries, tourism, planning, and rural development.
- Sustainable use or management is not the same as biodiversity-oriented management. The Russia Salmonids project successfully made this case, opening the door for conservation of commercially viable species to be targeted—that is, for biodiversity that is also a commercial resource.
- Rural development issues have been an important co-funded part of nearly every UNDP-GEF proj-

ect since the GEF's inception. Now, with the strategic priority on mainstreaming, this relationship is changing. In order to achieve mainstreaming, rural development becomes an area for active GEF input, where a number of opportunities may exist for biodiversity considerations to be integrated, whereas under "traditional" GEF projects it was seen as more of a peripheral, "co-funded" issue.

Engaging the Private Sector

- Projects are being designed to facilitate growing private sector opportunities in forest certification, organic agriculture, and tourism, among other areas. But the private sector remains a relatively unknown quantity for these case study projects due to lack of experience in these countries in working with the private sector on biodiversity issues.
- The private sector is an obvious area for future mainstreaming work in this region, given the transformation that is occurring. UNDP-GEF could begin thinking about what it can do to promote more private sector-based mainstreaming initiatives. UNDP country offices could consider the trends in their countries with respect to commercial sectors/government sectors, and identify promising opportunities, for example, through emerging private sector institutions, trade associations, trade unions, and chambers of commerce.
- Working effectively with the private sector will challenge UNDP and GEF in terms of staff time and skills. Coordinating private sector involvement requires ongoing stimulation from key staff and consultants. Also, project development must proceed more quickly and be allowed to engage the private sector in new and different ways.

Integrating with UNDP's Work as a GEF Implementing Agency

- UNDP's understanding and application of "mainstreaming" is influenced by UNDP's own emphasis on and experience with sustainable development.

■ Many UNDP country program initiatives provide opportunities for GEF incremental investments in mainstreaming. Mainstreaming approaches were facilitated in practical terms when projects built upon what UNDP's own country programs were doing in this area. For example, in Bulgaria the UNDP country office was already working in the Rhodope region to promote job creation and sustainable livelihood development, thus actively supporting small enterprise development, especially in medicinal plants processing, and marketing, as well as restoration of cultural heritage and promotion of sustainable tourism.

■ UNDP's emphasis on improving governance in terms of law, policy, decentralization, administration reform, and local empowerment provides many potential entry points for biodiversity mainstreaming efforts. The Mongolia project is good example of a project building upon UNDP's governance reform and support for decentralization.

Engaging Appropriate Stakeholders

■ Projects need to keep options open on the choice of lead agency until the project approach is clear. The decision on the lead agency is one that should be given more attention early on and as the project development process moves ahead. It is important to consider whether a project with the objective to mainstream biodiversity within a particular sector or region is best positioned in the ministry of environment, or in a relevant sectoral/cross-sectoral or regional agency.

■ A key lesson that emerges from many of the projects in this study is the need to engage the private sector early on, and to ensure that the project design process includes appropriate strategies for working with the private sector. This lesson applies equally to all project partners—to clarify and confirm their roles and responsibilities and level of engagement, as well as to devise appropriate mechanisms for information exchange, collaboration, and intersectoral coordination.

■ Real stakeholder buy-in to mainstreaming will have to be secured during project implementation. This is one question that should be moni-

tored closely as these projects continue along their implementation path. While broad directions have received support, most of the specific changes to be brought about by these projects are still not entirely clear; thus agreements and buy-in need to be secured as initial steps are taken toward defining mainstreaming approaches and identifying any specific changes that are required.

Measuring Success and Impact

■ Only 10 percent of indicators applied by case study projects focus on measuring impact of the project on the state and condition of biodiversity. There is more work to do in terms of understanding the kind of impact mainstreaming outcomes can have on the state of biodiversity.

■ To date, UNDP's approach to mainstreaming in countries in transition has focused on the practical aspects of mainstreaming. The highest percentage of indicators included in these projects measures "changes in practice." This distinct practical orientation to mainstreaming activities should not be lost but built upon, developing clear strategies to influence practice, as well as monitoring the linkages between changes in practice and the reduction of threats and improvement in state of biodiversity.

Economic Costs of Adopting the Mainstreaming Approach

■ Projects need to explore how to do more thorough cost-benefit analysis during the development phase, as well as during the project implementation process as an integral part of project monitoring. Some questions to pursue are: How can a quantification of ecosystem benefits be integrated into decision-making processes? How are our projects succeeding with the win-win approaches? What about the situations where net economic losses result from mainstreaming biodiversity? Are these situations being faced; and if so, how successfully?

■ It is important to consider how mainstreaming affects the "bottom line" for local people One particularly interesting lesson to be learned from the Mongolia Altai Sayan project will be in relation to this issue, and how mainstreaming affects herders. Will it really have no significant effect? Will it ultimately be too costly for them to undertake without some sort of subsidy? The local experience needs to be tracked and analyzed, and if additional payments are required, they must be carefully developed to provide incentives. These questions will be an important part of a project's adaptive management approach.

Replication Approaches—Strategies for Wider Adoption

- Our analysis has shown that projects are applying a number of different approaches to replication, from bottom up to top down, as well as horizontally to other sectors or geographic areas.
- In order to develop an effective and comprehensive plan to facilitate wider adoption, significant attention must be paid to this issue during project development.
- A project's replication plan should be adaptable, because it is difficult to determine how replication will occur before we know what specific results the project will achieve.

Postscript: New Projects and Future Directions in Mainstreaming

Since 2003, the number of UNDP-GEF projects focusing on mainstreaming issues has increased, and a broader range of approaches and strategies have been proposed. Several recent projects are working far more closely with specific sectors as well as with specific industries or commodity markets (for example tourism, coffee, cocoa, and medicinal plants). In fact, three distinct types of mainstreaming projects are emerging, focused: (1) on a specific landscape or territorial/jurisdictional area; (2) within a specific sector, including the government and private actors within that sector; and (3) within a specific industry or commodity market.

Bioregional approaches to conservation of specific habitats are also being taken (grasslands in South Africa, for example). This project focuses on key sectors that have an impact on the condition of grasslands, and aims to promote grasslands friendly production practices to reduce loss of priority grassland areas and species, and to guide sectoral planning in three key sectors by providing biodiversity information and promoting integrated planning.

Species-focused projects (such as Soaring Birds along the West Asian-East African flyway), are looking at ways to make development in key "bottleneck" sites along the flyway more "bird friendly," by seeking to influence key sectors in these areas such as agriculture, water management, energy, and infrastructure development, in order to protect soaring birds on their migratory routes along these flyways.

This paper is a preliminary effort by UNDP to analyze and draw lessons from this strategically important subset of projects being launched in transition countries. As these initiatives mature and new projects develop, UNDP will periodically take stock of how ongoing mainstreaming projects are progressing, what sort of success they are achieving and the roadblocks they are facing, and what emerging lessons and best practices can be shared with other mainstreaming projects. As more experience is generated and more guidance becomes available on areas identified here as needing more attention (such as engaging the private sector, measuring impact, and undertaking cost-benefit analyses), UNDP will facilitate continuing feedback to and interaction with these ongoing projects, in order to refine approaches and incorporate new guidance.

The authors acknowledge the support and advice of their colleagues who provided input on the case studies and who commented on earlier drafts of this study. They are grateful to John Hough, Dennis Fenton, Nick Remple, Nikhil Sekhran, Andrew Bovarnick, and Linda Ghanime.

Endnotes

1 Adviser, GEF Unit, Energy & Environment Group, Bureau for Development Policy, UNDP, New York, USA

2 Independent consultant to UNDP and GEF, Portland, Oregon, USA

3 Four of the six projects reviewed are being implemented, while two are still in the development stage. It is worth noting that the project development phase for GEF-funded projects is an important foundational stage that lays the groundwork for a common understanding among stakeholders of what the project will achieve, defining the project strategy, building partnerships among a range of actors, and mobilizing financial and institutional commitments.

4 A full-sized project is a project that receives over US$1 million in GEF funds to complement other co-funding that the project may have secured. A medium-sized project is one that receives less than US$1 million in GEF funding.

5 The term PDF stands for project development facility, which funds the preparatory stages of GEF project development. PDF-B refers to grants of up to $350,000 from the GEF used for development of projects above US$1 million (full-sized projects) and PDF-A refers to grants of $25,000, usually for projects under US$1 million (medium-sized projects).

6 For purposes of this case study, the term "production" is used to describe sectors traditionally not considered environmental.

7 This designation is in line with IUCN (The World Conservation Union) Category V, "Protected Landscape," which permits multiple uses of land.

8 Information from the Croatia project was not available at the time this paper was written, because economic aspects were still being studied.

9 For purposes of this study, the term "transition countries" is used to include Eastern European countries, the former Soviet Union, as well as Mongolia, which have all undergone dramatic social, economic, and political changes since the early 1990s.

References

Dublin, H., and C. Volonte. 2004. *GEF Biodiversity Program Study 2004.* Washington, DC: GEF Monitoring and Evaluation Unit.

GEF (Global Environment Facility). 2002. *Focusing on the Global Environment – The First Decade of the GEF: Second Overall Performance Study (OPS2).* Washington, DC: GEF.

———. 2003. "Emerging Directions in Biodiversity Under GEF 3: Information Document for the May 2003 GEF Council." GEF Secretariat, March 25.

UNDP (United Nations Development Programme). 2004. "Special Study on Mainstreaming Biodiversity Conservation". Prepared by UNDP as a contribution to the GEF Biodiversity Program Study 2004, April.

UNDP project documents, guidance notes, and progress reports of the six projects analyzed.

Part 4.

Mainstreaming in the Private Sector

11. Mainstreaming Biodiversity Objectives into the Tea Industry: A Case Study of the High Ranges, Western Ghats, India

Pramod Krishnan[1]

In India, until recently, natural forests were considered to be the sole repository of biodiversity. Not much attention was given to the need to conserve biodiversity in other biozones and economic sectors like agroforestry systems and commercial plantations. Today, however, it is recognized that managing biodiversity in production landscapes is critically important for maintaining regional ecological connectivity and enhancing ecosystem values and services. It is also understood that the dynamics in the surrounding production sectors have a direct impact on the biodiversity of "exclusive conservation areas" and vice versa.

The need to mainstream the objectives of biodiversity conservation into the management of production landscapes assumes paramount importance in this context. A classic case in this regard is the linkage between the tea gardens and the ecological integrity of a large, fragile rain forest zone, called "the High Ranges," in the Western Ghat mountains of peninsular India.

Perhaps the largest nonforestry land use activity ever undertaken in the Western Ghats was the establishment of the tea industry. Vast stretches of invaluable tropical rainforest formations were destroyed for this purpose over the last couple of centuries (see box 11.1 for a brief history of the region). Nevertheless, paradoxically, some of the best preserved remnants of rainforests exist inside tea gardens, especially along the crest line of mountains and valleys. These areas provide shelter and corridors for wildlife, and support essential ecosystem functions and services.

Almost all the tea gardens of the Western Ghats are strategically positioned and located in high value biodiversity zones close to protected areas.

As a result of fluctuations in the global economy, the tea industry is undergoing a crisis of unprecedented dimensions. The present crisis is having phenomenal repercussions for the ecology of the region, and is disrupting the relatively stable socioeconomic fabric of the region. The most disastrous consequence of this crisis is the loss of livelihood by the large labor force engaged in the tea industry, leading to labor unrest and the possibility of the plundering of forests and other bioresources in order to provide alternative livelihoods.

The present case study is an attempt to portray the critical link between biodiversity conservation and the tea industry, the pattern of the present crisis and its impact, the need to mainstream biodiversity into the tea industry by establishing effective partnerships for the long-term sustainability and conservation of the region, and the possibility of replicating this model elsewhere.

The Western Ghats: Conservation Values and Key Threats

The topographical entity called the Western Ghats of India is identified as one among 25 biodiversity hotspots in the world. Lying parallel to the western coast of peninsular India, this 1,400 kilometer-long mountain system spreads over 0.14 million square kilometers (km²) in extent. One of the oldest tropical mountain systems in the world, the Western Ghats is known for its immense biological and cultural diversity. It supports a human population of over 40 million, of whom about five million are indigenous people whose very survival depends on the natural resources of the region.

During the last couple of centuries, however, this unique geographical zone has been subjected to large-scale human interventions, with deleterious impacts on the regional ecology. The southern parts of the Western Ghats still have extensive, well-preserved climax vegetation and are among the best representative areas of the Indo–Malayan rain forest formation. The complex topography and rugged terrain of the Western Ghats have provided refuge for a racially varied set of microcultures as well (Nair 1991, p. 92).

The Western Ghats shapes the physical and cultural landscape of peninsular India through its impact on the climatic regime, hydrology and nutrient cycling, and its provision of a source of hydroelectric energy, raw material for forest-based industries, and a wide range of natural produce for local communities. Practically all cash crop cultivation in peninsular India is in the humid zones of the Western Ghats, and the whole economy of the region is dependent on this activity.

At present, the Western Ghats is witnessing large-scale ecological degradation as a result of the destruction of forests for commercial tree plantations, the clearance of large tracts of land for the cultivation of cash crops, such as cardamom, coffee, tea, rubber, and pepper, excessive cattle ranching, and unsustainable land-use practices. Road construction, urbanization, and mass tourism are factors as well. This leads to rapid erosion of biocultural diversity, triggering genetic, species, and ecosystem malfunctions and extinctions, and affecting the livelihood and security of local communities. The complex socioeconomic environment, created by high population density, heterogeneity in land cover, and irrational land-use practices compounds the problem and makes conservation and management of biodiversity in the Western Ghats a challenging task.

Box 11.1
History of the High Ranges

With planters from Europe moving in en masse, destruction of forest vegetation in the High Ranges became extensive by the 1850s. After the British started directing the administration of the region, forests became state property and intensive forest exploitation a state objective and monopoly. Hardwood, initially from natural forests and later from plantations of tree species such as Teak, Eucalyptus, Wattle, Pine, and Alnus, became a major source of revenue for the British government and local rulers. Revenue could also be generated through cash crops such as coffee, tea, cinchona, rubber, cocoa, and a host of subtemperate fruits and vegetables.

The High Ranges were viewed as an ideal location for coffee and tea cultivation, and in 1877 Mr. J.D. Monroe took on lease the extensive Kannan Devan Hills, part of the present High Ranges. Large-scale deforestation for plantation crops became a trend that extended to other parts of the southern Western Ghats as well. From the 1940s, the area saw large-scale development of river valley projects. Organized, massive forest encroachments became the order of the day from the 1950s, and there was a rapid build-up of population in the High Ranges.

Rampant deforestation in every part of the hills, ecologically unsustainable agricultural practices, and total disregard for ecological safeguards in developmental activities (including the construction of dams, roads, new townships, and commercial forestry) together contributed to a serious ecological crisis in the High Ranges. During the late 1990s, the High Ranges became a favorite tourist destination, and the region witnessed large-scale infrastructure developments in tune with the demands of the tourism industry.

The High Ranges

Geographical Positioning

The High Ranges, located in southern Western Ghats, is comprised of high mountain ranges rising to over 2,000 meters (m) above mean sea level, and includes the highest point on land in peninsular India, the Anaimudi Peak (2,695m), extending from approximately 9° 20' N latitude to 10° 20' N latitude and 76° 30' E longitude. It is roughly a horseshoe-shaped plateau with a few high ridges. The High Ranges and the adjacent hill tracts to the east in the state of Tamil Nadu together extend over 7,500-8,000 km². The area is characterized by steep rugged terrain and highly dissected valleys forming the major river systems of peninsular India. The High Ranges area is surrounded by other geographical zones of the Western Ghats called Nelliampathy Hills, Anamalai Hills, Cardamom Hills, and the eastern portion of Palani Hills.

Climate

Due to varying topographical features, the climate within the tract exhibits remarkable differences. During the southwest monsoon, from June to August, the wind blows throughout the day and night, and maximum precipitation is received during this period. An unpleasant extreme climate is experienced in the eastern slopes of the landscape during summer and in the high altitudinal Munnar area during winter. The average annual rainfall in the rain-fed part of the High Ranges varies from 3,000 to 8,890 millimeters (mm), and in the Anjanad Valley it goes as low as 1,270 mm. The temperature varies between subzero and 35° C. The dry season commences from January and lasts until May on the western side, and in the eastern valley it extends to July.

Biodiversity Values

The relatively stable geological history of the High Ranges provided ideal environmental conditions for the evolution of an exceptional ecological richness and diversity. This high plateau has at present mostly high-elevation subtropical evergreen forests called *sholas* along sheltered valleys, interspersed with grasslands and extensive tea and Eucalyptus plantations. The sholas are relict vegetation harboring species that have outlasted the gradual climatic and ecological changes since the last glaciation, 30,000 to 20,000 years ago. These Pleistocene refugia are mostly restricted to the High Ranges and are among the most endangered ecosystems in India. Eravikulam National Park, the last refuge of the endangered Nilgiri tahr, is an officially designated PA, located in the tract and acting as the nucleus of conservation in the region.

The High Range region is equally rich in faunal diversity and noted for its high degree of endemism. There is a high density of endangered species like the Nilgiri tahr (*Hemitragus hylocrius*), Indian elephant (*Elephas maximus*), tiger (*Panthera tigris*), gaur (*Bos gaurus*), sloth bear (*Melursus ursinus*), Sambar deer (*Cervus unicolor*), leopard (*Panthera pardus*), wild dog (*Cuon alpinus*), Nilgiri langur (*Trachypithecus johnii*), lion-tailed macaque (*Macaca silenus*), and threatened birds like the great Indian hornbill (*Buceros bicornis*) and black and orange flycatcher (*Ficedula nigrorufa*) in the region.

Considering the species richness, the diversity of vegetation, and the presence of unique habitats, the ecosystem value is of the highest order. The important functions of the ecosystem are hydrology, availability of water for hydroelectric power, irrigation, and drinking water purposes, and amelioration of the climate. In the absence of an established literature on ecosystem values for the region, such values cannot adequately be quantified. However, on a 10-point scale, it is argued that the ecosystem value of the High Ranges would range between 9 and 10 (Ramesh and others 2003).

Human Ecological Values

The High Ranges had a fairly large population of hill people and forest dwellers who showed a high degree of biocultural relationship with the natural environment. Prominent among them today are *Mannan, Muthuvan, Malasar, Malamalasar, Kadar, Paliyans, Mala Arayas, Malampandarams,* and *Hill Pulayas.* Subsistence farming and the collection of nonwood forest produce form their lifeline. However, the erosion of traditional survival strategies, illogical interventions by the government, and other changes have severely affected the sociocultural conditions of these people.

Apart from this, the High Ranges are occupied by a large number of settlers who live either in small townships or in scattered homesteads. The estimated population in the whole landscape is around 1.5 million. The primary occupations of the settlers are agriculture, the plantation industry, the collection and marketing of forest produce, forest-based labor, tourism, and other service sectors.

Land-Use Pattern

The current land-use pattern in the High Ranges presents a complex scenario. The High Range region still has about 50 percent of its area under forest cover. Large-scale conversions of forests have occurred to make way for cash crop plantations. Almost half of the total agricultural area is under plantation crops such as cardamom, tea, pepper, coffee, and rubber. At least 70,000–75,000 hectares of land is under nonfood crops. While there has been very little change in the cropping areas under tea, there has been a radical reduction in the cardamom plantations. The changes affecting the cardamom plantations and the uncertainties in the tea industry constitute the major ecological destabilizations affecting the High Ranges.

Cardamom Hill Reserve is a peculiar tenurial enigma of the High Ranges. Primarily used for cardamom cultivation, these evergreen forests have been subjected to irrational administrative actions which have adversely affected their biodiversity value to a considerable extent. Over the years, the area under cardamom cultivation has been reduced and the cropping pattern changed to more sun-loving crops such as pepper. This has resulted in a loss of top canopy vegetation in the region.

The human-inhabited areas of the High Ranges represent typical tropical agroforestry systems that are multispecies and multitiered, often simulating rainforest conditions. These systems are rich in agro-biodiversity, especially that of wild cultivars and edi-

ble plants. However, the influx of cash crops like coffee, rubber, pepper, tea, cardamom, and so forth has substantially reduced the area occupied by such age-old farming systems. Large tracts of the natural forests have been converted to monoculture plantations of Eucalyptus and Acacia.

The High Ranges harbor Eravikulam National Park, one of the premier and high-value protected areas of the southern Western Ghats. The region is fast becoming a mass tourism destination, with its associated negative impacts. Eravikulam National Park and the adjoining town of Munnar are testimony to this phenomenon. The floating population of visitors has started to upset the settled socioeconomic life of indigenous communities and plantation laborers. The shift in land use from agricultural to commercial plantations and to mass tourism places excessive pressure on limited natural resources, thereby reducing the quality of the landscape.

Other Conservation Issues

Other conservation issues confronting the High Ranges can be broadly categorized as follows:

- *Land-use issues:* Some of the major threats to the forests of the landscape include fire, poaching, marijuana cultivation, large-scale collection of nonwood forest produce, invasive alien species, tree felling, encroachment, and human–wildlife conflict. The area has become highly vulnerable to encroachments and resource dependency, because of certain global events and recent changes in government policies.
- *Human issues:* Conflict between forest-dwelling communities and the state-controlled forest department is increasing day by day. A lack of appropriate policies, limited livelihood options, heavy subsistence dependency on limited resources, a lack of mutually agreed access rules, the near absence of a comprehensive system of participatory management of natural resources, and the nonexistence of an ecological code for the region are among the reasons for this.

Box 11.2
Present Structure of the Indian Tea Industry

India is the largest producer and consumer of tea in the world. It produced 854 million kilograms of tea and consumed 673 million kilograms in the year 2001. Since independence, tea production in India has grown over 250 percent and presently accounts for 31 percent of the global production of tea. India also exports an average 180 million kilograms of tea every year. There are around 88,000 tea production units in India covering an area of 45,000 hectares, of which approximately 98.2 percent belong to small growers. However, these only account for 14.5 percent of the total area under tea and 11.1 percent of total tea production. The larger estates (greater than 400 hectares) account for about 48.3 percent of the total tea area and 53 percent of total tea production. These big plantations are part of a chain of plantations owned by large corporations and multinational companies. The estates that are between 200 and 400 hectares in size account for about 0.5 percent of the total number of estates but have 24.1 percent of the tea area and 25.2 percent of total tea production. Clearly, big corporate planters are the most influential players in the tea trade.

◼ *Institutional issues:* Major institutional issues concerning the landscape are inadequate coordination among agencies, interagency conflicts, ineffective planning, and improper implementation of various programs. The lack of a comprehensive conservation policy in the overall developmental process of the region compounds the problem.

Partnership between the Tea Industry and Biodiversity Conservation

Though the birth of the tea industry was marked by the large-scale decimation of primeval rainforests, interestingly, remnants of this industry have played a major role in the conservation of biodiversity of the High Ranges. Nestled in the high-value conservation zones of the Western Ghats, the majority of the tea gardens still have intact interspersed forest vegetations along the crest lines of mountains and in the sheltered valleys.

Right from the beginning, the managers of tea gardens were aware of the role of these remnant vegetation formations in maintaining essential ecological functions in the region. Like spokes in a wheel, these relict areas play a crucial role in ensuring linkages with other prime biodiversity zones and "Exclusive Conservation Areas" in the otherwise fragmented and manipulated landscape. These areas also act as corridors for the movement of wildlife and thereby ensure genetic flow across a large landscape. Of particular significance in this regard is the migration of elephant herds from Munnar to adjoining areas using these corridors.

Some of the important protected areas in the Western Ghats were formed through the active patronage of large tea estates. An example is Eravikulam National Park, which is 97 km^2 in extent and the last stronghold of the endangered Nilgiri Tahr. Surrounded by large corporate tea gardens, the National Park has a conservation history dating back to the establishment of tea plantations. The area was managed as a game preserve by the erstwhile Kannan Devan Hills Tea Produce Company and managed through the High Range Game Association. It was later taken over by the government and declared as a protected area in 1975 (Zacharias 2002, p. 103). Even now, the management of the tea estate is sensitive to the concerns of biodiversity conservation. The existing patches of forests in the tea gardens are zealously protected. Another corporate estate in the northern part of the Eravikulam National Park has a clear written policy and guidelines for safeguarding the interests of biodiversity in its tea gardens.

It can be seen that, though not part of any deliberate policy initiated by the government, the ethos of biodiversity conservation has been mainstreamed into the working of large corporate tea gardens of the High Ranges. The same is not necessarily true in the case of small-scale cultivators of tea. But their role is limited (see box 11.2 on the present structure of the industry). In short, the existing model of a conservation-production partnership in the tea industry is governed more by conventions originating in the colonial era than by macro-level interventions from the state, either in the form of any policy formulation or through large-scale political and financial support.

The Crisis in the Tea Industry and Its Impact on Biodiversity in the High Ranges

The tea industry is now experiencing an unprecedented crisis originating both from global economic forces and from locally caused environmental degradation (Centre for Education and Communication 2003, p. 89). Since 1999, the price of Indian tea has declined to such an extent that, for the producers, the price they earn is lower than the cost of production, thereby making tea production nonremunerative. One after another, tea plantations are closing production. The labor-intensive tea industry is the second largest employer in India (with more than 1.1 million workers on permanent payrolls), and the social implications are thus immense.

Tea plantations are not just economic production units, but rather stable social institutions. The enclave economy of the tea estates was built on the principles of exclusion, dependence, and heightened vulnerability. Located in remote localities, workers in these plantations lose not only employment, wages, and other statutory benefits like health, food, firewood, and education following the closure of a plantation. Workers also lose amenities like safe drinking water, sanitation, and electricity, and this often forces people to search for alternative livelihood options.

For the large unemployed labor force of the closed tea estates, the easiest option becomes plundering the biodiversity in the adjoining landscape. According to Sarkar (2003), in the federal state of West Bengal, around 70,000 workers of abandoned

tea estates have become solely dependent on forests for their survival and have decimated the forested slopes of the lower Himalayan Mountains. A similar disaster is just around the corner in the High Ranges as a result of the closing down of the tea estates. This could lead to a deteriorating law and order situation, social unrest among local communities, and a never-ending vicious cycle of poverty and environmental degradation.

Crisis looms large on the environmental front as well. Although the number of tea plantations has remained fairly stable during the past half-century, their environmental status has quickly deteriorated. In earlier times, the total area of plantations was small in relation to the large forests surrounding them; the buffering influence of forests not only safeguarded the agroclimatic regime suitable for the cash crops but also stabilized the hydrological cycle, loss of soil, and so forth.

But over the years, the forest cover has diminished drastically, exposing the plantations to extreme fluctuations in the local climate. As a result, the upstream water requirements in the drainage basins curtailed downstream water availability. Moreover, modern scientific changes in plantation management resulted in the extensive and intensive use of chemical fertilizers, pesticides, growth regulators, and other agrochemicals with severe environmental effects on soil and biota. These toxic agrochemicals released in the upper catchments flowed downstream through drainage channels and accumulated in backwaters and in coastal waters.

Rather than seeking long-lasting solutions, the trend so far has been to seek public subsidies and short-term technological remedies. Extensive areas of sensitive zones in the tea gardens were put under ecologically unsuitable monoculture plantations for quick profit (Nair 1991). The attempts of some of the tea garden managers to squeeze out that elusive profit by putting further land under tea cultivation, through converting natural forests, also added to the crisis. In short, the present scenario in the High Ranges has to be viewed against the backdrop of the enormity of the crisis in the tea industry, contributing factors (ecological, economic, and social), and the opportunity cost of maintaining an ecological equilibrium in the landscape.

Challenges for the Future

As discussed earlier, because of the scale of land use and the gravity of the crisis, the tea industry plays a pivotal role in maintaining the ecological health of the High Ranges. The present model of a conservation/development partnership in the sector has been driven largely by the concerns and sensitivities of the corporate tea industry to the objectives of biodiversity conservation, and has been marked by the inadequate intervention of the government. It is time that the state steps in with an appropriate and enabling policy framework to establish effective partnerships addressing the present uncertainties in the sector. Clearly, there are no easy "magic wand" solutions. The whole issue has to be approached in an integrated manner, in which the government, industry, local communities, and civil society join hands and generate synergy.

First, all land use activities in the landscape need a thorough review. Cost escalations and the consequences of environmental destabilizations may be temporarily warded off by financial juggling, state relief, and further suicidal withdrawals on the natural resource capital by some role-players. But in the long run, environmental costs will become unbearable even with these interventions. Interim adjustments will invariably be at the cost of society, particularly the less influential marginal farmers, tribal people, unorganized laborers, and others directly dependent upon common natural resources (Nair 1994, p.80).

Obviously, land ethics and restorative management practices need to be redefined and tailored to the requirements of local ecology. Intensive awareness-raising for policymakers, corporate managers, and members of local communities must be conducted, with the active collaboration of civil society. The

government has to create an appropriate enabling environment, and there needs to be consensus and clear policy direction regarding the conservation of remaining forest patches and the establishment of corridors in tea gardens. This is possible, because the majority of these tea gardens are not fragmented and are owned by the corporate sector. Any informed decisions taken at the top level can be implemented on the ground with relative ease. And this is the greatest ecological opportunity that exists for restoring the landscape in the High Ranges.

Second, the financial resilience of the tea industry is strained because of the vagaries of the global economy. The scale of the crisis is large and is dependent on a host of internal and external factors that require strategic planning and focused actions at different levels. At the micro level, the first and foremost priority is to ensure fiscal prudence in the industry, especially at the production stage. To ensure accountability and liability at all levels of the organization, actions are needed to address mismanagement, reduce the cost of production, increase the productivity of laborers, and prevent cartels in auctions-as are efforts to declare a support price, find alternative markets for export, add value by promoting organic tea, establish worker cooperatives, and introduce modern technology.

Other avenues to be explored include the possibility of supplementing the economy of the tea sector through collecting a water tax (for all of the streams originating from the region, and contributing to the economy of the nation through the generation of power, irrigation, and other purposes) as well as a tourism tax, and crop diversification. A nodal agency involving representatives from the government, industry, and workers' cooperatives could coordinate this operation. At the macro level, the government has to formulate appropriate policies and legislation, especially in matters related to the trade of tea, in consultation with all the partners and stakeholders.

Third, there is an urgent need to ensure social and livelihood security to the affected workers of the tea industry. Any effort in this direction should begin with immediate relief measures, such as the free supply of food grains, medical facilities (including mobile hospitals), drinking water, and assistance to school-age children. And workers' cooperatives could coordinate these rehabilitation efforts. In the Periyar Tiger Reserve, another protected area close to the High Ranges (and also affected by problems in the tea industry), there are examples of successful practices through which the socioeconomic status of the local communities has been strengthened without jeopardizing biodiversity. This has been accomplished in this community through cooperatives, and by augmenting their income through community-based ecotourism and alternative micro enterprises (through the India Ecodevelopment Project, supported by GEF). Even in the completely abandoned tea estates, these cooperatives are coordinating the collection and marketing of tea leaves. Nevertheless, there is a need for a holistic action plan and planned strategy for the region, rather than attempting piecemeal solutions.

In sum, it can be presumed that the present model of conservation-production collaboration in the tea industry in the High Ranges is at a crossroads. The existing system needs to be reinforced by effective interventions from the government and structural adjustments within the industry itself, taking into consideration the sociocultural sentiments and requirements of the local people. In this model, the existing protected areas act as the nucleus and pillars of conservation, but the production sectors, where the objectives of biodiversity are mainstreamed, perform vital supplementary and complementary roles.

Taking the High Range Experience to Scale

The High Range experience offers an opportunity for evolving better practices for mainstreaming bio-

diversity into production sectors, not only in the Western Ghats but also in the Eastern Himalayas (another biodiversity hotspot gravely affected by the crisis in the tea industry). The possibility of replicating the High Range model in other parts of the Western Ghats and Eastern Himalayas exists (with site-specific variations) because of the similarity in the pattern of and factors contributing to the crisis and its impact.

Because tea cultivation is the largest land use activity in the landscape, the impact of mainstreaming biodiversity in the tea industry will have implications for other production sectors as well. However, since the majority of other major agricultural production sectors in the landscape, like cardamom and coffee, are owned by a large number of individual farmers, mainstreaming biodiversity in these sectors may require more focus and concerted effort.

Conclusions

The ecological history of the High Ranges reveals a checkered past and complex present. It is now time for serious introspection on the ecological mishaps that have occurred, and to work out sound ecological and prudent economic practices for the future. The need to mainstream biodiversity in the tea production sector of the High Ranges is not a theoretical or romantic concern, but rather a question of survival, involving better management of the landscape in tune with the objectives of the Convention on Biological Diversity. The lessons learned from experience in the High Ranges and the refined model can act as the starting point for mainstreaming the ethos and objectives of biodiversity conservation into the overall developmental processes of the Western Ghats. The future of the Western Ghats depends on this.

Endnote

1 Deputy Director, Periyar Tiger Reserve, Kerala, India

References

Centre for Education and Communication. 2003. *Crisis in Indian Tea Industry: A Report.* New Delhi: Centre for Education and Communication.

Nair, S.C. 1991. *The Southern Western Ghats: A Biodiversity Conservation Plan.* New Delhi: Indian National Trust for Art and Cultural Heritage.

——. 1994. *The High Ranges: Problems and Potential of a Hill Region in the Southern Western Ghats.* New Delhi: Indian National Trust for Art and Cultural Heritage.

Ramesh, B.R., D. Lo Seen, P.V. Karunakaran, M. Balasubramanian, and M. Sankar. 2003. *Conservation Review for Rationalization of Protected Area Network in Kerala, Final Report.* Pondicherry, India: French Institute of Pondicherry.

Sarkar, D. 2003. "Burdensome Load: Laid-Off Tea Workers Fall Back on Forests in West Bengal." *Down to Earth* 12 (2): 42.

Zacharias, J. 2002. *Management Plan of Eravikulam National Park.* Thiruvananthapuram, India: Department of Forests and Wildlife, Government of Kerala.

12. Mainstreaming Biodiversity in the Energy Industry

Sachin Kapila[1]

Can the extraction of oil and gas resources be carried out in such a way as not to compromise the integrity of the world's biodiversity? This is a key challenge laid at the feet of society—to ensure continued development, given the increasing global population, while maintaining the health of the world's ecosystems to provide the basis for such development.

There is a solid body of scientific evidence that biodiversity is being lost, that it is happening quickly, and that this high rate of loss is a result of human impacts. Quite clearly, the oil and gas industry is a contributory factor. The range of direct or indirect (that is, primary or secondary) impacts is well documented, but what has been less well communicated is the business case for the industry both to manage its risks with regard to biodiversity impacts and to seek to make a positive contribution to biodiversity conservation.

This paper highlights the various steps that the industry as a whole has taken in response to the challenge, as well as the efforts of one particular company, Shell, in mainstreaming biodiversity into its operations.

Energy—The Fuel for Growth

Energy is the fuel for growth, an essential requirement for economic and social development. Changes in the energy system mark transitions in the economic and social development of countries and societies as they climb the energy ladder. Recent United Nations (UN) population forecasts point to a global population of 8.5 billion people by 2050 and 10 billion people by 2075.

Populations are aging, and it is estimated that over 80 percent of people are likely to live in urban environments by 2050. Increasing and more widespread affluence are also likely, with an estimated annual economic growth of 3.5 percent over the next 50 years. This should raise global average per capita incomes above US$20,000 by 2050 (see figure 12.1). Shell's long-term energy scenarios suggest that global primary energy demand could ultimately saturate at around 100 or 200 gigajoules (GJ) per capita, depending on how much investment is made in energy efficiency. At 100 GJ per capita by 2050, energy consumption would be just over twice what it is now, and at 200 GJ per capita, four times as much (Shell International Ltd 2001).

There is a real concern that there will be a scarcity of resources to meet this energy demand in the future. Just how quickly the traditional forms of energy (coal and oil or gas) will become scarce (if at all) depends on a number of factors, such as the advent of new technology, customer preference, and government choices. What is clear, though, is that a large proportion of the energy needed to meet future demand will come from traditional energy sources (hydrocarbons), with renewable forms of energy (solar, wind, biomass, geothermal, and so forth) contributing around 30 percent of the energy

Figure 12.1:
Energy Use in Relation to Gross Domestic Product

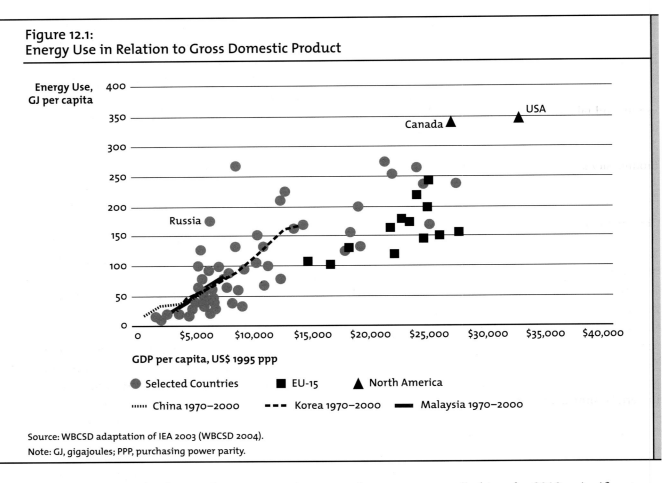

Source: WBCSD adaptation of IEA 2003 (WBCSD 2004).
Note: GJ, gigajoules; PPP, purchasing power parity.

The Biodiversity Problem

portfolio by 2050. That leaves 70 percent coming from coal, oil, and gas.

There is a solid body of scientific evidence that biodiversity is being lost at a rapid rate as a result of human impacts. There is also an emerging consensus that this could have profound consequences for the continued provision of ecosystem services, and the abundance and quality of natural products, both of which people have taken for granted for centuries. Recent international commitments have increased the pressure for action. For example, the European Union (EU) recently set a target to halt biodiversity loss by 2010.

The 2002 World Summit on Sustainable Development held in Johannesburg, South Africa, also set a target to "achieve by 2010 a significant reduction in the current rate of loss of biological diversity." Biodiversity has therefore become an issue of global environmental importance, featuring ever more prominently on the agenda of local and national governments, intergovernmental bodies, and pressure groups. Although the biodiversity "issue" is sometimes characterized as concern for particular threatened species or habitats, debate at the policy level is much more complex. At that level, the focus has shifted to the ecosystem functions that biodiversity provides and the need to maintain these. At the same time, there is a greater awareness of the impact of industrialization and corporate behavior on biodiversity—and of the importance of biodiversity in maintaining the ecosystem services on which certain companies depend. Thus the conservation of intact, healthy ecosystems is recognized as paramount to maintaining the full range of benefits that humans derive from nature.

Responses to the Problem

Increased Legislation

Governments have responded to the threat to biodiversity and taken action in many ways, including the Convention on Biological Diversity (CBD) and related conventions, and the drawing up of national biodiversity strategy and action plans (NBSAPs). In addition to the CBD, there are now several examples in place of how governments may apply the "polluter pays" principle to make companies responsible for the costs of their impacts on biodiversity. In Australia, Belgium, Brazil, Canada, and the United States legislation already exists establishing something akin to a biodiversity "levy." Operations causing damage to biodiversity are given permission to go ahead only on the basis that damage to biodiversity will be offset (made up for by "equivalent" biodiversity gains elsewhere), or that appropriate compensation will be paid to enable other parties to undertake similar offset activities.

The European Union's Environmental Liabilities Directive entered into force on April 30, 2004, and must be implemented by member states in national law by 2007. The directive specifically implements the "polluter pays" principle and is intended to result in a higher degree of environmental protection throughout Europe. Its fundamental aim is to hold operators whose activities have caused environmental damage financially liable for remedying this damage. In addition, the directive holds those whose activities have caused an imminent threat of environmental damage liable for taking preventive action. It is expected that this will result in an increased level of prevention and precaution. The Liabilities Directive puts in place, for the first time in the EU, a comprehensive liability regime for damage to the environment. In particular, it introduces a comprehensive regime for damage to protected species and natural habitats, on a scale that no member state has imposed so far.

Liability for biodiversity damage is something new in Europe, and so in order to have a precise and workable definition of biodiversity, this has currently been limited to damage to all species and habitats protected under the 1992 Habitats Directive, as well as most threatened species and migratory birds protected under the 1979 Birds Directive. The Habitats Directive lists 800 animal and plant species, and the Birds Directive identifies 181 vulnerable and threatened bird species. Protected areas under the Habitats Directive—part of the Natura 2000 network—are made up of over 15,500 individual sites and cover almost 14 percent of EU land territory. These protected species and areas represent biodiversity that has been found to be particularly rich and socially valuable in the EU. Ten years after the entry into force of the directive in the member states, this definition will be reviewed and, if appropriate, changed.

In addition, current proposals for forthcoming regulation in the United Kingdom (U.K.) will require all quoted companies to produce an operating and financial review (OFR). In the OFR, directors will be required to report on environmental and other issues, "both where they constitute a significant external risk to the company, and where the company's impact on others, through its activities, products or services, may affect its performance." The government's draft guidance to the OFR gives examples of the information that could be necessary for shareholders to make an informed assessment of the business. Among a number of examples given, two are of particular relevance to biodiversity:

- "how a company that is a heavy user of natural resources, which may become scarce or the price of which may change significantly, is intending to reduce its dependency on such resources," and
- "an explanation of the risk management approaches employed by a company to assess the operational impact on biodiversity, where failure to avoid or mitigate damage would put development consents at risk."

Increased Financial Scrutiny

On June 4, 2003, 10 multinational financial institutions announced their voluntary commitment to the

Equator Principles. The principles set an industry standard for determining, assessing, and mitigating social and environmental impacts in project finance. Developed in coordination with the International Finance Corporation (IFC), and based on the World Bank and IFC's safeguard policies, the principles apply to loans greater than US$50 million. "Equator banks" commit to ensuring that borrowers have developed projects in a manner that is socially responsible and reflects sound environmental management practices.

The principles specifically cite the protection of biodiversity, including endangered species and sensitive ecosystems, as examples of issues that must be addressed. Compliance with environmental and social standards is included in loan covenants, and noncompliance can trigger a default. As of August 2004, 27 financial institutions (comprising 25 banks, an export credit agency, and a multilateral agency) had committed to adopting the principles. These Equator banks currently represent in excess of 75 percent of the total project finance market, by deal volume.

In the United Kingdom, institutional investors (not to be confused with socially responsible investors) such as ISIS Asset Management and Insight Investment (both U.K.-based asset managers, with £62.6 billion and £71.8 billion of funds under management, respectively) have begun to turn their attention to the biodiversity risk faced by the extractive industry, including oil and gas companies. Both organizations have recently published reports benchmarking a number of extractive industry companies, comparing their performance with respect to how well they are managing biodiversity-related risks (Insight Investment 2004; ISIS Asset Management 2004).

Increased Pressure from NGOs

There is little doubt that, with the new technology available, specifically the Internet and high speed communications, campaigns coordinated by certain environmental nongovernmental organizations (NGOs) are becoming much more sophisticated. Not only is the way in which information is communicated changing (to include real time, webcams, high

quality photos, and live footage), but also the manner in which the campaigning is taking place. In addition to attention and pressure being placed upon a company in question (whether this is in the form of direct action at a specific location or using shareholder resolutions at company annual general meetings), attention is now also increasingly being placed at the doorstep of lending and credit agencies and the multi- and bilateral banks that support such projects.

The Energy versus Biodiversity Challenge

The challenge to society in the coming years will be to ensure continued development, while at the same time maintaining the health and integrity of the ecosystems on which such development depends. Part of this challenge stems from the need for increasing energy. If global energy demand is to be met, and much of it through traditional forms of energy, then this will inevitably mean access to new acreage and resources; and, no doubt, some of this from areas regarded as having high biodiversity value or sensitivity.

This presents a very real challenge to the industry, governments, conservation organizations, and civil society in general—the challenge of attempting to mix energy development and conservation. Can the extraction of oil and gas resources be carried out in such a way as not to compromise the integrity of an area's biodiversity values, whether or not it falls under protection? As one would expect, the issues are somewhat complex and emotive.

Why Should the Oil and Gas Industry Care?

Quite clearly, the oil and gas industry has an impact upon biodiversity. The range of impacts, direct and indirect, primary and secondary, has been well documented (see, for example, www.theebi.org). But the business case for managing risks with regards to biodiversity impacts and making a positive contribution to biodiversity conservation has been less thoroughly explored. Some of the key drivers for the industry can be summarized as follows:

- *Operating within the law.* This is an absolute minimum for any company—to stay within the law of any country in which it operates, or seeks to operate. This paper has touched upon some of the biodiversity/environment-specific legislation that either exists or is coming into force.
- *Complying with internal policies and principles.* Many, if not all, companies have their own policies and principles, which they expect their staff to abide by. Shell, for example, has its general business principles relating to issues such as human rights, and bribery and corruption, as well as a number of high-level policies.
- *Safeguarding current and future investments.* Critical to this industry's business growth aspirations is the ability to access new acreage. Becoming and staying an operator of choice with a host government is critical to safeguarding one's strategic investments. This is based on trust, credibility, and performance-including a demonstration of a company's ability to manage and control its risks.
- *Avoiding delays and driving down costs.* Central to any company's wishes is the wish to avoid delays, as this relates to financial over-run, which can affect the bottom line on a project.
- *Working for a company that cares.* Increasingly, companies are finding out that their staffs want to work for a company that has motivations and aspirations beyond those of just making money. They want to work for a company that operates in an environmentally and socially responsible manner and for a company that "puts something back." This is especially true when recruiting young staff and keeping them for at least five years.
- *Recognizing societal concerns and the real threats.* Being a responsible company includes listening to your stakeholders and responding to their concerns. There is no doubt that biodiversity (along with many other key issues) is on society's agenda. Failing to listen and respond may well result in reputations being damaged. Most companies (particularly those with visible brands) are only too aware of the damage caused by a crisis.

Industry's Response

The Energy and Biodiversity Initiative

The Energy and Biodiversity Initiative (EBI), established by several leading energy companies (BP, ChevronTexaco, Shell, and Statoil) and conservation organizations (Conservation International, Fauna and Flora International, IUCN [The World Conservation Union]), Smithsonian Institution, and The Nature Conservancy), provides a good example of mainstreaming. The organizations came together to develop and promote practical guidelines, tools, and models for integrating biodiversity conservation into oil and gas development. EBI addressed six important questions about the future of oil and gas development:

1. What is the business case for integrating biodiversity conservation into oil and gas development?
2. How can companies integrate biodiversity considerations into their systems and operations?
3. What are the potential negative impacts on biodiversity from oil and gas development, and what practices can companies adopt at their operational sites that will mitigate these impacts?
4. How can companies factor biodiversity criteria into decisions about where they will work?
5. How can a company measure a project's impact on biodiversity and its companywide performance in relation to biodiversity?
6. How can companies go beyond minimizing impacts and take actions that benefit biodiversity?

These questions were then used to develop a number of EBI tools and guidelines around mainstreaming biodiversity into the energy sector, namely the following:

Guides
- Integrating biodiversity into the environmental management system
- Integrating biodiversity into the environmental impact assessment
- Integrating a framework for biodiversity into the site-selection process

Box 12.1
Recommendations of the Energy and Biodiversity Initiative

1. Companies and conservation organizations view biodiversity conservation as an integral part of sustainable development.

2. Energy companies are familiar with the Convention on Biological Diversity, understand its implications for their industry, and contribute to its implementation.

3. Energy companies and conservation organizations work together in partnership to integrate biodiversity conservation into oil and gas development.

4. Energy companies and conservation organizations share information on biodiversity and make that information available in the public domain, whenever possible.

5. Stakeholder engagement includes biodiversity considerations that begin as early as possible and continue throughout the project lifecycle. Engagement is particularly important during impact assessment, indicator development, and evaluation of opportunities to benefit biodiversity conservation.

6. Where project development proceeds, it does so, where possible, in the context of a general plan for conservation and sustainable development on an appropriate geographic scale. Energy companies and conservation organizations participate with other key stakeholders in government-led spatial/regional land-use planning processes to map out priorities for biodiversity conservation and sustainable economic development.

7. Energy companies integrate biodiversity considerations into their environmental management systems.

8. Integrated environmental and social impact assessment processes are carried out for any new major development project. Potential impacts on biodiversity are fully assessed and analyzed when preliminary screening and scoping or subsequent review steps determine that the project may have significant impacts on biodiversity.

9. Companies recognize the integrity of protected areas. They understand that, while some governments may permit oil and gas development in certain protected areas, this can present significant risks to biodiversity. When operating in such areas, companies first take action to avoid impacts from their operations, and then mitigate or, where appropriate, offset any unavoidable impacts.

10. Companies recognize that areas of high biodiversity value exist both in and outside of protected areas. When considering whether to operate in such areas, companies evaluate alternative locations, routes, and technical solutions. If they do choose to operate in areas of high biodiversity value, companies employ a comprehensive set of management actions, including mitigation, compensatory measures, and investments in opportunities to benefit biodiversity conservation.

11. While biodiversity indicators may not be necessary for every project or activity, companies develop and use biodiversity indicators at appropriate organizational levels.

12. Companies seek opportunities to make positive contributions to conservation.

Source: EBI (2003).

Selecting biodiversity indicators for monitoring impacts and conservation actions.

Discussion papers
- Addressing negative secondary impacts from oil and gas development
- Outlining opportunities for benefiting from biodiversity conservation.

Resources
- Promoting good practice in the prevention and mitigation of primary and secondary impacts
- Providing online biodiversity information sources
- Explaining international conventions
- Presenting relevant glossaries
- Recommending topics for Power Point presentations.

To encourage progress in integrating biodiversity conservation into upstream oil and gas development, EBI has proposed a set of 12 recommendations, which are detailed in box 12.1.

Industry Working Group

In 2002, the Industry Environmental Conservation Association (IPIECA) came together with the upstream oil and gas producers' forum (OGP) to establish a joint biodiversity working group for the first time. The objectives of the group were to encourage information exchange, share best practice, liaise with external organizations, monitor, report, and engage with the Convention on Biodiversity (CBD) process, and raise awareness around and provide critical input into emerging issues.

The working group has, to date, conducted four regional workshops to raise awareness of biodiversity-related issues across the industry (both private and state-owned), collaborated with international processes such as the Millennium Ecosystem Assessment and the CBD, participated in international conferences such as the International Association for Impact Assessment (IAIA), the Society for Petroleum Engineers (SPE), the World Parks Congress, and the World Conservation Congress. The working group has also worked on developing specific products to share among its members, such as guidance on biodiversity action plans, biodiversity in the EIA lifecycle, and understanding what the ecosystem approach means for the industry. In addition, EBI documentation has been disseminated to all working group members and a discussion is taking place on how to make EBI become the industry "standard."

Case Study: Shell's Initiatives to Date to Mainstream Biodiversity

Shell has been working on mainstreaming biodiversity for over four years, focusing its efforts in three main areas:
- playing a role in the public policy debate around protected areas
- working to minimize its operational footprint

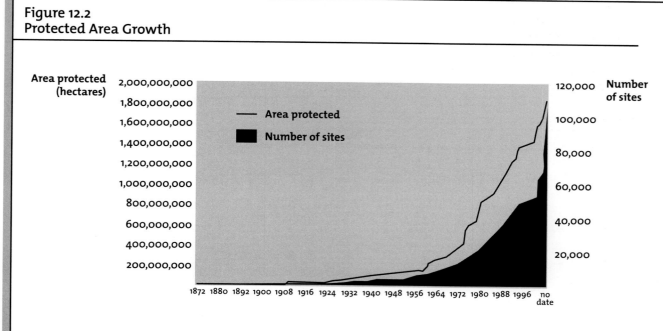

Figure 12.2
Protected Area Growth

Area protected (hectares) — Area protected — Number of sites

Number of sites

1872 1880 1892 1900 1908 1916 1924 1932 1940 1948 1956 1964 1972 1980 1988 1996 no date

Source: EBI (2003).

Box 12.2
Shell's Commitments on Protected Areas

■ Shell will not explore for, or develop, oil and gas resources within natural World Heritage Sites. This is the first time an energy company has publicly declared where it will not operate. Shell recognizes the outstanding universal value that these sites represent for society and feel they represent the "jewels in the crown."

■ Shell will further upgrade our operational practices wherever we operate in IUCN (The World Conservation Union) category I-IV protected areas or where an environmental, social, health impact assessment indicates high biodiversity values. Shell will become involved in spatial/regional planning exercises, assess our secondary impacts, implement Biodiversity Action Plans, and conduct appropriate baseline and monitoring studies.

■ Shell will publicly report on our activities in IUCN categories I-IV.

■ Shell will work with IUCN and others to develop and pilot ways of strengthening the management effectiveness of protected areas through providing key skills, creating sustainable livelihoods, and exploring options for sustainable financing.

■ making a positive contribution to biodiversity conservation.

The Public Policy Debate

One of the key issues for the industry and Shell revolves around protected areas. IUCN passed a "recommendation" at its 2000 Conservation Congress in Amman, Jordan, calling upon governments to prohibit mining (including oil and gas operations) from certain categories of protected areas, namely, the IUCN category I-IV protected areas. Given the proliferation of protected areas (currently standing at over 110,000 protected areas, or close to 12 percent of the Earth's surface, see figure 12.2), and the rising demand for energy, it is clear that this issue needs to be addressed, to avoid increased conflict between the conservation movement and the energy industry.

At Shell, protected areas are explicitly highlighted in the company's Group Biodiversity Standard ("We respect the basic concept of protected areas") published in 2001, and the first to emerge from an energy company. The company also recognizes, however, that biodiversity is important everywhere and not only in protected areas. At the time of publication, it was recognized that the statement did not go far enough for some NGOs. Shell spent two years defining exactly what this statement means for the company and, in 2003, announced a number of commitments with regard to protected areas. These are outlined in box 12.2.

During this period, in defining what exactly Shell meant by its reference to protected areas in its policy, the company was given the opportunity to contribute to the wider policy debate. Shell is a member of the steering committee for the Speaking a Common Language project, assessing ways in which the IUCN protected area management categories can be used to further conservation action on the ground. The objectives of the project are to:

■ establish the impact and effectiveness of the IUCN system of protected areas categories

■ examine what needs to be done to develop and promote the objectives-based system of protected area categories itself, and consider how it should be linked to other initiatives in protected area planning and management

■ guide the CBD's program of work on protected areas

■ provide technical advice on the categories system to a proposed program of work on protected areas for IUCN.

The project outputs will provide a review of progress in the implementation of the IUCN protected area management categories system, leading to recommendations for the system's refinement and development (see http://www.cf.ac.uk/cplan/sacl/ for more details).

Shell has been working to strengthen its relationship with the IUCN, both with the Secretariat and its regional offices. Shell benefited from a two-year IUCN secondment who helped work on the protected area issue and on specific projects on the ground. Shell has provided a return secondment to IUCN, from 2004, for a period of two to three years. IUCN's unique membership of government, government agencies, and NGOs has provided Shell with access to a wide range of stakeholders and views. One example of this is the role Shell played at the recent World Parks Congress, when for the first time industry was allowed to contribute to the congress proceedings.

Integration into Business Processes

Shell is currently working to embed its biodiversity policy into business operations and systems. Protected area and other sensitive region data (World Heritage Sites, IUCN categories I-VI protected areas, Ramsar wetlands, World Wildlife Fund Global 200 Ecoregions, and Conservation International's Biodiversity Hotspots) have been loaded onto an internal geographic information system. This "early warning system" helps staff developing new business opportunities to identify risks related to protected areas and other areas of biodiversity value/sensitivity.

Biodiversity has also been integrated into Shell's internal impact assessment (ESHIA) guidelines, also an industry first. Guidelines are currently being prepared that consider integrating biodiversity into Shell's health, safety, and environment management system (HSE-MS). Shell has also developed an internal assurance process (which includes questions on biodiversity) through which each operating company has to assure the committee of managing directors that they are complying with all policies, and provide a plan of how this will be remedied if it is not yet in compliance.

Shell is developing guidance for its operating units to produce biodiversity action plans at sites with high biodiversity value. The company believes that communicating all these efforts is important, both to raise awareness and to inform its staff of the lat-

est publications and activities. A biodiversity network, currently comprising some 200 staff members from around the Shell Group, has been established to discuss biodiversity-related issues, share best practices and lessons, and keep the group informed of internal and external issues. Shell recently published a management primer for senior staff members to help them understand better what the biodiversity standard means and what they need to do about it.

Making a Positive Contribution

Shell recognizes that, to be taken seriously, the company must demonstrate its commitments by taking action on the ground. Shell has over 130 biodiversity-related projects worldwide, including conservation, science, environmental education, capacity-building, and communication type projects (to view some of these in more detail, see www.shell.com/biodiversity).

An interesting area that Shell is currently exploring is the interface between business and conservation. If one takes a look at protected areas or protected area agencies, they have been or are typically run by conservationists who for one reason or another have had little grounding in business reality. These sites are often not run with business-type objectives, do not use business processes, and are not regarded as business assets-when in fact this is exactly what they are. Protected areas, just like businesses, require business plans, budgets, marketing plans, communication, and human resources skills, HSE management systems and protocols, safety awareness training, branding, and so forth, if they are to be run efficiently and on a sustained financial foothold. Business generally has these skills in abundance, since these are, after all, the types of skills that most businesses need to function and compete.

Shell has initiated two pilot programs aiming to build capacity through the transfer of business skills to protected areas and/or protected area agencies. It has begun a pilot with IUCN Asia HQ in Bangkok and with the Shell Foundation, the United Nations

Educational, Scientific, and Cultural Organization, and the University of Queensland, focusing on a number of World Heritage Sites. This pilot is about moving corporate thinking away from traditional forms of social investment, or corporate philanthropy, toward a model of more strategic relationships between the business and conservation sectors, building on the core skills of each sector toward delivering mutual goals. So what's in it for both sides? For the conservation community, Shell's human capital is available to address real business needs, and help in delivering organizational efficiency, as well as the opportunity to work closely with a large multinational that has significant convening power. For Shell, it helps the professionals involved to develop their leadership and personal development skills (for example, by working in a foreign environment where they have to think on their feet, work independently, and impart their own skills), act as an ambassador for the company, be exposed to an environment where profit is not a main driver, and be exposed to conservation aspirations.

Conclusions

There is a growing realization among global players in the oil and gas industry that biodiversity is a real business issue. A company like Shell can see that, if not addressed properly, biodiversity issues can increase the company's risks and potentially jeopardize its "license to operate." In addition, biodiversity presents great opportunities for Shell and other companies to work in partnership, empower staff, make a positive contribution, and play an active role in the public policy debate.

Shell has been working hard to mainstream biodiversity into its business operations in order to reduce its operational footprint. It has also, over the past few years, developed working relationships and partnerships with key conservation organizations, such as Conservation International, Earthwatch, Fauna and Flora International, IUCN, National Fish and Wildlife Foundation, Nature Conservancy Canada, Smithsonian Institution, The Nature Conservancy, Wetlands International, the World Wildlife Fund, and others.

Shell sees the need for pragmatic and yet innovative approaches when it comes to balancing the challenges between energy demand and conservation. Shell does believe that there are some areas too sensitive to operate in, namely the natural World Heritage Sites. But the company also feels that, through a transparent process, working in partnership with conservation organizations on a case-by-case basis, it is possible to operate responsibly in some areas under protection and other areas of high biodiversity value.

Endnote

1 Shell International, London, UK

References

EBI (The Energy and Biodiversity Initiative). 2003. *Integrating Biodiversity Conservation into Oil and Gas Development.* www.theebi.org/pdfs/ebi_report.pdf.

Insight Investment. 2004. *Protecting Shareholder and Natural Value: Biodiversity Risk Management: Towards Best Practice for Extractive and Utility Companies.* www.insightinvestment.co.uk/Responsibility/project/biodiversity.asp.

ISIS Asset Management. 2004. *Is Biodiversity a Material Risk for Companies? An Assessment of the Exposure of FTSE Sectors to Biodiversity Risk.* www.earthwatch.org/europe/news/biodivrisk.html.

Shell International Ltd. 2001. *Energy Needs, Choices, and Possibilities - Scenarios to 2050.* www.shell.com/static/royal-en/downloads/scenarios.pdf .

WBCSD (World Business Council for Sustainable Development). 2004. *Energy and Climate Change. Facts and Trends to 2050.* www.wbcsd.ch/web/publications/Basic-Facts-Trends2050.pdf.

Web sites

The Energy and Biodiversity Initiative: www.theebi.org

International Oil and Gas Producers Association (OGP): www.ogp.org.uk

International Petroleum Industry Environmental Conservation Association (IPIECA): www.ipieca.org

Shell: www.shell.com/biodiversity

Speaking a Common Language Project: http://www.cf.ac.uk/cplan/sacl/

13. Mainstreaming Biodiversity in the Mining Industry: Experiences from Alcoa's Bauxite Mining Operations in Western Australia

Carl Grant[1] and John Gardner[1]

Alcoa's land management and mine restoration activities in the jarrah forest of Western Australia, as this paper demonstrates, represent world best practice in these fields. One of the cornerstones of this success has been the research and development activities directed to returning biodiversity to mined areas. Some of the experiences that led to this outcome are unique to Alcoa, but others have application to other mining operations and other resource sectors. The following experiences have been important:

■ A long-term, large-scale lease and an adaptive regulatory framework have provided the impetus for Alcoa to tackle large issues such as minimizing the impact of its operations on biodiversity.

■ Opposition to Alcoa's mining operations in the unique jarrah forest ecosystem in the late 1970s and early 1980s highlighted for the company the importance of setting the benchmark in environmental management of its mining operations.

■ The company recognized the need for protected areas that are representative of key elements of the jarrah forest ecosystem. The company actively participated in a number of land-use planning cycles that have established a comprehensive, adequate, and representative (CAR) reserve system overlaying the mining lease. This has led to many millions of tons of ore being relinquished.

■ The definition of Alcoa's environmental policy, restoration objective, and completion criteria have been drivers for continual improvement and internal standards that exceed regulatory requirements.

■ The company's internal recognition of excellence in mining restoration in Western Australia has led to the development of standards throughout Alcoa's worldwide operations, and the utilization of this expertise to improve performance in other mining operations.

■ A commitment to undertaking applied research using internal and external expertise has been critical to achieving biodiversity milestones and has made a significant contribution to training undergraduate and postgraduate students over the past 30 years.

Alcoa's commitment to biodiversity in its restoration has been recognized through a number of national and international awards. These include being listed on the United Nations Environment Programme (UNEP) Global 500 Roll of Honour in 1990 and receiving the Society for Ecological Restoration Model Project Award in 2003.

Background to Alcoa's Operations in Western Australia

Location

Alcoa World Alumina Australia operates two bauxite mines at Willowdale and Huntly in the Darling

Range of southwestern Western Australia, 80-140 kilometers south of Perth. A third mine at Jarrahdale operated from 1963 to 1998, and has now been completely decommissioned and restored. The Huntly mine is the largest bauxite producer in the world. The bauxite from the two mines is processed into alumina at three refineries at Kwinana, Pinjarra, and Wagerup. The alumina is then shipped interstate or overseas for smelting to produce aluminium.

Mining takes place in the jarrah (*Eucalyptus marginata*) forest entirely within the water supply catchment of Perth and the surrounding region. The jarrah forest has high conservation value, is the basis of a major sawmilling industry, and is widely used for recreational pursuits. The jarrah forest has a diverse flora estimated to include more than 780 species, and is part of the South-western Botanical District, acknowledged as one of the biodiversity hotspots of the world. The forest, with these multiple uses, is managed by the state government authorities. The uniqueness of the jarrah forest and its proximity to Perth present an enormous challenge in terms of environmental management and restoration.

The Business

Alcoa's mining and refining operations in Western Australia supply alumina to produce approximately 15 percent of the world's primary aluminium. With assets of over $A8 billion in Western Australia, the company directly employs over 4,000 people, and contributes around $A1.1 billion each year to the state's economy. Most of the alumina is exported worldwide and generates sales revenues of nearly $A2.2 billion a year. The company is a major contributor to Australia's balance of payments, with an average net inflow of $A3.9 million per day for the past eight years.

Mining Operations

The bauxite ore is relatively shallow, averaging 4 to 5 meters deep in extent, and is usually located less than one meter below the soil surface. The mine pits range in size from a single hectare to tens of hectares. Alcoa has been restoring its bauxite mines since 1966, and approximately 550 hectares are currently mined and restored annually. All areas cleared for mining and infrastructure are restored. After timber harvest, the mining sequence involves: clearing the remaining vegetation, removing the soil, blasting the cemented bauxite layer or ripping it with a bulldozer, removing and crushing the bauxite, and transporting it to the refineries.

Alcoa's mining operations commenced in 1963, and since then nearly 14,500 hectares have been disturbed and 12,200 hectares rehabilitated. The area disturbed so far represents less than 1 percent of the total jarrah forest of 1,480,000 hectares. Over an expected 100-year life of the viable bauxite reserves, Alcoa will have disturbed approximately 2.7 percent of all jarrah forest. Each year, similarly sized areas are cleared and rehabilitated, with the remaining area open required for mining infrastructure, haul roads, sumps, and topsoil storage.

Impacts from Mining

The main potential environmental issues for the mining operation are water catchment protection, loss of flora and fauna diversity, the spread of *Phytophthora* dieback disease, loss of timber production, and impacts, such as noise, dust, and access to the forest, on neighbors and local communities. Both mines are ISO 14001-certified (International Organization for Standardization), with environmental management systems that are critical to the effective management of mining impacts. This paper focuses on those impacts directly related to biodiversity (that is, flora, fauna, and dieback).

Prior to mining, flora and fauna surveys are carried out. Flora surveys map site-vegetation complexes, search for rare or threatened species and communities, help identify habitat of endangered and threatened fauna, and prepare species lists for restoration seed mixes. Where rare or threatened species or communities are identified, management plans are developed to protect them. Fauna surveys provide baseline data on the presence and abundance of mammals, reptiles, and birds; help identify the presence of endangered or threatened species; and locate high value habitat. Mine plans are then altered to avoid disturbance of high-value habitats such as large swamps.

Many plant species, including jarrah, are susceptible to dieback, a disease that has been present in the forest for at least 100 years. The disease is caused by the microscopic pathogen *Phytophthora cinnamomi*, which attacks the roots of plants and causes them to rot. This kills the plant by stopping the uptake of water and nutrients. The pathogen is spread mainly by the movement of infested soil and by the flow of infested water. An intensive dieback management program is integrated into all mining and restoration operations. This program is an essential component of Alcoa's environmental management program for mining, and aims to minimize the effects of mining on the health of the forest and rehabilitated mined areas.

Restoration Process

The restoration process starts with shaping the mine pit, returning the soil, and ripping to 1.5 meters deep using a bulldozer with a winged tine. Logs and rocks are returned to provide habitat for native fauna. Seeds of local plants are spread, and nursery-grown plants are planted for species where seed is not a viable method of establishment. A fertilizer mix is then applied in late winter or early spring using a helicopter. Establishment of vegetative cover is rapid. A more detailed description of the restoration process is provided elsewhere (see, for example, Ward and others 1996; Gardner 2001).

Factors that Influenced the Mainstreaming of Biodiversity

It is not possible to provide a comprehensive account of the history and multiple factors that have led to the mainstreaming of biodiversity in Alcoa's operations, within the limitations of this paper. We have, therefore, identified a number of factors and processes that have been the major influences, and

discuss these briefly. There are lessons to be learned from these factors, as identified in the literature on mainstreaming biodiversity (see Pierce and others 2002). For example, supportive legislation and policy, effective research, effective involvement by non-governmental organizations (NGOs), and scientific knowledge and understanding are all discussed in relation to Alcoa's operations, pointing out opportunities for and limitations on the broader application of these factors.

Regulatory Framework

The Kwinana alumina refinery and Jarrahdale bauxite mine were established under the provisions of an agreement between Alcoa and the state of Western Australia in 1961. The agreement was given statutory effect by the passage of the Alumina Refinery Agreement Act in 1961. Major amendments were made to the principal agreement in 1969 and 1978, to provide for the establishment of the Pinjarra and Wagerup refineries and their associated bauxite mines at Huntly, Del Park, and Willowdale.

The 1978 (Wagerup) Agreement required the company to produce a detailed environmental review and management program (ERMP) for approval by the state before construction commenced, and subsequently to implement the environmental management program as approved. The ERMP gave specific commitments in relation to the submission of mine plans for agreement on by the state, rehabilitation of mined areas to meet designated land-use priorities, protection of water catchments, control of spread of dieback disease, rehabilitation of forest adjoining mined areas, noise control, and the implementation and reporting of environmental research and monitoring programs. In a strictly legal sense, the much more stringent environmental and planning controls included in the 1978 agreement apply only to the Wagerup refinery and Willowdale mine operations, but Alcoa voluntarily applies them to all Western Australian operations.

Although the legislation and mining lease provide Alcoa with a relatively secure resource, Barry

Carbon, the company's environmental manager in the 1980s, summarized Alcoa's position by saying:

In the short term, the security for Alcoa to maintain access for bauxite resources is protected by legal agreements. In the long term, however, it is the general community that will decide on this issue. As long as the community perceives that the benefits of the mining and refining operation exceed the costs of that operation, then ongoing access to resources is likely. If, however, the community perceives an excess in costs, and these costs are mainly environmental, then access to bauxite is not so secure.

It has therefore been the continued policy of Alcoa to make every effort to minimize the environmental costs to the community of its bauxite operation,

through an ongoing, intensive effort at rehabilitation. Put simply, we want to be treated responsibly in maintaining access to resources and, in order to earn that access, we must in turn be responsible, and be seen to be responsible.

Each year Alcoa submits rolling five-year mine plans to a multiagency committee known as the Mining and Management Programme Liaison Group (MMPLG) for approval (see figure 13.1). The MMPLG includes representatives from all of the relevant government agencies. The submission of advance mine plans allows the activities of the other forest users to be integrated; in particular, forest silviculture, logging, and prescribed fuel-reduction burning operations. The flexibility that the MMPLG provides Alcoa has allowed them to minimize the area cleared

Figure 13.1
Mine Planning Approval and Monitoring Flow Diagram Showing the Bodies Represented in the Various Groups

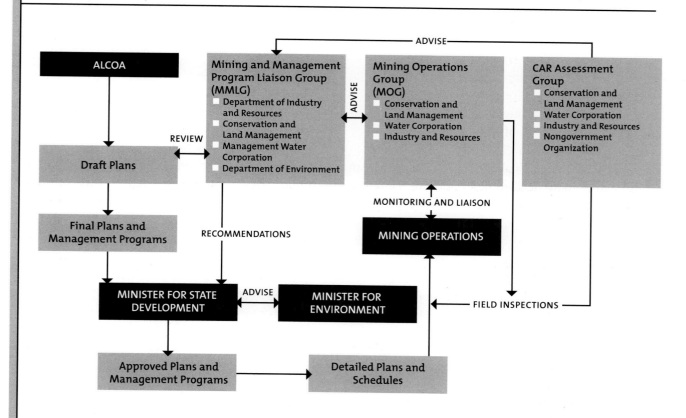

for their bauxite operations. In contrast to projects that are assessed at a single point in time, which are likely to overestimate the required clearing, Alcoa can fine-tune their mine plans on an annual basis, leading to a better environmental outcome.

One of the outcomes of a regional forest agreement process undertaken in 1996 to develop a CAR reserve system was the identification of informal CAR reserves in addition to the formal reserves. These are often linear buffers along streams, isolated small pockets of remnant old growth forest, and diverse ecotype zones such as swamps and granite outcrops. The company endeavors not to disturb these areas but occasionally haul roads must cross stream zones and disturb these informal reserves. Through consultation with the regulatory agencies, Alcoa has established a procedure for seeking approval for disturbance of areas within informal reserves. Following baseline flora, fauna, and heritage surveys, and selection of the lowest impact route, plans are submitted to the MMPLG for approval. A subcommittee, which includes an NGO representative, inspects these areas in the field before recommending approval (figure 13.3).

Opposition to Alcoa's Mining Operations

Opposition to Alcoa's mining operations in the unique jarrah forest ecosystem in the late 1970s and early 1980s made the company realize the importance of setting a benchmark in environmental management of its mining operations. In a critique of bauxite mine rehabilitation in the jarrah forest, Schur (1985) demonstrated the passion felt by protesters at that time, arguing that "Rehabilitation represents a trial-and-error, corporate gardening exercise" and that "Alcoa environmental scientists' job is to justify unimpeded corporate access to bauxite reserves." It was critically important, he said, "to prevent Alcoa from mining within the lower rainfall zone of the Northern Jarrah Forest. This could entail a specific campaign to prevent any trial mining being implemented there."

Roger Vines, Executive Director of Alcoa's Western Australian Operations in the 1990s, indicated the resultant shift in Alcoa's rehabilitation policy when he stated that:

Regardless of the effort that the industry applies to rehabilitation, in the end it is public perception rather than a measure of inputs or outcomes that defines success. The environment might "belong" to all species, and animal species can indicate success by recolonizing a rehabilitated landscape, but only the human species can articulate success. Generally, this results from perception and attitude rather than evaluation of facts.

Conservation Reserves, Mining Lease, and Broader Forest Management

The northern jarrah forest of Western Australia is covered to a large extent by a mineral lease granted to Alcoa in 1961. During the subsequent 44 years, a series of reviews of conservation reserves (protected areas) has been undertaken to improve biodiversity protection in this region. Alcoa's mineral lease (ML1sa) was granted in 1961 under a state agreement act (SAA). Initially the lease covered an area of 1,260,000 hectares, which included forested areas in the Darling Range, where the bauxite reserves occurred, as well as a significant area of mostly private land on the coastal plain, encompassing the refinery sites and transport corridors. In 1994, the lease was amended to cover only the bauxite resource, reducing the area to 712,900 hectares (Gardner and Stoneman 2003). Of the remaining area, Alcoa has relinquished over 34,000 hectares (5 percent of the remaining lease area, 21 percent of the lease area that contains economically viable bauxite) of land containing economically viable bauxite over the past 30 years. This has occurred through a number of additions to the conservation reserve and negotiations with Alcoa that are detailed in another paper (Gardner and Stoneman 2003).

Alcoa's bauxite resources in the jarrah forest have some features that have allowed flexibility to negotiate over conservation reserves. The deposit is large, dispersed, and highly viable. In other situations, where a mineral reserve is small, concentrated and marginally viable, the same opportunities may not arise. In such cases, the conflict between mining and biodiversity protection will be more difficult to resolve.

Alcoa and the Department of Conservation and Land Management (CALM) have worked together on a range of projects that benefit biodiversity in the broader jarrah forest, beyond the boundaries of the company's operations. Alcoa is a major sponsor of Operation Foxglove, a feral animal control program to remove the threat of predation by feral foxes on small and medium-sized native mammals. Operation Foxglove is part of a wider feral animal control program, Western Shield, which covers an area of over 3 million hectares. These projects have led to the recovery of populations of a number of threatened fauna species and have also allowed reintroductions of locally extinct species like the Noisy Scrub Bird and Tammar Wallaby. Alcoa has also contributed directly to threatened species recovery programs and has sponsored rare plant propagation initiatives.

Since 1989, Alcoa has been actively working with farmers, government, and NGOs to repair degraded land, conserve biodiversity, and protect regional waterways through the Landcare program. These activities are generally undertaken outside of Alcoa's mining lease area. Rural communities throughout Australia were facing alarming land degradation problems that were caused by several complex problems: clearing of native vegetation, erosion, salinity, fertilizer run-off, and loss of wildlife habitat. Alcoa has committed resources, expertise, and more than A$20 million to community, environment, and Landcare projects that have demonstrated the practical results of various Landcare management techniques. The Alcoa Landcare Project also includes educational packages for schoolchildren and Alcoa-sponsored education centers.

Internal Standards Exceeding Regulatory Requirements

The definition of Alcoa's environmental policy, restoration objective, completion criteria, and botanical milestone have been drivers for continual improvement and internal standards that exceed regulatory requirements.

Environmental, Health, and Safety Policy

It is Alcoa's policy to operate worldwide in a safe, responsible manner that respects the environment and the health of its employees, its customers, and the communities where it operates. This involves a commitment not to compromise environmental, health, or safety values for profit or production. All Alcoa employees are expected to understand, promote, and assist in the implementation of this policy and the accompanying principles. Part of the mission statement of the mining group in Western Australia outlines that the company will "be the world leader in restoration of mined land and an international benchmark for environmental management." Such policies and mission statements, while corporate in nature, are important in obtaining environmental commitment from all levels within an organization.

Restoration Objective

In 1990, Alcoa's restoration objective was identified as being "To restore a self-sustaining jarrah forest ecosystem, planned to enhance or maintain water, timber, recreation, and conservation values." Management signed off on this objective, which was somewhat ambitious when first proposed. In subsequent years, the identification and agreement of this restoration objective has been a key driver for continual improvement. In an endeavor to meet the objective, management has agreed to fund various research and operational trials. A fundamental mistake that has been made by other mining companies is not to agree on their restoration objective at an early stage in their operations.

Figure 13.2
Species Richness of Restored Areas from 1990 to 2001 When Compared to the Unmined Forest

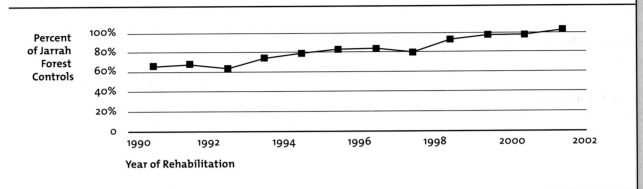

Completion Criteria

Completion criteria have been defined as restoration performance objectives (Grant and others 2001). They represent milestones in the biophysical processes of restoration that provide a high degree of confidence that a rehabilitated mine site will eventually reach the desired, sustainable state (that is, restoration objective). Alcoa developed completion criteria for post-1988 restoration in the 1990s, with the regulatory authorities and other stakeholders agreeing to these criteria in 1998 (DoIR 2002).

Alcoa defined the following broad completion criteria for rehabilitated bauxite mines in the jarrah forest: meets land-use objectives, is integrated into the landscape, exhibits sustained growth and development, vegetation is as resilient as the jarrah forest, and can be integrated with forest management (Elliott and others 1996). These criteria were then assessed under five time categories (from planning to greater than 15 year-old restoration). For each criterion, the intent, guidelines for acceptance, accepted standard, and corrective actions were identified (DoIR 2002).

The definition of criteria that will allow Alcoa to relinquish their responsibilities over rehabilitated

areas has been a driver for research into the long-term successional development and management and provided options for these areas. This has led to the identification of issues such as fire and weed management, and brought about alterations in the current restoration prescription, resulting in a better biodiversity outcome. For example, the density of short-lived legume species in rehabilitated areas has been decreased in recent years because many of these species represent a fire risk when they senesce (Grant 2003). These legume species also out-compete other smaller plants that contribute greatly to biodiversity. Decreasing the density of legumes in rehabilitated areas has therefore assisted in long-term management, and has also increased biodiversity in rehabilitated areas in the shorter term.

Botanical Milestone

One of the key drivers for the restoration of a self-sustaining jarrah forest ecosystem is the return of the diverse understory flora. In recognition of this, a botanical milestone was defined in 1990, stating that "[t]he average number of indigenous plant species in 15 month-old restoration is 80 percent of the number found in representative jarrah forest sites." This target was first achieved in areas restored in 1995. A new milestone was then set, stating that "[t]he average number of indigenous plant species in 15 month-old restoration is 100% of the number found in representative jarrah forest sites, with at least 20% of these from the recalcitrant species priority list." Recalcitrant species are plants that are common in the unmined jarrah forest but are difficult to reestablish and are historically absent or underrepresented in the restored mined areas. These internal milestones were created even though the agreed completion criteria state that rehabilitated areas need only have a species richness that is greater than 50 percent of the unmined forest controls.

To measure botanical richness in restoration areas, a rigorous, scientifically based sampling system was developed. Each year in spring, when a restoration is 15 months old, 50 plots of 80 square meters are randomly selected at each mine. All native plant species in each plot are counted. Identically sized plots in the native forest adjacent to each mine are used for comparison. Improved soil management and greater richness in the applied seed mix led to gradual improvement in species richness to over 80 percent by 1995 (figure 13.2). By further improving soil handling methods, using improved seed technology, and planting recalcitrant species, the botanical milestone of 100 percent species richness was achieved by 2001 in restored areas.

Continuous Improvement

Underpinning a philosophy of internal standards that exceed regulatory requirements is the desire for continual improvement. The bar is being set higher and higher, as demanded by the general public, and no company can afford to rest on its laurels. Alcoa has striven to become the best and to stay in that position. Roger Vines, Executive Director of Western Australian Operations in the 1990s, summarized this ethic in a presentation in 1991:

> If we were to select the single most important characteristic of our environmental effort I believe I would point to our philosophy of continuous improvement. Never being content to rest at any level of achievement, always wanting to push

> towards a higher goal, always looking for the next piece of the jigsaw.

An example of continuous improvement in environmental practice is provided by the dieback management systems utilized at the two mine sites. Dieback has been identified as a key process threatening biodiversity in Australia. The dieback management system was reviewed by an internationally recognized plant pathologist, Professor Everett Hansen, in 1999 and he summarized his comments in a discussion paper sent to Alcoa:

> To my knowledge, the Alcoa programme is unprecedented and unparalleled in the world, including other disease management efforts in Western Australia. The challenge is immense: widespread distribution of P. cinnamomi in the operating area, and operations that require logging, road building, and mining activities that have led to disease increase in other situations around the world. The Alcoa programme is marked by commitment to success at all levels of the organization, boldness of objectives in the face of a daunting challenge, willingness to invest in the expensive operations necessary to halt Phytophthora, and openness to evaluation by the public and collaboration with the scientific community. Against the odds, the effort appears to be successful, although final evaluation must wait until some years after the mining operations are finally closed.

Applying Best Practice throughout the Company

Alcoa's internal recognition of excellence in mining restoration in Western Australia has led to the development of standards throughout the company's worldwide operations and the use of this expertise to improve performance at other mining operations. Alcoa's corporate mine rehabilitation standard and guidelines were developed with input from its rehabilitation staff throughout the world, and are applicable to all mining operations. These are published on Alcoa's intranet for reference by the company's staff, as well as at the following Web site: http://www.alcoa.com/global/en/environment/pdf/bauxite_mine_rehab_standards.pdf.

The standard also forms the basis for a corporate environmental audit protocol on land management, with which all Alcoa mining locations must work toward full compliance. Improvement activities have included initial assessments of mine rehabilitation performance at all Alcoa mining locations worldwide, regular reviews of progress at locations where improvement is most needed, exchange and coaching of inexperienced rehabilitation staff, and an internal workshop in 2002 attended by rehabilitation staff from all bauxite mining locations.

Research and Training

In 1970, Alcoa employed a consultant to review the performance of early mine rehabilitation and to advise on how it could be improved. This led to the appointment of a professional environmental officer in 1971, and a major internal review of the environmental impact of the mining operations in 1974. An outcome of that review was to expand significantly the resources applied to environmental management, including the appointment of the first environmental research personnel in 1975. To have secured such resources nearly 30 years ago indicates a wealth of strategic vision and conviction on the part of those involved (Slessar 1994).

Alcoa has made a statutory and moral commitment to carry out and support scientific research in relation to its operations in Western Australia. The company has strong links to all of Western Australia's universities and to other research institutes such as the Australian Centre for Mining Environmental Research (ACMER) and Kings Park and Botanic Garden, funding and supporting basic and applied biological research by these organizations. Alcoa funded a lecturer position in plant ecology at the University of Western Australia from 1978 to 1990. This was in response to a perceived need to establish a center of excellence in the study of native plant ecology in the state. Alcoa also funded a lectureship position in plant pathology at Murdoch University from 1994 to 1998. Again, this developed into a center of excellence to study plant diseases, and particularly Phytophthora dieback disease in Western Australia.

Alcoa environmental staff have supervised or co-supervised approximately 100 honors, masters, and doctoral students over the years. Alcoa also financially supports these projects. In 1999, 2000, and 2001 Alcoa had a total of 28 students working with the company. These projects provide Alcoa with important research information and give the students valuable training in environmental matters associated with the resource sector. All environmental management courses in Western Australian universities include at least one visit to Alcoa's mine restoration operations. Several courses also include one or more lectures from Alcoa environmental staff. A significant flow-on benefit is that these students, their university supervisors, and other associated researchers communicate the research results to the rest of the resource sector. In addition, many of these students are subsequently employed in the resource sector.

Alcoa currently directly employs nine staff in its mining environmental research department. Since 1975, staff members of the research department have been authors or coauthors on more than 80 peer-reviewed articles in journals, 16 book chapters or monographs, and over 100 conference proceedings. Obtaining peer review and presenting research findings at conferences has been important in ratifying the research that Alcoa has conducted. A failure to publish research findings in peer-reviewed literature has often been a weakness of other mining companies and resource sectors.

Integration of Environmental and Operations Management

The benefits of integrating environmental management with operations planning and management are obvious. If protection of the environment is perceived by operations personnel to be an "add-on cost" or an afterthought, or something that is mainly the responsibility of environmental personnel, it is unlikely to be done well or efficiently. Integration not only helps ensure that environmental issues are adequately considered in all stages of the planning and production process, but also imposes the discipline of cost- and time-effectiveness on environmental management activities.

Clear assignment of accountability for environmental performance is an important aspect of integration with operations management. The mine manager should feel as accountable for the quality of mine restoration and environmental management as he or she does for the quality and quantity of ore the mine produces. In Alcoa, this accountability is fostered by a clear division of responsibility between mine and environmental department personnel. Mine environmental personnel report to the mine manager in relation to performance, and to the manager of the environmental department for technical guidance (Slessar 1994).

Conclusions

Alcoa's bauxite mine restoration in Western Australia is regarded as one of the best large-scale examples of native ecosystem restoration in the world. Identification of a clear restoration objective and botanical milestone, commitment from all levels of the company to achieve these targets, and decades of applied ecological research have been the key drivers to this success. Alcoa's commitment to biodiversity in its restoration has been recognized through a number of national and international awards.

Endnote

1   Alcoa World Alumina, Applecross, Australia

References

DoIR (Department of Industry and Resources). 2002. *Alcoa World Alumina Australia Darling Range Bauxite Mine Rehabilitation Completion Criteria*. Perth, Australia: DoIR.

Elliott, P., J. Gardner, D. Allen, and G. Butcher. 1996. "Completion Criteria for Alcoa of Australia Limited's Bauxite Mine Rehabilitation." Presented at the Third International and the 21st Annual Minerals Council of Australia Environmental Workshop, Newcastle, Australia, October 14-18.

Gardner, J. 2001. "Rehabilitating Bauxite Mines to Meet Land Use Objectives: Bauxite Mining in the Jarrah Forest of Western Australia." *Unasylva* 52: 3-8.

Gardner, J.H., and G. Stoneman. 2003. "Bauxite Mining and Conservation of the Jarrah Forest in South-west Australia." Presented at IUCN and ICMM Workshop on Mining Protected Areas and Biodiversity Conservation: Searching and Pursuing Best Practice and Reporting in the Mining Industry, Gland, Switzerland, July 7-9.

Grant, C.D. 2003. "Post-Burn Vegetation Development of Rehabilitated Bauxite Mines in Western Australia." *Forest Ecology and Management* 186: 147-57.

Grant, C.D., J. Duggin, I. Meek, and M. Lord. 2001. "End Point Criteria and Successional Pathways for Manganese Mining Rehabilitation on Groote Eylandt, Northern Territory." Presented at 26th Annual Minerals Council of Australia Environmental Workshop, Adelaide, Australia, October 14-18.

Pierce, S.M., R.M. Cowling, T. Sandwith, and K. MacKinnon, eds. 2002. *Mainstreaming Biodiversity in Development: Case Studies from South Africa*. Washington, DC: World Bank.

Schur, B. 1985. *Jarrah Forest or Bauxite Dollars?* Perth, Australia: Campaign to Save Native Forests.

Slessar, G.C. 1994. "Environmental Management of Alcoa of Australia's Bauxite Mining Operations in Western Australia." Presented at Conference on Economic Growth with Clean Production, Melbourne, Australia, February 7-10.

Ward, S.C., G.C. Slessar, D.J. Glenister, and P.S. Coffey. 1996. "Environmental Resource Management Practices of Alcoa in Southwest Western Australia." In D. Mulligan, ed., *Environmental Management in the Australian Minerals and Energy Industries: Principles and Practices*. Sydney, Australia: UNSW Press.

Part 5.

Achieving Mainstreaming Outcomes

14. Achieving Mainstreaming Outcomes: Guidelines for Effective Interventions

Workshop Participants[1]

A primary goal of the Cape Town workshop on biodiversity in production landscapes was to assist in designing more effective interventions for the achievement of mainstreaming outcomes. Discussion at the workshop drew on the papers presented in this volume and the rich experience of participants to build a picture of the current state of mainstreaming biodiversity across the globe. Sectoral discussions explored the gains made and obstacles faced in economic sectors including agriculture, tourism, forestry, mining, energy, infrastructure, transport, and construction. An attempt was made to identify the core and potentially unique features of each sector, the special opportunities for mainstreaming existing in the sector, the biodiversity values upon which mainstreaming approaches should focus, and the critical factors for success in the sector.

Ultimately, the workshop came to the conclusion that, while specific opportunities for mainstreaming biodiversity do exist in each sector, a sectorally based approach is insufficient. The potential "targets" of mainstreaming are not limited to sectors, but may be larger or smaller, or cut across two or more sectors. Targets include specific industries, individual enterprises, landowners, businesspeople, and consumers. They can include spatial targets—entire bioregions, landscapes, individual properties, and specific sites; and they can include all levels of governance-international bodies, national governments, and lower tiers of government—as well as international donor agencies and banks.

At times, a very focused mainstreaming initiative at a local scale will be appropriate, while at other times, initiatives will occur at a broad landscape scale, taking into account a matrix of land uses and a number of role-players. At the other end of the scale are global mainstreaming initiatives, in which biodiversity is placed on the agenda of development policymakers and planners. Cross-sectoral mainstreaming programs will also need to be carried out, since many of the threats to biodiversity cut across economic sectors and are cumulative.

Many of the barriers to effective mainstreaming are also common across sectors, relating both to the enabling environment-improving policy and institutional capacity—and to the need to create markets for biodiversity goods and services. The workshop decided to focus on developing three key products (principles, priorities, and indicators), which can assist the Global Environment Facility (GEF) and its Implementing Agencies in meeting the opportunities for mainstreaming biodiversity conservation and overcoming the barriers.

Principles and Conditions for Effective Mainstreaming

In a broad sense, the 10 principles of the ecosystem approach listed in box 1.1 inform much of the work currently being undertaken to mainstream biodiversity conservation into production sectors and landscapes. At the same time, however, the workshop felt that a set of principles and conditions specific to mainstreaming approaches could be useful in guiding future initiatives.

The 10 principles outlined in this paper, and summarized in box 14.1, are informed by the fact that biodiversity is critically important to all sectors of human society and is the insurance for life itself. While biological resources are used for human livelihoods, this use is often unsustainable, and many human activities totally ignore any consideration of biodiversity, at a high cost to human development.

The Cape Town workshop agreed that the objective of mainstreaming biodiversity is: "to internalize the goals of biodiversity conservation and the sustainable use of biological resources into economic sectors and development models, policies and programmes, and therefore into all human behaviour."

In order to conserve biodiversity, protected areas must be supplemented by integrating the concerns and values of biodiversity conservation into the wider landscape. Investment in mainstreaming can both generate immediate benefits and act as a safeguard for sustainable development in the long term.

Mainstreaming may involve difficult choices and will require well-informed decisions on:
- Trade-offs between the interests of biodiversity conservation and conventional forms of economic production, in both the short and long term
- Trade-offs between those who gain the benefit and those who bear the cost.

The importance of each of the 10 principles is explored the following section, in relation to examples taken from the papers presented at the workshop and published in this volume.

Awareness and political will from the highest levels, providing support for implementation

The importance of this level of support is shown clearly in Carlos Toledo's paper on mainstreaming biodiversity in rural development programs in

---

Box 14.1
Principles for Effective Mainstreaming

Effective mainstreaming requires:

1. Awareness and political will from the highest levels, providing support for implementation
2. Strong leadership, dialogue, and cooperation at all levels
3. Mutual supportiveness and respect between biodiversity and development priorities
4. A strong focus on economic sectors, supported by cross-sectoral approaches, securing sector-based biodiversity conservation
5. Analysis and understanding of the changing motivations and opportunities of each sector, including the effects of globalization
6. Identification and prioritization of entry points and the development of sector-specific tools and interventions (such as international codes of conduct or standards)
7. Awareness within sectors of the relevance of biodiversity conservation and the capacity needed for implementation
8. A coherent set of economic and regulatory tools and incentives that promote and reward integration and added value, while discouraging inappropriate behaviors
9. Sustained behavioral change within individuals, institutions, and society, and in both public and private domains
10. Measurable behavioral outcomes and biodiversity impacts.

Mexico. Toledo shows the difficulties faced by mainstreaming projects working with marginalized rural farming communities, in the absence of high-level political support. He points to the contradictions between mainstreaming projects based on a model of integrated conservation and development on the one hand, and a political environment on the other hand, which favors direct financial compensation to peasant farmers who are adversely affected by trade liberalization. Toledo's case study also stresses the importance of environmental institutions having a significant influence within the arrangement of national governmental institutions, in order to win support for mainstreaming initiatives.

Strong leadership, dialogue, and cooperation at all levels

The paper in this volume by Trevor Sandwith, Kristal Maze, Mandy Barnett, Sarah Frazee, and Mandy Cadman on bioregional conservation programs in southern Africa illustrates the importance of a multiple-scale approach to mainstreaming. The authors report on landscape-scale conservation initiatives that have been effective by using a combination of "bottom-up" and "top-down" approaches involving Implementing Agencies in the management of projects at several scales, with site-specific interventions both responsive to and informing higher-level policy and programs.

Mutual supportiveness and respect between biodiversity and development priorities

Several of the papers in this volume highlight the need for biodiversity conservation initiatives to address socioeconomic development priorities-not merely internalizing the goals of biodiversity conservation into economic sectors and development programs, but also ensuring that development goals are internalized in conservation programs. Gonzalo Castro's paper on biodiversity in the GEF portfolio points out that individual, narrowly focused, site-specific projects have in the past largely failed to address the root causes of biodiversity loss, including economic and social policies, and that project links to social and political aspects of sustainable development need to be improved in the future.

A strong focus on economic sectors, supported by cross-sectoral approaches, securing sector-based biodiversity conservation

The need for an approach that crosses economic sectors is illustrated by Robert McCallum's paper on mainstreaming biodiversity conservation initiatives in New Zealand. The paper reports on a recent shift away from relying on the support of government agencies, conservation nongovernmental organizations (NGOs), and other "traditional" conservation proponents to working with a range of role-players including those in the industries reliant on conservation estate-forestry, agriculture, and tourism. The paper by Trevor Sandwith and others reports on an approach that goes beyond this focus on economic sectors to one that is truly cross-sectoral and includes, for example, initiatives with collaboration between sectors on social priorities such as addressing rural poverty, youth development, and community health by including a component of biodiversity conservation.

Analysis and understanding of the changing motivations and opportunities of each sector, including the effects of globalization

This significance of this principle is highlighted in Pramod Krishnan's case study of the tea industry in the mountainous High Ranges area of the Western Ghats region of India. The paper outlines the historical contribution of the large tea estates to maintaining corridors of biodiversity in remnants of rain forests along mountains and valleys. In today's context, the paper highlights the damaging effects of fluctuations in global markets on the tea industry and the social and ecological crisis that is resulting. Krishnan points to the opportunities thrown up by the crisis for mainstreaming biodiversity into the tea industry by establishing effective partnerships for the long-term sustainability and conservation of the region, and the possibility of replicating this model elsewhere.

Identification and prioritization of entry points and the development of sector-specific tools and interventions (such as international codes of conduct or standards)

This principle is illustrated by Carl Grant and John Gardner's paper on mainstreaming biodiversity in Alcoa's bauxite mining operations in Western Australia. In this setting, the definition of a clear environmental policy, restoration objective, and completion criteria have been drivers for continual improvement and internal standards that exceed regulatory requirements, and the development of standards throughout the company's worldwide operations. It is argued that prioritizing entry points and interventions specific to the company's mining operations has enabled conservation goals and targets to be effectively mainstreamed into day-to-day company operations.

Awareness within sectors of the relevance of biodiversity conservation and the capacity needed for implementation

This principle is illustrated by Sachin Kapila's paper on the response of the oil and gas industry in general, and Shell in particular, to the dual challenge of managing its risks with regard to biodiversity impacts. These companies are seeking to make a positive contribution to biodiversity conservation using the approach of mainstreaming biodiversity into their operations. Biodiversity is a real business issue that, if not addressed properly, can increase risks and potentially jeopardize a company's "license to operate." Simultaneously there is an awareness that biodiversity conservation presents great opportunities for companies to work in partnership, empower staff, make a positive contribution, and play an active role in the public policy debate. The experience of this industry shows the importance of raising awareness of biodiversity concerns in a manner that focuses on core business operations rather than corporate philanthropy.

A coherent set of economic and regulatory tools and incentives that promote and reward integration and added value, while discouraging inappropriate behaviors

The paper by Paul Elkan and Sarah Elkan on mainstreaming wildlife conservation in multiple-use forests of the northern Republic of Congo reports on an initiative that provides a good example of this principle in action. The initiative has involved working with logging companies to put in place a detailed set of incentives and disincentives to achieve the objectives of halting hunting encroachment and pressures around a national park, extending protection to endangered and rare species across a large area of important habitat, establishing a locally recognized and supported system of community hunting and no-hunting zones, identifying and protecting key wildlife habitat areas within logging concessions, and creating the conditions necessary for the sustainable off-take of legally hunted game species in combination with alternative protein sources. The economic and regulatory tools and incentives used in the case study

are an innovative response to the challenges of meeting these objectives.

Sustained behavioral change within individuals, institutions, and society, in both public and private domains

This principle is explored in Richard Cowling's paper on the conditions necessary for successful mainstreaming initiatives, and the constraints facing such initiatives. Cowling points out that mainstreaming is achieved "by changing the behavior of individuals and organizations through the creation of institutions (including incentives) that bind actors to supporting norms, values, and practices that promote biodiversity persistence." He discusses the constraint on effective mainstreaming posed by the dwindling awareness of biodiversity among the citizenry of most countries of the world, as people become increasingly disconnected from nature. He argues that there is a high degree of ignorance of ordinary people about the importance of biodiversity to their livelihoods, and that sustained behavioral change can only come about once the biodiversity community takes up the challenge of communicating its messages more effectively, through media that strike the right emotional chords by telling stories that touch people's values.

Measurable behavioral outcomes and biodiversity impacts.

The importance of having measurable project outcomes is demonstrated in the paper by Tehmina Akhtar and Jeffrey Griffin, which reviews the experience of mainstreaming initiatives in six countries in economic transition: Bulgaria, Croatia, Hungary, Mongolia, Russia, and the Slovak Republic. The paper analyzes the project results in detail and critically examines what kinds of impact the projects are looking to measure, what types of indicators are used to assess project success, and the broad question of how project implementers can know whether mainstreaming has been successful. The paper points out how infrequently actual impacts on biodiversity on the ground are measured, while highlighting this as a central area for future initiatives to address.

Priority Areas for GEF Intervention

In mapping a way forward for mainstreaming biodiversity initiatives, the Cape Town workshop focused on recommending the kinds of activities that could be supported by the GEF and its Implementing Agencies in the future. The activities identified here are indicative of the types of initiative that may be supported by GEF on a cost-sharing basis under the GEF's Strategic Priority 2 for Biodiversity: Mainstreaming Biodiversity in Production Landscapes and Sectors—to integrate biodiversity conservation into agriculture, forestry, fisheries, tourism, and other production systems and sectors, in order to secure national and global environmental benefits.

The workshop noted that the GEF will finance the incremental costs of measures to mainstream biodiversity in production landscapes and sectors, without subsidizing the costs of enterprises in doing regular business, and taking due precautions to ensure the sustainability of outcomes, and that the GEF will fund country-driven activities that respond to national priorities. The focus in Strategic Priority 2 is on conservation efforts outside of protected areas, although opportunities will be sought to complement GEF-funded and other interventions to strengthen protected area networks. Knowledge management activities in support of mainstreaming opportunities may also be funded under Strategic Priority 4 for Biodiversity: Generation and Dissemination of Best Practices.

The activities recommended below fall into three priority areas:
(1) Strengthening capacity at the systemic level
(2) Establishing markets for environmental goods and services
(3) Improving production practice.

These are in line with the GEF's commitment to fund efforts to remove key barriers to the development and uptake of mainstreaming opportunities in different production landscapes and sectors, by strengthening capacities at the systemic, institutional, and individual levels, and undertaking demonstration activities to catalyze innovation in production processes and increase management know-how.

1. Strengthening Capacity at the Systemic Level

Strengthening policy
- ◼ *Policymaking:* Strengthen capacities among policymakers outside the traditional environmental institutions to accommodate biodiversity management objectives in policy-making processes within and across production sectors.
- ◼ *Legislation:* Integrate biodiversity management objectives into legal reform processes in production sectors.
- ◼ *Best practice guidelines:* Incorporate best practice guidelines into national legislation covering specific production sectors.

Incorporating biodiversity management considerations into spatial and sector planning
- ◼ *Sector planning:* Strengthen institutional capacities to integrate biodiversity conservation objectives into sector planning and growth strategies at local, national, and global scales.
- ◼ *Spatial planning:* Strengthen capacities for integrating conservation objectives in cross-sectoral spatial planning systems at the landscape level, including poverty alleviation strategies.
- ◼ *Bioregional programs:* Establish multi-stakeholder programs at the level of the ecoregion or bioregion, as an effective approach to mainstreaming biodiversity across a production landscape, providing institutional and governance mechanisms for vertical integration between scales.
- ◼ *Strategic environmental assessments (SEAs):* Strengthen capacities at the institutional and individual level for undertaking SEAs as a means of identifying the cross-sectoral impacts of production activities on biodiversity in target landscapes.
- ◼ *Information systems:* Construct user-friendly information and knowledge management systems to inform planning activities within and across different production sectors at different scales (local, national, regional, global).

■ *Networking:* Strengthen partnerships and networks between different institutions and stakeholder constituencies, including governments, industries, civil society, and NGOs.

Awareness/advocacy

■ *Awareness:* Build awareness of the ecological goods and services provided by species and ecosystems, and their contribution to production sectors, sustainable livelihoods, and the wider economy.

■ *Mass media:* Strengthen the capacity of mass media to highlight the importance of biodiversity conservation and sustainable use.

■ *Advocacy:* Sensitize top decision makers and investors across public institutions and private enterprises to the economic and social benefits of biodiversity conservation and the public and private costs of ecosystem degradation and biodiversity loss, including the impact of invasive alien species.

■ *Business monitors:* Support the establishment of business monitors in countries where these are not yet present.

■ *Community empowerment:* Support innovative demonstration projects that educate local communities and empower them to benefit from biodiversity conservation and sustainable use.

2. Establishing Markets for Environmental Goods and Services

Markets for ecological services

■ *Knowledge management:* Distill, evaluate, and disseminate in a user-friendly format lessons and best practices in establishing markets for ecological services in different countries.

■ *Resource valuation:* Work to establish or strengthen the policy, legal, and institutional framework for resource pricing to signal the true economic values of ecological services to production activities.

■ *Market-based instruments:* Design and pilot cost-effective, market-based instruments for biodiversity conservation suitable for different jurisdictions to complement regulatory measures (including tradable development rights, mitigation banks, or other schemes).

■ *Payments for ecological services:* Design and pilot payment schemes for ecological services to compensate resource users for off-site ecological service benefits associated with conservation-compatible land-use practices; such schemes should be developed and adapted with a view to mass replication, and to ensure their financial sustainability.

Supply chain initiatives

■ *Certification:* Strengthen fair trade or eco-labelling schemes to improve their biodiversity content; provide one-time support to small and medium-sized producers to remove barriers to market access for certified produce. Examples may include the creation of producer cooperatives to assure economies of scale in supply to community-based enterprises, improvement of product distribution systems, measures to shorten market chains so as to improve value capture at the producer end for local enterprise, and capacity support to meet the initial social and environmental criteria for market entry.

■ *Procurement:* Work with large national and multi-national companies and the public sector to create supply chain guidelines, accommodating biodiversity objectives and procurement systems that motivate small and medium-sized suppliers to meet these guidelines.

■ *Deal flow facilitation:* Facilitate financial deal flows between investors and financial intermediaries and prospective small and medium-sized ecoenterprises by sensitizing capital markets to the business case for such enterprises, bundling investments to reduce transaction costs, or other one-time activities to remove barriers to sustainable financing.

3. Improving Production Practice

Promoting best practice in different sectors

■ Demonstration activities: Demonstration projects may be supported at the local level to test and adapt production systems to protect biodiversity better, while assuring profitability at the enterprise level.

■ *Partnerships:* Promote the systematic adoption of best practice guidelines and protocols through strategic partnerships with industries, and utilization of industry associations or other vehicles.

■ *Adapting production:* Provide technical support to small and medium-sized enterprises to adapt existing production systems so as to better conserve biodiversity, building on traditional knowledge where appropriate.

■ *Integrated extension:* Provide technical assistance for the establishment of integrated extension systems to inform small and medium-sized enterprises of the impacts of production on biodiversity, and win-win mitigation options.

■ *Voluntary measures:* Support the establishment of schemes to recognize good practices at the enterprise level, including award schemes.

Mitigating secondary impacts in sectors that open up wildlands

■ *Mitigation measures:* Strengthen the capacity of small and medium-sized enterprises to identify, plan, and implement mitigation measures against secondary impacts associated with their primary business.

■ *Secondary impacts:* Integrate requirements to address secondary impacts into permit conditions.

■ *Monitoring:* Provide technical assistance for the establishment of monitoring systems by small and medium-sized enterprises to monitor their impacts on biodiversity and to create links with global monitoring systems.

Impact Indicators to Assess the Effectiveness of Mainstreaming

The Cape Town workshop considered some of the kinds of indicators that could be developed in future mainstreaming initiatives and categorized these according to the various targets of mainstreaming biodiversity, as outlined in this section. The nature of the target will influence the way in which indicators for the impact of mainstreaming are defined.

The top three indicators suggested as possible priorities for the GEF were:

(1) Spatial—the percentage of a priority area/key biodiversity area (defined at any level from ecosystem to species) under biodiversity-compatible management is significantly increased. (This requires understanding and agreement on priority areas, as well as standards to define what is considered biodiversity-compatible management.)

(2) Institutional—the level of resource allocation to biodiversity conservation by key government departments other than the environmental departments is increased and departments are leading biodiversity programs.

(3) Market—the volume of biodiversity friendly products is increased.

These, plus additional potential indicators in relation to specific targets, are detailed in the following section. These need to be carefully considered in the context of specific mainstreaming interventions, and refined in order to be effective in guiding the relevant actors. Consideration should also be given to the possibility of linking these indicators to existing monitoring and evaluation programs of public and private sector actors and donor agencies (for example, to processes such as the World Bank's Poverty Reduction Strategy Papers or the United Nations' Millennium Development Goals). This would enable those programs to improve the extent to which they explicitly evaluate the mainstreaming of biodiversity considerations. Additional comments from workshop participants included the need to maintain a focus on biophysical indicators as well as stress reduction indicators. These would, however, need to be identified in relation to specific contexts.

1. Potential indicators for spatial targets include:

■ The percentage of a priority area/key biodiversity area (defined at any level from ecosystem to species) under biodiversity-compatible management is significantly increased. (This requires understanding and agreement on priority areas, as well as standards for defining biodiversity-compatible management in a particular context.)

This may include:

- The area of land under protected area management within production landscapes (emphasis on encouraging industry to cede parts of their landholding to protected area management, which does not necessarily require a change of ownership)
- The area of land under biodiversity-compatible management (biodiversity friendly/compatible land uses) which is also meeting technically informed biodiversity standards.
- There is a decrease in habitat fragmentation.
- Siting of major infrastructure is guided by biodiversity priorities.
- Species diversity is maintained or enhanced (for example, for species requiring large ranges, increase in numbers can measure impact of improved connectivity in the landscape).

2. Potential indicators for government targets include:

- Planning authorities have integrated biodiversity priorities into a greater number of their plans.
- Communication and partnership mechanisms focused on biodiversity concerns are institutionalized (including intergovernmental and public-private expertise).
- A greater number of policy statements reflecting biodiversity priorities are in place.
- Number (or percentage) of government staff with an environmental qualification is significantly increased.
- Biodiversity issues have a significant presence in election campaigns.
- A wide range of nonenvironmental government departments/sector agencies is participating in and/or coordinating biodiversity programs or projects, to which sufficient resources have been committed (indicated by percentage of budgets, number of staff, policies, publications, and so forth)
- There is a national consensus on valuing ecosystem services (indicated, for example, by a surcharge on water services).
- No perverse incentives are in place (can apply at national and international levels).

- A government is a signatory to or has ratified relevant international conventions, and demonstrated progress on implementing them, for example, through producing a national biodiversity strategy and action plan (NBSAP).
- NBSAPs incorporate strategies to mainstream biodiversity in production landscapes and sectors.
- Legislation that contributes positively to biodiversity conservation is in place and is enforced.
- There is a significant increase in the percentage of bilateral/multilateral funding allocated to biodiversity conservation.
- Speeches by ministers (nonenvironment, and especially finance ministers) make reference to biodiversity issues.
- Biodiversity issues are integrated into the national education curriculum.

3. Potential indicators for private sector targets include:

- An increased number of sector players have adopted best practices and standards relating to biodiversity.
- Key sectoral players are acting as champions on biodiversity issues.
- There is an increase in the number of partnerships for collaboration on conserving biodiversity.
- Corporate planning departments have internalized biodiversity priorities into their plans.
- Biodiversity departments have been established in key large companies.
- There is a presence of priority biodiversity issues in policy statements.
- Budgets include biodiversity conservation allocations.
- There is an increase in the percentage of budgets allocated to biodiversity conservation through nontraditional internal alliances and realignment.
- Government policy frameworks are influenced by the actions of companies in conserving biodiversity.
- Processes are in place to develop and internalize biodiversity standards in key sectors and industries.
- Incentives are provided for maintaining biodiversity friendly land uses and production systems,

and more people are employed in such uses and systems (for example, farmers planting indigenous crop varieties).

4. Potential indicators for **individual targets** include:

- There is a marked change in relevant consumer behavior, with a significant increase in willingness to pay for biodiversity-sensitive or lowest-impact products.
- Greater shelf space in shops is allocated to merchandise produced through biodiversity friendly activities.
- There is an increase in visitor numbers to sites of biodiversity value, with appropriate safeguards in place.
- There is increased awareness by consumers of the links between biodiversity and their purchasing (mind shift as an intermediary activity).
- Greater numbers of volunteers and other actors are participating in biodiversity conservation activities.
- There is an increase in viewership of nature programs, and the number of advertisements with a biodiversity conservation message on television channels.
- Sustainable use is made of indigenous species.
- There is an increase in membership numbers and active participation in biodiversity/"green" organizations.

5. Potential indicators for **multilateral donor organization targets** include:

- Representatives of biodiversity issues are participating in international forums (such as the World Trade Organization).
- There is a significant increase in the percentage of budgets of donor organizations allocated toward biodiversity conservation.
- More training programs for staff on biodiversity issues are in place.
- Conditionalities relating to impacts on biodiversity are placed on projects to a greater extent.
- More biodiversity safeguards are in place.

- There is an increased number of pages in annual reports focused on biodiversity activities.
- Speeches by leadership figures mention biodiversity issues more frequently.
- A greater number of staff are participating in carbon-offset programs for their travel.
- Best practices are institutionalized for organizational activities (for example, recycling, decision making on environmentally responsible products, carbon-offset, and videoconferencing when appropriate).
- Initiatives are in place and funding sourced to replicate routine private-sector best practices relating to biodiversity.
- There is an increased number of projects in portfolios that are supporting new biodiversity-based products or services.

6. Potential indicators for **poverty alleviation agenda targets** include:

- Programs are using biodiversity sustainably to eradicate poverty (for example, ensuring food security, employment generation, invasive alien species removal).
- Crisis funds are available to mitigate the effects of natural disasters/stresses (such as droughts, floods, tsunamis) on ecosystems.
- Biodiversity conservationists are engaging with poverty alleviation agendas, to minimize negative impacts on biodiversity and increase the contribution of biodiversity resources to alleviating poverty.

7. Potential indicators for **markets-for-ecosystems-services targets** include:

- New biodiversity-based commodities are emerging.
- Biodiversity considerations are taken into account in setting up supply chains.
- There is an increase in the number and diversity of products certified as biodiversity friendly.

These are broad suggestions for the kind of indicators that could be built into project design in mainstreaming initiatives in order to ensure that the process, products, and outcomes of such initiatives are being thoroughly recorded, monitored, assessed, and analyzed. The exact nature of specific indicators, as well as mechanisms for monitoring and follow-up actions, will need to be developed in the context of particular projects.

Conclusions

The challenges of internalizing values and goals relating to the conservation and sustainable use of our planet's biological diversity into the mainstream of social and economic development are enormous.

The Cape Town workshop provided an opportunity to pause and assess how far we in the environmental community have come, drawing on a broad range of experience and expertise from around the world. At the same time, the gathering was able to make constructive suggestions for the way forward in the three areas outlined in the previous section-principles and conditions for effective mainstreaming, priority areas for GEF intervention, and impact indicators to assess the effectiveness of mainstreaming. It is hoped that the recommendations of this document will be taken forward by the GEF and its Implementing Agencies and will help to shape this area of work as it grows in size and importance over the next few years.

Endnote

1   A list of names of the Cape Town workshop participants appears in an appendix at the end of this volume.

Appendix: Workshop Participants

Mainstreaming Biodiversity in Production Landscapes and Sectors

Workshop of the Scientific and Technical Advisory Panel
of the Global Environment Facility
Cape Town, South Africa
September 20-24, 2004

Tehmina Akhtar, UNDP, New York, NY, USA   tehmina.akhtar@undp.org

Phoebe Barnard, Global Invasive Species Programme, Cape Town, South Africa   barnard@sanbi.org

Mandy Barnett, Cape Action for People and the Environment (CAPE), Cape Town, South Africa   mandy@capeaction.org.za

Karla Boreri, BP America Inc., Washington, DC, USA   karla.boreri@se1.bp.com

Gonzalo Castro, GEF, Washington, DC, USA   Gcastro@thegef.org

Mark Collins, UNEP, Nairobi, Kenya   mark.collins@unep.org

Richard Cowling, University of Port Elizabeth, Port Elizabeth, South Africa   rmc@kingsley.co.za

Holly Dublin, IUCN Eastern Africa Regional Office, Nairobi, Kenya   holly.dublin@ssc.iucn.org

David Duthie, UNEP, Nairobi, Kenya   david.duthie@unep.org

Paul Elkan, Wildlife Conservation Society, New York, NY, USA   pelkan@uuplus.com

Saliem Fakir, IUCN, Pretoria, South Africa   saliem.fakir@iucn.org

Sarah Frazee, Conservation International, Cape Town, South Africa   sfrazee@conservation.org

Nicole Glineur, GEF, Washington, DC, USA   nglineur@worldbank.org

Carl Grant, Alcoa World Alumina Australia, Applecross, Australia   carl.grant@alcoa.com.au

John Hough, UNDP, New York, NY, USA   john.hough@undp.org

Brian Huntley, SANBI, Cape Town, South Africa   huntley@sanbi.org

Jon Hutton, Fauna and Flora International, Richmond, UK jon.hutton@fauna-flora.org

Sachin Kapila, Shell, London, UK sachin.kapila@shell.com

Pramod Krishnan, Periyar Tiger Reserve, Kerala, India edo@periyartigerreserve.org

Kathy MacKinnon, The World Bank, Washington, DC, USA kmackinnon@worldbank.org

Kristal Maze, SANBI, Pretoria, South Africa maze@sanbi.org

Robert McCallum, Department of Conservation, Auckland, New Zealand rmccallum@doc.govt.nz

Jeffrey McNeely, IUCN, Gland, Switzerland jam@hq.iucn.org

Robert Nasi, CIFOR, Montpellier, France r.nasi@cgiar.org

Khungeka Njobe, CSIR, Pretoria, South Africa knjobe@csir.co.za

Caroline Petersen, SANBI, Cape Town, South Africa petersenc@Sanbi.org

Guy Preston, Working for Water Programme, Cape Town, South Africa GPreston@dwaf.gov.za

Glenn Prickett, Conservation International, Washington, DC, USA g.prickett@celb.org

Kent Redford, Wildlife Conservation Society, New York, NY, USA kredford@wcs.org

Alan Rodgers, UNDP—GEF, Nairobi, Kenya alan.rodgers@undp.org

Trevor Sandwith, CAPE, Cape Town, South Africa trevor@capeaction.org.za

Peter Schei, Fridtjof Nansen Institute, Lysaker, Norway pjs@fni.no

Nik Sekhran, BDP-GEF, Pretoria, South Africa nik.sekhran@undp.org

Carlos Toledo Manzur, Mexico Sustainable Development Network, Mexico City, Mexico toledocarlos@prodigy.net.mx

Jo Treweek, International Association for Impact Assessment, Devon, UK jo@treweek.fsnet.co.uk

Christopher Whaley, STAP Secretariat, Washington, DC, USA christopher.whaley@rona.unep.org